MONOCHAETIA AND PESTALOTIA

MONOGRAPH OF
MONOCHAETIA
AND
PESTALOTIA

by

EMIL FREDERICK GUBA

Professor, Plant Pathology, University of Massachusetts
Waltham Field Station, Waltham, Massachusetts

1961

HARVARD UNIVERSITY PRESS

Cambridge, Massachusetts

Library of Congress Catalog Card Number 61-5249

Manufactured in the United States of America

PREFACE

The author has devoted nearly forty years to the systematic study of the genera *Monochaetia* and *Pestalotia* of imperfect fungi, as an auxiliary project of his professional work in mycology and phytopathology. The preparation of a critical monographic account of these fungi has been a challenge and one not without its moments of confusion and despair. It is my humble hope that the systematic study presented hereafter will be useful to those who may have occasion to work with these fungi and that it will constitute an acceptable contribution to the general advancement of mycological science.

A large number of species of *Monochaetia* and *Pestalotia* have been described as new since 1839, when the genus *Pestalotia* was established. All too often the authors have considered their new species distinct because the host or matrix on which they were found differed from those of other similar species or because new geographic areas were concerned. Classification of these essentially saprophytic and widely distributed forms on such grounds is not basically sound. Many of the species have been inadequately described, lacking any mention of conidial sizes or other essential morphological characters. Illustrations, a most desirable feature, are quite generally not provided. The original descriptions must be sought in the literature of many countries and languages, and some have been found only after patient effort and with the assistance of helpful colleagues elsewhere.

Saccardo, in his *Sylloge Fungorum*, brought together in various volumes diagnoses of known species, but no such compilation has appeared since his last volume was issued in 1931. The flood of alleged new species has continued unabated, mycologists all too often following the practice, by no means confined to *Pestalotia*, of setting up new binomials without bothering to search the older literature. Such descriptions serve a useful purpose in providing new distribution and host records but clutter up the taxonomic picture needlessly.

The preparation of this monograph has been greatly facilitated by the cooperation of many mycological colleagues who have provided specimens, data and helpful criticism. Edith K. Cash, formerly Mycologist, National Fungus Collections, Beltsville, Maryland, reviewed the manuscript in detail, provided Latin diagnoses for the new species and assisted in the preparation

v

of the comprehensive host and fungus index, a very necessary feature of the book. S. F. Blake, New Crops Research Branch, Beltsville, Maryland, checked all phanerogamic binomials appearing in the text for accuracy and uniformity. John A. Stevenson, Principal Mycologist in Charge, National Fungus Collections, prepared a critical review of the preliminary draft of the manuscript and edited and rearranged the final copy. To these associates who have assisted me in this long effort I offer my heartfelt gratitude.

The University of Massachusetts Research Council provided funds for the preparation of the manuscript. The Foundation for Microbiology, Rutgers University, Dr. Selman A. Waksman, President, contributed a substantial grant toward the cost of publication. I am deeply indebted to these institutions for their aid and to Dr. Waksman for his personal interest in my work.

EMIL FREDERICK GUBA

Waltham, Massachusetts
September 25, 1959

CONTENTS

MONOCHAETIA AND PESTALOTIA

INTRODUCTION

Some years ago the writer published two papers (Phytopathology 19:191–232,1929, and Mycologia 24:355–397,1932) entitled *Monograph of the genus Pestalotia*. These contributions were intended to crystallize our knowledge of the common species of the genus *Pestalotia*, as well as to bring together the pertinent literature. With further study and the greater accessibility of type material, a more complete treatment of the genus is now possible. As a result of the broader knowledge obtained, it became necessary to study not only the genus *Pestalotia*, but also all those genera characterized by having fusiform, multiseptate conidia of four or more cells, with intermediate colored cells and exterior hyaline or subhyaline cells, and crowned with a varying number of setulae. Thus there arose the need for determining the status of each of the following genera in addition to the genus *Pestalotia*: *Labridella, Pestalotiopsis, Truncatella, Monochaetia, Hyaloceras,* and *Seiridium*. The problems arising from these studies have been resolved by the acceptance of the two genera *Monochaetia* and *Pestalotia*, as will be explained in the following pages.

NOMENCLATURE

The Genus Monochaetia

The genus *Monochaetia* was established as a subgenus of *Pestalotia* (as *Pestolozzia*) by Saccardo (Syll. Fung. 3:797,1884) and given generic rank by Allescher (Rabenhorst, Krypt. Flora 1, Abt. 7:665,1902). A few years later Saccardo (Syll. Fung. 18:485,1906) concurred. Allescher recognized 23 species but did not indicate a type. It seems in order to accept *Monochaetia monochaeta* (Desm.) Allescher as the type, as has been done by Clements and Shear (The Genera of the Fungi, 1931, p. 384), since this is the first species given by Saccardo (Syll. Fung. 3:797,1884 and 18:485,1906). In Allescher's account, three species precede his description of *M. monochaeta*, but they are species not listed by Saccardo in his first account. A substitute binomial, *M. desmazierii* Sacc. (Syll. Fung. 18:485,1906), is available if the specific epithet is considered a tautonym, which does not appear to be the case.

At least 75 species of *Monochaetia* have been described and more than 40 are recognized as acceptable in this monograph. In addition to Saccardo, most general mycological works recognize the genus, including Allescher as noted (Rabenhorst, Krypt. Flora 1, Abt. 7), Migula (Krypt.-Flora v. Deut. u.s.w. Band III, 4 Teil, Abt. 1), Vassiljevsky and Karakulin (Fungi Imperfecti Parasitici, pars II, Melanconiales), Clements and Shear (Genera of Fungi), Ainsworth and Bisby (Dictionary of the Fungi). All species are associated with leaves and other plant parts to a greater or less extent, and several in particular are of economic importance as parasites. *Monochaetia* has been the generic name used almost uniformly in the extensive phytopathological literature on the subject.

Two generic names appear to have priority, *Seiridium* (*Siridium* of Clements and Shear) and *Hyaloceras*. *Seiridium* was first published by Nees v. Esenbeck (Das System der Pilze und Schwämme, 1817, p. 22). The single species described (*S. marginatum*) occurred on rose stems in Germany and was reported as having colored, many-septate conidia that were linked in pairs or chains by a filament, the chains of conidia arising from an acervulus. Fries (Syst. Mycol. 3:473,1829) placed this species first under his genus *Coryneum*, the second and only other recognized species being *C. umbonatum*, now generally accepted as the type of the genus (Clements and Shear, Genera of Fungi, p. 384). In discussing the first species Fries noted that "under the microscope the septate conidia are seen to be wholly those of *Coryneum*,

3

differing only in the more slender pedicels and the hyaline terminal, filiform, apiculus of the conidia." This would indicate that Fries regarded the second species as the true *Coryneum*, a view now universally accepted. Krombholtz (Abbild. Beschreib. essb. schäd. verd. Schwämme, Heft 1:6,1831) appears to have been the first post-starting point author to recognize *Seiridium*. In common with other writers of the period, including Corda (Anleit. zum Stud. Myc., 1842) and Bischoff (Allgem. Ubers. Org. Phan. u. Krypt. Pflanzenkr., 1851), he reproduced the original figure of *Seiridium* of Nees, thus perpetuating the error of conidia produced in chains held together by slender filaments.

Fuckel (Symb. Mycol., 1869, p. 391) studied the fungus microscopically and was the first to present dependable data concerning it. He found it to be a species with 6-celled conidia with brown center cells and hyaline end cells. He issued the fungus under the name *S. marginatum* (Fries) Nees in Fungi Rhenani, No. 2136. Hazelinsky (Verh. zool.-bot. Ges. Wien 20:214,1870) also used this binomial for a different fungus with 4-celled conidia. Saccardo confused the issue by accepting this later usage for the binomial and giving a new name, *Pestalotia seiridioides*, to the Nees species as studied by Fuckel.

Von Hoehnel (Sitzb. K. Akad. Wiss. Wien, Math.-Naturw. Kl. 125:29–23, 1916) reviewed the history of *Seiridium* and studied Fuckel's specimen. As a result he decided the fungus was not melanconiaceous and he accepted the genus in the sense of Fuckel with *S. marginatum* Nees as the type. He recognized *Monochaetia* as belonging in the Melanconiaceae, the genera of which "do not have closed stromata and whose conidia are not bound together by a heavy slime." The present writer finds that these criteria for separating the genera do not hold and that *Monochaetia* is therefore synonymous with *Seiridium* Nees ex Krombh. *Seiridium* has been recognized (Clements and Shear, Ainsworth and Bisby, and other recent workers) as a genus of the Melanconiaceae characterized by conidia in chains as suggested by the original figure of Nees. Other than this imaginative figure there is no evidence to support the conidia in chains theory. Other species assigned to the genus have been long since transferred to *Phragmidium* and *Phragmotrichum*[1] or are known only from old and inadequate descriptions.

Seiridium could possibly be disposed of by considering it a *nomen confusum*, but in the light of the studies by Fuckel and von Hoehnel, the situation can be best met by conserving *Monochaetia* against it.

[1] *Seiridium marginatum* Schw. on dead canes of *Rosa corymbosa* Ehrh. (Trans. Am. Philos. Soc. 4:306,1834) is apparently the same as *Phragmidium apiculatum* Fries (Summa Veg. Scand., 1846, p. 474), but to it Fries (Syst. Mycol. 3:496,1829) earlier gave the name *Aregma speciosa* Fr. Later this species was named *Phragmidium speciosum* (Fries) Cooke (Grevillea 3:171,1875; Syll. Fung. 15:329,1901) and this is the currently accepted name. *Seiridium smilacis* Schw. in the Schweinitz herbarium at the Philadelphia Academy of Natural Sciences, is also *Phragmidium speciosum* according to Fries (Syst. Mycol. 3:496, 1829) and Bartholomew (Handbook N. Am. Uredinales, 2nd ed., 1933, p. 37). *S. lignicolum* (Cda.) Sacc. is pictured with muriform conidia and is therefore properly *Phragmotrichum lignicolum* Cda. as originally described.

Hyaloceras was described by Durieu and Montagne (Flore d'Algerie Crypt., 1846, p. 587) with one species *H. notarisii*. About five additional species have been added to the genus in the years since 1846. Hoehnel (Sitzb. K. Akad. Wiss. Wien, Math.-Naturw. Kl. 119:663–664,1910) pointed out that *Monochaetia* was synonymous with *Hyaloceras* and added that the species of the former genus should accordingly be transferred. He did not make any actual transfers. Diedicke (Krypt. Flora Mark Brandenb. 9:877–881,1915) followed von Hoehnel's suggestions, citing five species in *Hyaloceras*. Von Hoehnel later (Sitzb. K. Akad. Wiss. Wien, Math.-Naturw.Kl. 125:33:1916) changed his mind and recognized *Monochaetia*. Apparently no further transfers have been made from *Monochaetia* to *Hyaloceras* and the generic name has been ignored in recent years.

Monochaetia should be conserved against *Seiridium* Nees ex Krombh. and *Hyaloceras* Dur. & Mont. since it is the generally accepted generic name for the fungi involved. A large number of transfers would otherwise be necessary.

The Genus Pestalotia

The genus *Pestalotia* as established by de Notaris (Mem. R. Acad. Sci. Torino II, 3:80–81,1839) was based on a single species found on grape canes (*Vitis vinifera*) in Italy and dedicated to Fortunato Pestalozza. Saccardo, noting after whom the genus was named, changed the spelling to *Pestalozzia*, which violates Article 72 of the International Code of Botanical Nomenclature. This rule provides that "The original spelling of a name or epithet must be retained." Guba (Phytopathology 19:191–193,1929) and Guba and Linder (Mycologia 24:415–416,1932) have discussed the nomenclatorial problem involved and have emphasized that the correct spelling is *Pestalotia*.

The type species of the genus, *P. pezizoides*, is characterized by having 6-celled conidia of which the four middle cells are deeply colored or dark and the terminal ones usually hyaline. The conidia, provided with two or more simple or branched bristles at the apex, or with one branched appendage, are formed in an acervulus resting on a gelatinous well-developed stroma. Steyaert (Bull. Jard. Bot. État Bruxelles 19:285–354,1949) regarded these colored cells more properly as refracting globular masses or locules or as four strongly delimited zones separated by pseudo-septa rather than well-characterized cells with true septa such as characterize the 4- and 5-celled forms. Nevertheless the compartments, or refracting globular masses, germinate like single-celled conidia and the distinction asserted by Steyaert is hardly valid.

The diagnostic characters presented by the type species of *Monochaetia* and *Pestalotia* have had to be modified since, with an increase in our knowledge of the genera and with the addition of many new species, the concepts of the genera had of necessity to be broadened to include species with 4- to 6-celled conidia produced in acervuli with little or with well-developed stromatic tissue, and even with a pycnidial structure. Since there are all degrees of intergradation between the extremes, this conservative treatment seems advisable or otherwise the genera would have to be split into a number of genera which in turn would have to be placed, although closely related, in different families of the Fungi Imperfecti. Thus the distinction between the two genera rests essentially upon the number of appendages rising from the superior hyaline cell. The number of cells constituting the conidium has provided the basis for dividing the genus *Pestalotia* into sections (Klebahn, Myc. Centralbl. 4:1–19,1914) designated *Quadriloculatae, Quinqueloculatae,* and *Sexloculatae,* and this arrangement was adopted by Guba (Phytopathology 19:191–232,1929). The same subdivisions apply to *Monochaetia.*

The beginning of the process of splitting *Pestalotia* into a number of genera was made by Brenckle (Fungi Dakotenses, fasc. 27, no. 663, Oct. 1929; Mycologia 22:160–161,1930) who described the genus *Labridella* in the Leptostromataceae. The type of the genus, *L. cornu-cervae,* herbarium material of which also bears the unpublished epithet *Pestalotia cornu-cervae* Brenckle, in contrast to *P. pezizoides* de Not. has conidia with five colored cells, each of which is crowned with an attenuated branching setula. The basal cell is slightly colored, and the acervulus is a cup-like or apothecioid structure analogous to that of *P. pezizoides.* Since these two species, *L. cornu-cervae* and *P. pezizoides,* differ only in the number and coloration of the cells of the conidia, there is no reason for recognizing Brenckle's genus and it is therefore relegated to synonymy.

More recently Steyaert (Bull. Jard. Bot. État Bruxelles 19:285–354,1949) has done away with the genus *Monochaetia,* preferring to distribute these forms in the section *Monosetulatae* in each of two newly proposed genera, *Truncatella* for the 4-celled conidial forms and *Pestalotiopsis* for the 5-celled forms. The genus *Pestalotia* is reserved for the single species *P. pezizoides* de Not. The genera *Truncatella* and *Pestalotiopsis* are divided into additional sections, that is, *Bisetulatae, Trisetulatae,* and *Multisetulatae.*

The genus *Truncatella* is further distinguished by a hyaline epispore which envelops the two colored cells and which may be shown by immersing the spores in an aqueous solution of caustic potash. The *Monosetulatae* are subdivided further into sections Simple Setulae and Branched Setulae. The *Trisetulatae* of the genus *Pestalotiopsis* are broken down into sub-groups comprising species with concolorous and versicolorous conidia, fusiform and claviform conidia, and spatulate and non-spatulate setulae. The genus *Pestalotia* is removed from the *Melanconiaceae* to the *Discellaceae (Sphaeropsidales)* but the new genera are retained in the *Melanconiaceae.* Steyaert's deflection from the traditional vocabulary and understanding of these genera has been the subject of disapproval by Moreau (Rev. Mycol. Fr. 14: Suppl.

Colon. 2:101–103,1949), Servazzi (Nuovo Gior. Bot. Ital. 60 (n.s.) 4:943–947, 1953) and Guba (Mycologia 47:920–921, 1955). Steyaert's defense (Bull. Jard. Bot. État Bruxelles 25:191–199,1955; Mycologia 48:767–768,1956) has served to clarify his position and to invite further disapproval (Guba, Ann. Microb. Enzimol. Milan 7:74–76,1956).

Variations in the fruiting structure of the different species of *Pestalotia* and *Monochaetia* are suggested by the specific epithets *phyllostictea, depazeoides, excipuliformis, hysteriiformis, pycnoides, pezizoides,* and *vermiformis.* The emphasis on the structure of the fruiting body rather than on the conidial type has given rise to groups of organisms or genera in the *Melanconiales* and *Sphaeropsidales* with identical conidial morphology. While admitting that the orders *Sphaeropsidales* and *Melanconiales* are distinct in their extreme forms, there is nevertheless a group of genera in each order which show transitional characters that make separation of the members of the groups into the two orders a difficult task, and of extremely doubtful value. The acervulus of *Pestalotia guepini* Desm. and *Hyaloceras ceratospora* (de Not.) Hoehn. may be considered a poorly developed pycnidium with little developed stromatic tissue, whereas the structure of *P. pezizoides* de Not. shows varying degrees of stromatic development. The relative degree of development of the stromatic tissue, since it varies so within the genus and the species as well as with age, is of relatively little value for the segregation of species and is of even less significance when it comes to breaking up the genera *Pestalotia* and *Monochaetia* and distributing the resulting groups among different families and orders. The relatively uniform morphology of the conidia indicates the strong morphologic and perhaps phylogenetic relationship between the species of *Pestalotia* and of *Monochaetia* and argues against the usefulness or desirability of splitting the genera.

To illustrate the chaos that would arise from segregating groups of species into different genera which would be distributed among different families rather than to regard the aggregate of species as one genus which is usually placed in the single family *Melanconiaceae*, it is only necessary to furnish a partial list of the family assignments already suggested by various workers. Thus Archer (Ann. Mycol. 24:66–67,1926) considers that the development of the acervulus is like that of *Sphaeropsis* which would therefore place certain of the species in the *Sphaeropsidaceae*. Elenkin and Ohl (Zhurnal Bolezni Rastenii St. Petersburg 6:77–122,1912) created the genus *Pseudopestalotia* which they placed in the *Pseudosphaeroidaceae*. Hoehnel placed *Pestalotia* in the *Gymnostromaceae* and Leiniger (Centralbl. Bakt. II, 29:3–35,1911) assigned the genus to the *Pseudopycnidiaceae*. Mention has already been made of the assignment of *Labridella* [=*Pestalotia*] to the *Leptostromataceae*. Steyaert (Bull. Jard. Bot. État Bruxelles 19:285–354,1949) asserted that *P. pezizoides*, because of its stromatic apothecioid fruiting pustules, belongs to the *Discellaceae* (*Excipulaceae*) of the order *Sphaeropsidales* and all other species with distinct acervuli to the *Melanconiaceae*, order *Melanconiales*. The classic paper by Montemartini (Atti Ist. Bot. Pavia II, 6:78–82,1900) describing the modifications in the fructifications among various groups of the *Melanconiales*, including *Pestalotia*, and the phylogenetic relationships of the groups based on structure and stroma, is relevant to the subject.

Until more is known in regard to the relations between the conidial and the ascigerous phases, little is to be gained by dividing either *Pestalotia* or *Monochaetia* into a number of genera to be placed in one or more families. It is far more practical at present to subdivide the genera into sections on the basis of conidial form, color, and number of cells, and the position, number, and character of the setulae.   Whether or not the genus *Pestalotia* is kept in the *Leptostromatacae* or the *Melanconiaceae* is a matter of interpretation of the structure of the acervulus and whether or not a sharp line of demarcation can be found to divide the transitional stages of development of the acervulus. From the writer's studies, such a line of demarcation is not obvious.   For this reason, we have adopted the simple yet effective system proposed by Klebahn (Myc. Centralbl. 4:1–19,1914) of dividing the genus into sections which are characterized by the number of cells in the conidia, that is, the *Sexloculatae*, *Quinqueloculatae*, and *Quadriloculatae*, rather than Steyaert's plan, which provides a new genus for each group.

CULTURAL STUDIES

In the preceding pages it has been shown that the imperfect fungi having acervuli on which are produced colored, septate conidia with characteristic appendages, may be placed in either *Pestalotia* or *Monochaetia*. Cultural studies, however, appear to throw some doubt on the validity of *Monochaetia* as distinct from *Pestalotia*. Christensen (Bull. Torrey Bot. Club 59:525–544, 1932) reported that he obtained from monoconidial cultures from the acervuli of a species of *Pestalotia* on *Pinus palustris* Mill., races which conformed to the characters of both *Pestalotia* and *Monochaetia* and as a result suggested that the salient characters used to distinguish the two genera are not entirely dependable and that the genus *Monochaetia* could not be maintained as distinct from *Pestalotia*. The present author does not accept this point of view.

La Rue (Genetics 7:142–201,1922) reported that selection for abnormal number of appendages within a strain isolated from *Hevea* gave progeny with the normal number of three appendages. In another paper, La Rue and Bartlett (Am. Jour. Bot. 9:79–92,1922), employing precise and narrow biometric differences in the length of conidia and appendages, resolved a total of 35 isolations of *Pestalotia* from cocoanut palm (*Cocos nucifera*), oil palm (*Elaeis guineensis*), betel nut palm (*Areca cathecu*), *Hevea* and *Thea*, collectively regarded as the nominal species *P. guepini*, into 14 groups distinct from each other in regard to certain biometric measurements and independent of host relationships. None of these is *P. guepini* in the sense of the type specimen and actually they represent several distinct species. Thus their evidence to support the assertion that *P. guepini* is a widely cosmopolitan fungus in a plastic condition is not convincing. Christensen (Bull. Torrey Bot. Club 59:525–544,1932) resolved 150 monoconidial isolations of a *Pestalotia* from *Pinus palustris*, which he misdetermined as *P. funerea*, into 15 cultural races, and from cultures of these 15 races, 10 distinct variants arose through sectoring.

Since it is well known that the *Fungi Imperfecti* may undergo considerable variation when they are grown on artificial media, it may be assumed that many of them are extremely variable under these conditions, but it does not seem plausible to conclude that, because of this, a given fungus will be equally variable on the natural substratum and under the conditions that exist in nature. On the basis of the writer's study of many hundreds of specimens and a lesser number of cultures from all over the world, it is felt that the species in almost all cases, by a comparison with the type specimen or a knowledge of it, can be accurately defined and that aberrances should be considered as of little or no taxonomic importance.   It is realized, however, that while many species may be specific to a given host, the range of other species may be much more extensive.   To determine the host range of the individual species requires extensive inoculation experiments and until these can be accomplished it is necessary for the present to rely, in part, on the host relationship for the classification of the species, and in part, the greater part, on the morphology of the conidia.   It is significant to note that form, color, and measurable characters within the nominal species show no dissimilarities with age of cultures, and agreement has been reported by LaRue (Genetics 7:142–201, 1922) and Christensen (Bull. Torrey Bot. Club 59:525–544,1932).   This fact should help to render dependable any carefully prepared and accurate description of the species.

Mycologists have failed to provide comprehensive and accurate species descriptions.   It can be stated that the descriptions of the nominal species are generally in no degree diagnostic and when the common characters in the descriptions are cancelled, nothing remains but different host plants and geographic locations.   Mycology has recognized this state of affairs, yet continues to describe new species in the same conventional manner and without regard for those existing.   Steyaert (Bull. Jard. Bot. État Bruxelles 19:285–354,1949) in his revision of the genera *Monochaetia* and *Pestalotia*, has not simplified the nomenclature.

PATHOLOGICAL CONSIDERATIONS

Newly described species of *Monochaetia* and *Pestalotia* continue to be identified with plant disease. However, earlier studies are generally consistent in recognizing the secondary and saprophytic role of the species. The pathogenic aspects of the subject have been studied and reviewed by numerous investigators, notably Doyer (Med. Phytopath. Lab., "Will. Comm. Scholt." 9:41–72,1925), Guba (Mycologia 24:357–359,1932), Christensen (Bull. Torrey Bot. Club 59:525–544,1932), and Servazzi (Boll. Lab. Sper. R. Osserv. Fitopat. Torino. 12: nos. 1 and 4,1934; 13: no. 1,1935; 15: nos. 5–6,1936). Doyer reported that none of the species of *Pestalotia* is pathogenic. She worked especially with species alleged to be pathogenic to tea, palm, rhododendron, sapodilla, and conifers. No biologic studies were undertaken by the present author. He has, however, compiled the pertinent literature relating to each species for which biologic studies are reported.

The more recent literature has reported many instances of the association of species of *Monochaetia* and *Pestalotia* with plant disease and of successful artificial infection experiments. The recovery of species from diseased stems and roots has been frequent, especially among woody host plants in the orders Coniferales, Salicales, Rosales, and Ericales, and in regions of the North Temperate Climatic Zone.

The genera *Monochaetia* and *Pestalotia* are represented in the microflora of the soil and in polluted streams of water. Other forms are associated with the deterioration of wood, paper, tentage, and fabrics of military importance (Weston, Research Rep., QMG Microbiol. Lab., Ser. no. 15, Ser. QMC Project 60, Aug. 1949). Michalska (Acta Microbiol. Polon 6:27,88,1957, illus.) recognized *Pestalotia* as one of several destructive fungi involved in the decay of sheep fleece. Dorset (Text. Mfr. 80: no. 956,421–425 and no. 957, 474–477,1954, illus.) reported the genus as a problem in the deterioration of cotton fabrics and chemical means of control. One brief report by Cole and Vanderwyk (Jour. Am. Pharm. Assoc. Sci. Ed. 43: no. 1,56–58,1954) explored a few species of *Pestalotia* for sources of antibiotics but nothing in this respect has been done with the genus *Monochaetia*.

Thus *Monochaetia* and *Pestalotia* have significance in the biology and economics of nature and man's concern. The novel architecture of the conidia was the main feature about these fungi, in the beginning, to arouse the curiosity and interest of the naturalist and artist. The work of Hartig and Tubeuf in Germany, in the primitive era of forest tree pathology, aroused interest in these organisms as plant pathogens and gave impetus to an entirely new conception of their importance.

11

ASCIGEROUS FORMS

A few authentic connections between the ascigerous and conidial stages of *Pestalotia* and *Monochaetia* have been reported. For the most part, the ascigerous stages that have been reported are based on the occurrence of the two stages on the natural substratum and not on cultural experiments. As a result and in view of the diverse relationships shown, it is necessary to confirm all such reports by cultural experiments.

Fuckel (Symb. Mycol. II, 1873, Nachtr. p. 28, fig. 6) described the perfect stage of *Seiridium marginatum* Nees [not *S. marginatum* (Fr.) Nees] and gave it the name *Massaria marginata* Fckl. The two stages appeared together on canes of *Rosa canina* L. collected by du Morthier, near Neuchâtel in the Jura Mountains. According to Fuckel, both forms originated in the same stroma from the same mycelium. Later, Hoehnel (Sitzb. K. Akad. Wiss. Wien, Math.-Naturw. Kl. 125:29–33,1916) observed the same relations in material collected in the Tirol.

Hoehnel (Sitzb. K. Akad. Wiss. Wien, Math.-Naturw. Kl. 126:4–5,348–349,1917) announced the occurrence of both *Ceratostoma vitis* Fckl. and *Pestalotia truncata* Lév. on *Humulus lupulus* L. in specimen No. 580 of Krieger, Fungi Saxonici. It is possible that the two forms are genetically related, but until this observation has been repeated or until cultural studies prove the actual relationship, the statement should be accepted with reservation.

The relation existing between *Pestalotia cornu-cervae* (Brenckle) Guba (syn.: *P. pezizoides* var. *longiseta* Dearn., *Labridella cornu-cervae* Brenckle) and its perfect stage has been obscured by the occurrence of two pyrenomycetous species on the same host. According to Hoehnel (Sitzb. K. Akad. Wiss. Wien, Math.-Naturw. Kl. 128:61,1919) there are two species, *Dothidotthia symphoricarpi* (Rehm) Hoehn. (syn. *Pseudotthia symphoricarpi* (Ell. & Ev.) Rehm; *Otthia symphoricarpi* (Ell. & Ev.) Ell. & Ev.) and *Griphosphaerioma symphoricarpi* (Rehm) Hoehn. (syn., *Plowrightia symphoricarpi* Ell. & Ev.; *Plowrightia symphoricarpi* Rehm).

Griphosphaerioma symphoricarpi (Rehm) Hoehn. is the species that is of interest in connection with the relations between the conidial and ascigerous stages since it was issued in Brenckle Fungi Dakotenses, No. 100, under the incorrect name, (fide Hoehnel) of *Zignoella morthieri* Fckl. Another specimen was received from Brenckle under the name of *Curreyella symphoricarpi* (Rehm) Petr. and it was accompanied by a letter in which Brenckle stated that

Curreyella symphoricarpi and *Pestalotia cornu-cervae* are more or less associated and have been found by culture to be related. Since these two specimens are identical, having 2- to 4-celled hyaline spores, and since Hoehnel states that the former belongs under the name *Griphosphaerioma symphoricarpi*, it is evident that this should be the perfect stage of *Pestalotia cornu-cervae*. This is evidenced by Brenckle's statement and borne out by the fact that the conidial and ascigerous stages are in intimate association in the two specimens mentioned above.

Zeller (Mycologia 26:291,1934) described as new, *Dermatea brunneo-pruinosa* in leaves of *Gaultheria shallon* Pursch. where it occurred in spots with *Pestalotia gibbosa* Harkn. He suggested that the two forms might be organically connected and this was later confirmed by Bonar (Mycologia 34:180,1942), who demonstrated that when the ascospores were germinated in culture, the resulting mycelium produced the *Pestalotia* stage. Subsequently, Seaver (Mycologia 34:298,1942) recognizing that the ascigerous stage did not fit well in the genus *Dermatea*, and because it was associated with the conidial genus *Pestalotia*, placed it in his new genus *Pestalopezia* as *P. brunneo-pruinosa* (Zeller) Seaver. Thus *Pestalotia gibbosa* Harkn. may be confidently accepted as the conidial stage of *Pestalopezia brunneo-pruinosa*. At the same time Seaver reported the association of another member of the ascigerous genus with *Pestalotia macrotricha* Kleb. which occurs on *Rhododendron maximum* L. To the perfect stage of this imperfect fungus he applied the binomial *Pestalopezia rhododendri* Seaver.

Hansen *et al.* (Phytopathology 46:637,1956) obtained in culture the perfect stage of *Pestalotia palmarum* Cooke (det. by author) corresponding to the genus *Leptosphaeria*. In a letter (Dec. 17, 1953) Hansen alleged that *Dermatea brunneo-pruinosa* Zeller and *Pestalopezia rhododendri* Seaver have no connection with *Pestalotia*, in spite of the apparent proof cited in the text above.

APPENDAGES OR SETULAE

The crest of appendages or setulae crowning the conidia has aroused considerable speculation regarding their significance. Vize (Trans. Woolhope Nat. Field Club, 1885,363–364,1890) likened the appendaged conidia to parachute heads of composite seeds. "They cannot be useless or they would not be created and beyond their being made for the pleasure of the Great Creator we are not able to supply any specific cause for them." However, Vize surmised that the appendages may aid in attaching the spore to the place where it begins its vegetation. Smith (Gard. Chron. Eng. 22 (n.s.) 429,1884) believed that the appendages which he drew to appear like setae (tapered pointed extremities) may aid in the distribution of the conidia by helping them to sail in the air, or they may get tangled on the bodies of insects and be carried from one position to another.

Desmazières (Ann. Sci. Nat. Bot. II, 13, Pl. 4, 1840), Corda (Icones Fung. II, 1838, tab. 9, fig. 46), Clements and Shear (Genera of Fungi, 1931, pl. 52, fig. 9), and others have illustrated these filaments with pointed tips like setae, but the error of such representation was revealed as early as 1856 by de Lacroix (Ann. Soc. Linn. Angers 2:10–16). He described the development of the setulae from their point of origin. In the growth of the conidia the rudimentary filaments appear as one or more spicules at the summit of the hyaline conical cells. At first the extremities are somewhat swollen; later these swellings disappear, and the walls of the appendages remain parallel for their entire length. In certain forms, however, the swellings persist as a constant character and aid in the identification of the species.

The novel appendaged character of the conidia also intrigued Crié (Bull. Soc. Linn. Norm. III: 111–115,1877; Ann. Sci. Nat. Bot. VI, 7:55–60,1878; Rev. Sciént. Fr. II: 22;514–616,1878). He gave the name *Diplopestalozzia* to an indefinite form combining didymous, one-septate and multisetulate conidia present in the same pycnidium (Crié, fig. 4). He reported that the conidia of *Hendersonia* are sometimes crowned with setulae. He considered *Hendersonia* and *Pestalotia* as *Diplodia* with multiseptate and setulate conidia. His study is dubious and no type material or specimens are designated.

EXAMINATION OF SPECIMENS
AND USE OF KEYS

Generally the fructifications of *Monochaetia* and *Pestalotia* are acervuli. Sometimes they show more or less stroma formation. The 4- and 5-celled conidial forms show the least stroma, or none of it, and the 6-celled conidial forms the most. The stroma in the 6-celled conidial forms can be extensive, underlying and enveloping the base and sides of the sporogenous layer as to resemble an apothecioid structure. There is considerable uniformity among the fructifications *in vivo* and considerable variation *in vitro*. The fructifications show variations in form according to the character of the matrix. In general, the fructifications are not considered significant in the definition of species. There are exceptions.

The fructifications are usually borne in the matrix and are freed by the rupture of the epidermis or covering tissue. They are black, carbonaceous, scattered or confluent, and sometimes densely aggregated. The contents are erupted in black coils or masses, leaving a black sooty deposit over the area. The black pustules can be observed with the naked eye, or better with a hand lens or binocular, and they appear in spots or dead areas on leaves, bark, wood, paper, and other plant materials. Their distribution is usually irregular and without order. A punctiform arrangement in leaf spots appears frequently, but the arrangement, number, distribution, and even size of fruiting pustules are not significant in the definition of species.

The fruiting area is treated with a speck of water which is allowed to soak into the matrix. The pedicels, exterior hyaline cells, and crest of setulae are essential to the identification of the species, and a smear of water applied to the fructifications aids in the removal of the conidia without the loss of their attachments. A bit of fungus or conidial material is placed in a drop of water on a glass slide and covered for examination under the microscope.

The position of the specimen in the author's scheme of classification should be promptly recognized. Are the conidia provided with one, or more than one, apical setulae? Does the specimen belong to *Monochaetia* or *Pestalotia*? [Fig. 1a,c; Fig. 2e,f]. Then determine the number of cells comprising the conidia. The exterior or extreme hyaline cells added to the number of colored cells will total 4, 5, or 6 cells, thus placing the specimen in either the Quadri-, Quinque-, or Sexloculatae section of the genus [Fig. 1b,c; Fig. 2b,c]. From here on, the color of the conidial cells, number and peculiarities of the setulae, and biometric measurements are used to key out the species. Aber-

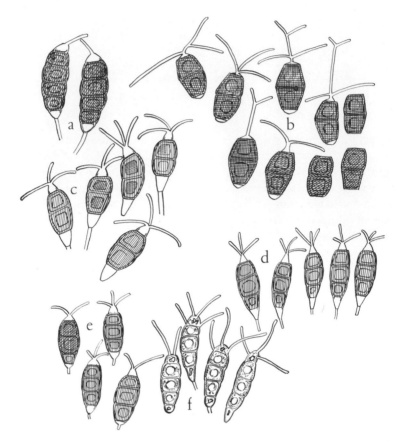

FIG. 1.   Conidia of (*a*) *Monochaetia unicornis*, (*b*) *Pestalotia hartigii*, (*c*) *P. stevensonii* (*d*) *P. micheneri* (=*P. microspora*), (*e*) *P. cryptomeriae*, (*f*) *Pestalozzina unicolor*.

rant conidia and characters should be disregarded.   Figures 1–4 will serve to illustrate the variation in number, form, and color of conidial cells and variations of the setulae.

The exterior or terminal cells of the conidia are hyaline or usually so. Rarely are they dilute yellow or faintly colored.   The coloration of the intermediate cells is an important diagnostic character.   These cells may be faintly colored, brown or yellow-brown, and equally colored (concolorous) [Fig. 1c,d,e].   They may be of two colors or versicolored and slightly or strongly contrasted.   The upper two colored cells may be brown or umber in contrast to the pale or yellow-brown color of the lowest of the three colored cells [Fig. 3b,f,g].   These color contrasts appear only among the 5-celled conidial forms with three intermediate colored cells.   The upper two colored cells may be dark brown or nearly black and opaque (fuliginous) and most

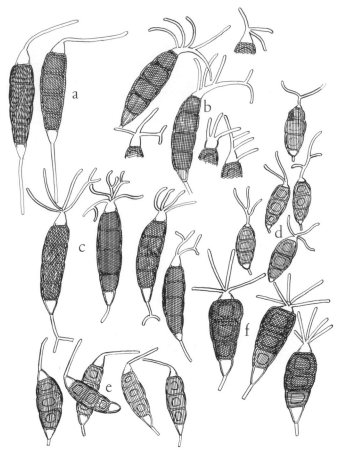

FIG. 2.   Conidia of (a) *Monochaetia seiridioides*, (b) *Pestalotia cornu-cervae*, (c) *P. pezizoides*, (d) *P. guepini*, (e) *Monochaetia ilicina* (= *M. monochaeta*), (f) *Pestalotia funerea*.

distinct from the lowest colored cell [Fig. 4b].   This is the extreme color difference between the upper two and the lowest colored cells.   The intense dark color can obscure the septum dividing the two upper colored cells.

If the conidia of a given specimen have concolorous olivaceous or pale brown cells the specimen belongs in the section *Concolorae, Olivae-Pallidae*. A portion of the conidia under observation may show a slight contrast in the coloration of the intermediate cells.   If the color contrast is not striking or not consistent throughout the mass of conidia in the microscopic mount, the specimen remains in the section *Concolorae, Olivae-Pallidae*, and should be keyed to the species in that category.

If there is a distinct and consistent color difference between the upper two and the lowest colored cells of the conidia, that is, brown or umber vs. olivaceous or yellow-brown, then the specimen belongs in the section *Versi-*

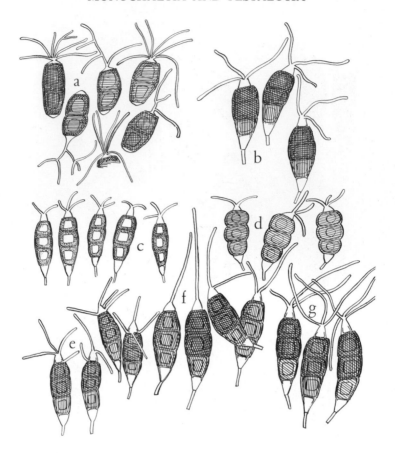

FIG. 3.   Conidia of (*a*) *Pestalotia caulicola*, (*b*) *P. oleandri*, (*c*) *P. podocarpi*, (*d*) *P. torulosa*, (*e*) *P. gravesii*, (*f*) *P. monochaetioides*, (*g*) *P. conigena*.

colorae, Umbrae-Olivae.   If the contrast is extreme, that is, the upper two colored cells usually swollen, of an intense or chocolate brown color (fuliginous) and even opaque, the lowest colored cell olivaceous or yellow-brown, then the specimen belongs in the section *Versicolorae, Fuliginae-Olivae.*   In addition, the conidia may be strongly constricted at the septa dividing the colored cells [Fig. 3d], or usually the fuliginous and the olivaceous colored cells [Fig. 4b].   These color contrasts are illustrated in the text by figures of conidia of representative species embraced within the three categories of the author's system of classification.

The conidia are of different forms.   In some species they are clavate, in others narrow fusiform.   The exterior hyaline cells may be acute, long or short, cylindric, turbinate, or conic.   These peculiarities are useful distinguishing characters in defining species.

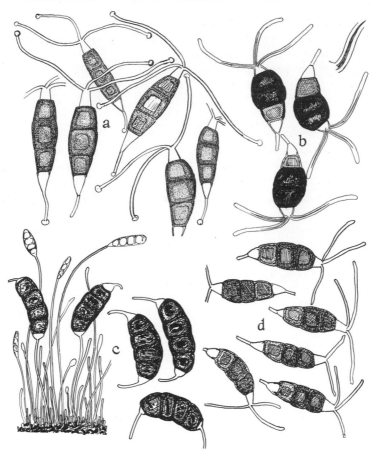

FIG. 4.   Variation in form and color of conidia.   (*a*) *Pestalotia theae*: three concolorous olivaceous or pale brown intermediate cells; setulae with knobbed or spatulate extremities. (*b*) *Pestalotia*: conidia with three versicolorous intermediate cells, the upper two of them fuliginous or dark brown and opaque; stout setulae with lumen.   (*c*) *Monochaetia cera-tospora*: sporogenous layer; conidia with hyaline exterior cells and four fuliginous, opaque intermediate cells.   (*d*) *Pestalotia*: conidia with three versicolorous intermediate cells, the upper two of them brown or umber, the lowest one olivaceous or pale brown.

The setulae, in addition to number and size, may show other peculiarities. They may arise together at the summit of the apical cells or they may be dis-connected.   They may be far apart or they may arise from the slope or even from the bases of the apical cells [Fig. 3e].   The setulae may be filamentous and flexuous or coarse and rigid, projecting forward and widely divergent or reflexed backward.   If coarse and thick, they may show a lumen extending from the base of the setulae toward their middle point [Fig. 4b].   They may be simple or branched, or both.   The length of the setulae and their number, if reasonably constant, are useful specific characters.   The extremities of the setulae may be capitate or spatulate [Fig. 4a].   Consideration of all these features appears in the keys to the species and the species descriptions.

Units of measure can be useless if the calibration of the microscope is inaccurate or if low-power lenses are used.   Measurements are changed by the culture of the fungus on different substrata and they are increased by growth on artificial nutrient media.   The subject of variation of the species and the influence of substrate on the form and dimensions of the conidia have been treated by numerous investigators and recently by Tandon (Proc. Nat. Acad. Sci. India 25, 1–2, 11–14,1956) and Gambogi (Nuovo Gior. Bot. Ital. n.s. 63, 2–3, 248–256,1956). Therefore, latitude must be recognized in employing the measurements in the text, and small differences in width and length between descriptions and specimens are insignificant.   With this approach the keys should be helpful in the identification of specimens and in discouraging the erection of superfluous species.

There are still too many species of *Pestalotia*.   The specimen must be distinctly different from anything that is recognized to be considered new. To the student disposed to naming new species, let me advise caution and judgment.   If the traditional system of describing new species continues, then some bolder plan of regulation and administration more effective than the present method is necessary to curb the practice.   Otherwise a monographic study can be futile and virtually impossible of accomplishment in view of the magnitude of the work and the inaccessibility of type material.

MONOCHAETIA

Melanconiales, Melanconiaceae, Phaeophragmiae

Monochaetia (Sacc.) Allescher, Rabh. Krypt. Flora 1, Abt. 7,665,1902.
Seiridium Nees ex Krombh., Abbild. Beschr. essb. schäd. verd. Schwämme.
    1:6,1831.
Hyaloceras Dur. & Mont., Flore d'Algerie Crypt., 1846, p. 587.
    Fruiting bodies black, carbonaceous, usually true acervuli with or without stromatic area, sometimes pycnidia or pseudopycnidia, but usually without a true ostiole and rarely as loose fertile hyphae without a distinct stratum or stroma. Conidia fusiform, straight or curved, 4- to 6-celled, crowned with a single hyaline setula; exterior cells hyaline or rarely dilutely colored; rarely with contents; intermediate cells equally or variably colored pale brown to almost black, guttulate; pedicels hyaline, simple, attached to the base of the conidia.

Section *Quadriloculatae*

Conidia 4-celled; two intermediate colored cells

Species Nos. 1–8

a. Intermediate cells of conidia greenish
    b. Conidia narrow fusiform, $20–30 \times 6–7\ \mu$ . . . .   1. *M. monorhincha*
a. Intermediate cells of conidia olivaceous or
    brown
    b. Conidia $12–16 \times 4–5\ \mu$
        c. Setulae $3–7\ \mu$ long, sometimes up to $10\ \mu$ 2. *M. saccardiana*
    b. Conidia $13–18 \times 3–5\ \mu$
        c. Setulae $3–5\ \mu$ . . . .   3. *M. rhododendricola*
    b. Conidia $15–17 \times 5–6\ \mu$
        c. Setulae $5–7\ \mu$ long. . . . .   4. *M. paeoniae*
        c. Setulae $18–30\ \mu$ long. . . . .   5. *M. excipuliformis*
    b. Conidia oblong, pyriform, $15–20 \times 6–8\ \mu$
        c. Setulae about $7\ \mu$ long . . . .   6. *M. depazeaeformis*
                                 7. *M. syringae*
    b. Conidia elliptic fusiform, $19–21 \times 7.5–9\ \mu$
        c. Setulae $3–5\ \mu$ long. . . . .   8. *M. berberidicola*

Section *Quinqueloculatae*

Conidia 5-celled; three intermediate colored cells

Species Nos. 9–25

a. Intermediate cells olivaceous to umber brown
   b. Conidia 13–18 × 4–5 μ
      c. Setulae 4–15 μ long.................. 9. *M. bicornis*
   b. Conidia 18–20 × 4–4.5 μ
      c. Setulae 12–14 μ long................. 10. *M. camelliae*
   b. Conidia 15–21 × 5–8 μ
      c. Setulae up to 19 μ, usually less than 15 μ
        long .... 11. *M. monochaeta*
                                             12. *M. alnea*
                                             13. *M. osyrella*
                                             14. *M. rosae-caninae*
   b. Conidia 18–24 × 6–8 μ
      c. Setulae 5 μ long..................... 15. *M. phyllostictea*
   b. Conidia 20–23 × 8–9.5 μ
      c. Setulae 8–10 μ long.................. 16. *M. schini*
   b. Conidia 20–26 × 6–9 μ
      c. Setulae up to 10 μ long .... 17. *M. berberidis*
      c. Setulae 5–15 μ long.................. 18. *M. concentrica*
      c. Setulae 10–38 μ long................. 19. *M. kansensis*
   b. Conidia 25–35 × 6.5–9.5 μ
      c. Setulae 9–13 μ .... 20. *M. hysteriiformis*
   b. Conidia 30–35 × 7–10 μ
      c. Setulae 8–10 μ .... 21. *M. miersii*
   b. Conidia 35–38 × 7 μ
      c. Setulae up to 15 μ................... 22. *M. macropoda*
a. Intermediate cells chocolate brown, fuliginous, opaque
   b. Conidia 20–23 × 6–9.5 μ
      c. Setulae 9–13 μ .... 23. *M. russeliae*
   b. Conidia 18–29 × 5.5–6.5 μ
      c. Setulae 12–16 μ .... 24. *M. osyridella*
   b. Conidia 22–30 × 7–10 μ
      c. Setulae 20–32 μ .... 25. *M. cryptomeriae*

Section *Sexloculatae*

Conidia 6-celled; four intermediate colored cells

Species Nos. 26–41

a. Intermediate cells olivaceous brown or fuliginous
   b. Conidia 18–22 × 9–11 μ, fuliginous
      c. Setulae 8–10 μ .... 26. *M. terebinthi*

b. Conidia 19–23 × 6–7 μ, olivaceous brown
   c. Setulae 12–16 μ .... 27. *M. curtisii*
b. Conidia 20–23 × 7.5–8.5 μ, umber
   c. Setulae 6–10 μ .... 28. *M. breviaristata*
                                            29. *M. juniperi*
b. Conidia 21–32 × 7.5–10 μ
   c. Setulae up to 8 μ................... 30. *M. diospyri*
   c. Setulae 6–13 μ .... 31. *M. unicornis*
                                            32. *M. turgida*
                                            33. *M. tecomae*
   c. Setulae 10–18 μ .... 34. *M. veneta*
   c. Setulae 23–25 μ .... 35. *M. rhododendri*
   c. Setulae 30–45 μ .... 36. *M. jefferisii*
b. Conidia 25–35 μ
   bb. Conidia 7–9 μ wide, umber............. 37. *M. crataegina*
   bb. Conidia 9–12.5 μ wide, fuliginous .... 38. *M. ceratospora*
b. Conidia 30–40 × 7.5–9.5 μ
   c. Setulae 8 μ .... 39. *M. plagiochaetia*
   c. Setulae 9–35 μ .... 40. *M. seiridioides*
b. Conidia 35–37 × 12 μ
   c. Setula 12 μ .... 41. *M. coryneoidea*

Species Descriptions

Section *Quadriloculatae*

Species Nos. 1–8

1. **Monochaetia monorhincha** (Speg.) Sacc., Syll. Fung. 18:485,1906.
   Pestalotia decolorata Speg. var. *monorhinca* Speg., Anal. Soc. Ci. Argent.
      13:22–23,1882.
   P. monorhincha (Speg.) Sacc., Syll. Fung. 3:798,1884.

Conidia 4-celled, 20–30 × 6–7 μ, intermediate cells greenish, exterior cells
hyaline, drawn out into beaks at the apices which are often curved.

On wilting leaves of *Eugenia uniflora* L. Quilmes, Argentina, July 1881.
Saccardo made a species of the variety and also changed the spelling of the
specific name to *monorhynca*. The type specimen was not examined so that
the position of the species remains uncertain.

2. **Monochaetia saccardiana** (Vogl.) Sacc., Syll. Fung. 22:1229,1913.
   Pestalotia saccardiana Vogl. Atti Soc. Ven.-Trent. Sci. Nat. Padova
      9:233 (reprint, p. 27), 1885, pl. X, fig. 32.

P. microspora Ell. & Ev., Jour. Mycol. 4:46,1888; Syll. Fung. 10:489,1892;
    non *P. microspora* Speg., Anal. Soc. Ci. Argent. 10:31–32,1880.
P. minor Ell. & Ev., N. Am. Fungi ?178,1889.
P. ellisii Sacc. & Syd., Syll. Fung. 14:1030,1889; 15:242,1901.
Coryneum mucronatum Massal., Malpighia 8:208,1894, tab. IV, fig. 17;
    Syll. Fung. 11:577,1895; Allescher in Rabh. Krypt. Flora 1: Abt.
    7,656,1902.
Monochaetia mucronata (Massal.) Maire, Bull. Soc. Bot. Fr. 53:187,1906;
    Syll. Fung. 22:1229,1913.

Pustules sparse or gregarious, amphigenous, generally distributed over
the matrix or limited to spots, subepidermal, erumpent, black, globose to
lenticular. Conidia small, narrow elliptic, 4-celled, $12–16 \times 4–5\ \mu$, the two
intermediate cells olivaceous, equally colored, $8–11\ \mu$; exterior hyaline cells
acute, the small apical cells attenuate; setulae short, curved, filiform, $3–7\ \mu$
long, rarely up to $10\ \mu$ long; pedicels slender, $18–25\ \mu$, or shorter, $6–10\ \mu$ long.

On dead areas in persisting or fallen leaves of *Quercus*, New Jersey.

Specimens examined: On fallen leaves of *Quercus coccinea* Muench.,
Newfield, N. J., March 1882 in Ell. & Everhart, N. Am. Fungi No. 2178,
sub *P. minor* Ell. & Ev. (*P. microspora* Ell. & Ev.). Fructifications of *M.
monochaeta* (Desm.) Allesch. similar to the fungus in Ellis & Everhart, N. Am.
Fungi No. 1353, sub *P. monochaeta* Desm., are also present in the matrix.
On dry leaves of *Q. pedunculata* Ehrh. [= *Q. robur* L.], Italy, leg. Spegazzini
sub *Pestalotia saccardiana* Vogl.; on *Q. pubescens* Willd. Verona, Italy, Feb.
1890, leg. Scaveaghe, sub *Coryneum mucronata* Massal.; on spots on persisting leaves of *Quercus lusitanica* Lamk., Tlemcen forest near Hafir, North
Africa, April 21, 1906.

The fungus was also described with the name *Pestalotia microspora* Ell.
& Ev. This is a later homonym of *P. microspora* Speg., occurring on leaves
of *Hedera* (Anal. Soc. Ci., Argent. 10:31–32,1880; Syll. Fung. 3:789,1885,
and Guba, Mycologia 24:372,1932). Ellis and Everhart, in 1899, offered
the new name *P. minor* Ell. & Ev. Saccardo and Sydow, not aware of the
circumstances, proposed the new name, *P. ellisii* Sacc. & Syd., in 1899. The
fungus described by Ellis and Everhart belongs to the genus *Monochaetia*
while Spegazzini's fungus belongs to the genus *Pestalotia*. The first valid
published specific name for the species under consideration is that of Voglino
(1885); hence the accepted name is *Monochaetia saccardiana* (Vogl.) Sacc.
The illustration of this fungus, in Saccardo Fungi Italici, tab. 1119,1881, is
incorrectly designated *Monochaetia monochaeta* Desm. An earlier description and illustration of *M. saccardiana* by Saccardo (Atti Soc. Ven.-Trent.
Sci. Nat. Padova 2:198,1873, pl. 17, fig. 25) incorrectly carries the name
Pestalotia monochaeta Desm. Maire (Bull. Soc. Bot. Fr. 52:187,1906)
reported that *Coryneum mucronatum* Massal. belongs to the genus *Mono-*

chaetia because the apex of the conidia possesses a short appendage-like mucron which is sometimes elongated as in *Monochaetia monochaeta* (Desm.) Allescher.

3. **Monochaetia rhododendricola** Yoshii, Sci. Rep. Matsuyama Agr. Col. 13: 33–36,1954.

Spots at first dark brown on upper surface, pale brown beneath, round, 0.5–1.5 mm diam, becoming larger and angular, 3–15 mm diam, bordered by the veins of the matrix, sometimes with brown or purple border, the centers becoming grayish white, confluent, forming large dead areas. Pustules small, dotting the upper surface, 90–150 μ in diam. Conidia 4-celled, oblong or cylindric fusiform, somewhat constricted at septa, erect or curved, 13.2–17.8 (mean 16 μ) × 3.2–4.4 μ (mean 3.7 μ); intermediate colored cells olivaceous, concolorous; exterior cells hyaline; setulae 2.2–4.4 μ long; pedicels 14.8–25.4 μ long.

In spots on living leaves of *Rhododendron obtusum* Planch. var. *kaempferi* (Planch.) Wil., Ehime, Japan, H. Yoshii, July 17, 1948; H. Yoshii and K. Fukuda, July 24, 1948.

4. **Monochaetia paeoniae** (Maubl.) Sacc. & D. Sacc., Syll. Fung. 18:485,1906.
   Pestalotia paeoniae Maubl., Bull. Soc. Mycol. Fr. 92–93,1905, pl. 7, fig. III.
   Hyaloceras paeoniae Curzi & Barbarini, Atti. Ist. Bot. Univ. Pavia, Ser. III, 3:188,1927, tab. 12, fig. 5.

Acervuli subepidermal, later erumpent, 250–300 μ in diam.; hymenium dark-olivaceous, superficial. Conidia erect or curved, 3-septate, not or only slightly constricted at septa, dark olivaceous; exterior cells subhyaline; 15–17 × 5–6 μ; one setula at apex, somewhat divergent, 5–7 μ; pedicels hyaline, 7–10 μ.

On dead twigs of *Paeonia arborea* Donn. [=*P. suffruticosa* Andr.] near Paris, associated with other fungus saprophytes, secondary to *Botrytis paeoniae* Oud.

The same fungus collected on decorticated twigs of the same host plant at Aternum, Italy, was described as *Hyaloceras paeoniae* Curzi & Barbarini in 1927. The species was described with 4-celled conidia, 20–30 × 4–5 μ, and filiform setulae, 10–15 μ long. The measurements seem unreasonable for a 4-celled conidial form. Table 12, fig. 5, shows both 4- and 5-celled conidia.

5. **Monochaetia excipuliformis** Bubak, Ann. Mycol. 4:120,1906; Syll. Fung. 22:1229,1913.

Pustules borne under the epidermis, later erumpent and surrounded by torn shreds of epidermis; black, standing in more or less thick groups and covering the matrix, round, elongate or irregular in outline, pulvinate or patellate, often confluent, 50 μ thick. Conidia 3-septate, elliptic or spindle-form, 11–18 × 4–5.5 μ; intermediate cells olive-brown; exterior cells hyaline or slightly colored, rounded, tapering; setulae 18–30 μ; pedicels 20–30 μ, straight or curved.

On dead twigs of *Salix* sp. along Moldau River, near Prague, Bohemia. In habit the fungus appears like one of the *Excipulaceae*.

6. **Monochaetia depazeaeformis** (Auers.) Allescher, Rabh., Krypt. Flora 1; Abt. 7,666–677,1902; Syll. Fung. 18:485,1906.
   Pestalotia depazeaeformis Auers. Oest. Bot. Z. 18:209,1868; Syll. Fung. 10:494,1892.

Pustules pyreniform, epiphyllous, scattered, seated in ash-colored spots with dark-purple margin. Conidia 18 × 8 μ, oblong, dark, 4-celled, crowned with a single setula.

On leaves of *Arbutus uva-ursi* L. [= *Arctostaphylos uva-ursi* Spreng.], near Seis, Tirol, 1866, leg. Franciscus Leber, Baron de Hausmann (H. Heufler) and described as like *Depazea* or *Phyllosticta*. The fungus is not well understood and may possibly belong elsewhere.

7. **Monochaetia syringae** (Oud.) Allescher, Rabh. Krypt. Flora 1; Abt. 7,675, 1902; Syll. Fung. 18:485,1906.
   Pestalotia syringae Oud., Nederl. Kruidk. Arch. 5: Ser. 2, 510, 1889, fig. 40; Syll. Fung. 10:494,1892.

Pustules erumpent across the crevices of the periderm, sometimes solitary or in groups of two or three. Conidia 4-celled, pyriform or oblong, erect, sometimes inequilateral, 15–20 × 6–7 μ, intermediate dark cells pallid, the exterior cells paler; one setula, 7 μ long, pedicels 35 μ long, remnants up to 7 μ long, remaining attached to the basal cell, the setula and pedicel thus easily confused.

On twigs of *Syringa vulgaris* L. Rijswijk, Netherlands, February 1889, Mlle. Destrée.

8. **Monochaetia berberidicola** Vassiljevsky, Vassiljevsky and Karakulin, Fungi Imperf. Par. 2:466,1950.
   M. berberidis Girzitska, Bull. Jard. Bot. Kiev (U.S.S.R.), 5–6:167,1927, pl. 1, fig. 1.

Pustules punctiform, sparse, black, innate, 250–350 μ diam. Conidia fusiform, 3-septate, not constricted at septa, 19–20.6 × 7.6–9 μ; two intermediate cells olivaceous, exterior cells somewhat olivaceous; setulae filiform, hyaline, 3–5 μ long; pedicels hyaline, septate, 30–50 μ long.

On branch of *Berberis vulgaris* L., Bot. Gard., Kiev, U.S.S.R., 1926. The new name was necessary since *M. berberidis* Girzitska is a later homonym of *M. berberidis* Lind in Rostrup's Danish Fungi, 1913, 489, pl. 8, fig. 104; Syll. Fung. 25:610,1931.

Section *Quinqueloculatae*

Species Nos. 9–25

9. **Monochaetia bicornis** (Dur. & Mont.) Sacc., Syll. Fung. 18:485,1906.
   Pestalotia bicornis Dur. & Mont., Flore d'Algerie Crypt. 1:586,1846; Syll. Fung. 3:797,1884.

Pustules punctiform, sparse, or gregarious, often coalescing, 150–250 μ, globose to lenticular, innate-erumpent, carbonaceous and sooty, largely epiphyllous, seated in pale, definitely bordered, brown or ash-colored areas. Conidia narrow fusiform, usually erect, acute at both ends, usually 5-celled, sometimes 4-celled, 13–18 × 4–5 μ; 3 intermediate cells pale olivaceous, equally colored, guttulate, 9–13 μ long, hardly constricted at septa; setulae short, curved or oblique, 4–15 μ, usually less than 12 μ long; pedicels oblique or curved to one side, 3–16 μ, but usually less than 10 μ long.

On spots on leaves of *Quercus coccifera* L., Algeria, Durieu, in herb. Mus. d'Hist. Nat. Paris (*lectotype*); on leaves of *Quercus* sp., California, Harkness, herb. Ellis No. 2065, in herb. Farlow; on spots on living leaves of *Quercus* sp. caused by *Taphrina caerulescens* (Mont. & Desm.) Tul., College Station, Texas, May 8, 1915, F. H. Blodgett, in Nat. Fungus Coll., sub *Monochaetia taphrinicola* (Ell. & Ev.) Sacc.

The original description is based on two distinct fungi, one on leaves of *Phillyrea media* L. collected at Stora, Algeria, which is a *Cryptostictis*, the other on leaves of *Quercus* collected in Algeria by Durieu which is a *Monochaetia*. The conidia are stated to have 3 cells and to bear at each extremity a single curved appendage. Montagne's drawings of conidia of the fungus on *Phillyrea* show 2 and 3 cells, with setulae at apex, pedicel at base, and a lateral setula at the base of the lowest cell whence the specific name "bicornis." Conidia are shown with and without a basal hyaline cell. Another conidium is drawn reversed with 2 setulae crowning the hyaline superior cell, which is actually the pedicel and setula at the base, then 3 colored cells and a curved setula at the base, actually the apex. Montagne's drawing of a conidium of the fungus on *Quercus* shows 3 colored cells, with pedicel at base and a setula at apex, but no exterior hyaline cells. This was the error of the illustration.

The name *Monochaetia bicornis* (Dur. & Mont.) Sacc. is retained for the fungus on *Quercus* even though the binomial conveys a conflicting meaning. The emended description is drawn from the lectotype specimen established above. The fungus on *Phillyrea* is characterized by 5-celled conidia, intermediate dark cells, exterior hyaline cells, one apical setula, one setula projecting from the basal cell, and a coarse pedicel indicating the genus *Cryptostictis*, and the name *Cryptostictis bisetulata* Guba nom. nov. is here established for it.

10. **Monochaetia camelliae** Miles, Mycologia 18:167,1926.

Pustules punctiform, gregarious, smoky black, subcutaneous, 300–400 μ in diam, rupturing the cuticle irregularly. Conidia 4-septate, fusoid, pointed at each end, not constricted, 18–20 × 4–4.5 μ, intermediate cells dark olivaceous, basal cell usually dilutely colored, apical cell hyaline and terminated by a stipitate, filiform, hyaline setula, straight or bent at a right angle near the point of union with the conidium, 12–14 μ long.

On leaves of *Camellia japonica* L., Columbus, Miss., No. 460 (type).

11. **Monochaetia monochaeta** (Desm.) Allescher, Rabh., Krypt. Flora 1: Abt. 7,667,1902.

Pestalotia monochaeta Desm., Ann. Sci. Nat. Bot. III, 10:355–356,1848. Voglino, Atti Soc. Ven.-Trent. Sci. Nat. Padova 9:235 (reprint, p. 29), 1885, pl. 10, fig. 27; Syll. Fung. 3:797,1884.

Hendersonia acuminata Lév., Ann. Sci. Nat. Bot. III, 10:253–254,1848; Cooke, Nuovo Gior. Bot. Ital. 10:27,1878.

Coryneum rostratum Fckl., Syll. Fung. 3:797,1884; Fuckel, Fungi Rhenani, No. 1657, 1866.

Pestalotia ilicina Sacc., Nuovo Gior. Bot. Ital. 8:198,1876.

P. peckii G. W. Clint., Peck, Rep. Bot. in Rep.; N. Y. State Mus. 28:59, 1879; Syll. Fung. 3:797,1884; 15:242,1901; 18:485,1906.

P. saccardoi Speg., Michelia 1:480,1879; Syll. Fung. 3:797,1884.

Cryptostictis ilicina (Sacc.) Sacc., Syll. Fung. 3:443,1884; 15:242,1901.

Pestalotia taphrinicola Ell. & Ev., Jour. Mycol. 4:104,1888; Syll. Fung. 10:495,1892.

P. pallida Ell. & Ev., Jour. Mycol. 4:46,104,132,1888; 5:143,156,1889; Syll. Fung. 10:495,1892.

P. affinis Ell. & Ev., Jour. Mycol. 5:156,1889. Not *P. affinis* Sacc. & Vogl. Atti Soc. Ven.-Trent. Sci. Nat. Padova 9:2:216,1885, tab. 8, fig. 6.

P. nervalis Ell. & Ev., Jour. Mycol. 5:157,1889; Syll. Fung. 10:495,1892.

P. uncinata Ell. & Kellerm., Jour. Mycol. 5:143,1889; Syll. Fung. 10:495, 1892.

P. everhartii Sacc., Syll. Fung. 10:492,1892; 15:241,1901.

P. monochaeta Desm. var. *gallicola* Trotter. Atti R. Ist. Ven. Sci. lett. arti 59:728,1900, fig. 44; Syll. Fung. 16:1016,1902.

M. monochaeta (Desm.) Allescher var. *gallicola* Trotter, Rabh. Krypt.-Flora 1: Abt. 7,668,1902.

M. saccardoi (Speg.) Allescher, Rabh., Krypt.-Flora 1: Abt. 7,671–672, 1902.

M. desmazierii Sacc., Syll. Fung. 18:485,1906; 22:1229,1913.

M. everhartii Sacc., Syll. Fung. 18:485,1906.

M. nervalis (Ell. & Ev.) Sacc., Syll. Fung. 18:485,1906.

M. taphrinicola (Ell. & Ev.) Sacc., Syll. Fung. 18:485,1906.

M. uncinata (Ell. & Kellerm.) Sacc., Syll. Fung. 18:485,1906.

M. pallida (Ell. & Ev.), Sacc., Syll. Fung. 18:485,1906.

M. quercina Politis Mem. Soc. Hist. Nat. Afr. Nord. Hors.-Ser. 2:269, 1949.

M. rhododendri Yoshii, Sci. Rep. Matsuyama Agr. Col. 13:30–33, Nov. 1954.

Hyaloceras monochaetum (Desm.) Died. var. *gallicola* Trotter in Diedicke, Krypt. Flora Mark Brandenb. 9:878,1915.

H. pachysporum Bubak var. *brevicorne* Bubak, Ann. Mycol. 14:154–155, 1916.

Brown or grayish indefinite spots or areas in leaves sometimes delimited by sharp margins, frequently zonate or concentrically divided, the infected areas sometimes insect-eaten or infected with the fungus *Taphrina caerulescens* or confined to dead lobes or margins or generally distributed over the dead leaves. Pustules punctiform, globose to globose-lenticular, scattered or gregarious and confluent, usually subepidermal, erumpent, surrounded by torn shreds of the epidermis, the contents oozing out in small black heaps, sooty, staining the matrix, 75–225 μ, usually 100–150 μ in diam.

Conidia 5-celled, elliptic, or narrow fusiform, erect, or slightly curved, tapering toward the extremities, 15–21 × 5–8 μ, usually 5–7 μ wide; three intermediate colored cells pale olivaceous, pellucid, rarely darker, equally colored, guttulate, 10–15 μ long, hardly constricted at septa, exterior cells hyaline or yellowish, conic or pointed, basal cell rather acute, usually with some contents; apical cell elongated, prolonged into a short oblique setula, 5–19 μ long, usually less than 15 μ long; pedicels oblique, like setulae, slender, equal to conidia in length or shorter.

On dry wilting leaves of *Quercus*, France, 1848, sub *Pestalotia monochaeta* Desm. in herb. Mus. d'Hist. Nat., Paris.

The fungus is widespread on oak leaves. The original description of *P. monochaeta* Desm. is incomplete. Only such information as: "conidia 4-septate, 20 μ long and pale olivaceous intermediate colored cells" is helpful. This fungus was renamed *Monochaetia monochaeta* (Desm.) Allescher (1902), and is accepted as the type of the genus as noted previously. Saccardo (1906) applied the new name *M. desmazierii* Sacc. and its validity was recognized by Graves (Mycologia 4:172,1912). It has been heretofore the accepted name.

Pestalotia ilicina Sacc. (Fungi Veneta (Sec. V) in Nuovo Gior. Bot. Ital. 8:198:1876) was described on wilting leaves of *Quercus ilex* L., Arco, Trentino, Italy, Sept. 1874. The original description reported ovoid, 5-celled conidia, $15 \times 7 \mu$, oblique setulae at apex, filiform pedicels $30 \times 1.7 \mu$. Specimens are distributed in Saccardo Mycotheca Veneta No. 327. The conidia are 5-celled, 15–19×5–7.5μ, 3 intermediate cells pale brown; setulae 6–13μ, pedicels 3–13μ. Saccardo later (Syll. Fung. 3:443–444, 1884) republished the original description of *P. ilicina* Sacc. but substituted the name *Cryptostictis ilicina* Sacc., a bad error. Thus Saccardo (Syll. Fung. 15:242,1901) reported *Pestalotia ilicina* Sacc. [= *Cryptostictis ilicina* Sacc.], which is wrong. *P. ilicina* Sacc., described on leaves of *Quercus ilex* L., is the same fungus as *Pestalotia monochaeta* Desm.

Specimens examined: On decaying leaves of *Quercus* in forest, Conegliano and Montello, Italy, 1876–77, sub *P. saccardoi* Speg.; Germany, in Fuckel *Fungi Rhenani*, No. 1657 (1866), sub *Coryneum rostratum* Fckl.; herb. Desmazières 1863, No. 8, March-April 1849 in herb. Mus. d'Hist. Nat., Paris, sub *P. monochaeta* Desm.; Angers, France, Guepin, herb. M.L.R. Tulasne in Mus. d'Hist. Nat., Paris, sub *P. monochaeta* Desm.; Montand, France, Castagne, in Mus. d'Hist. Nat., Paris, sub *P. monochaeta* Desm.; Angers, France, leg. Guepin, in herb. Roussel, Mus. d'Hist. Nat., Paris, sub *P. monochaeta* Desm.; on leaves associated with lesions caused by the fungus *Taphrina caerulescens*, College Station, Texas, May 8, 1915, F. H. Blodgett.

On leaves of *Quercus alba* L., Ohio, June 1883, W. A. Kellerman, No. 258, sub *P. pallida* Ell. & Ev.; New York, May and July, C. H. Peck in herb. N. Y. State Mus., sub *P. saccardoi* Speg.; *ibid.*, Buffalo, N. Y., May, G. W. Clinton, sub *P. peckii* G. W. Clinton; in lesions with *Taphrina caerulescens* (Mont. & Desm.) Tul., Newfield, N. J., Aug. 1888, in Ellis & Everhart, N. Am. Fungi No. 2179, sub *P. taphrinicola* Ell. & Ev.; Louisiana, A. B. Langlois, No. 1151, sub *P. taphrinicola* Ell. & Ev.; Racine, Wisc., Sept. 2, 1888, J. J. Davis, herb. J. J. Davis, University of Wisconsin sub *P. nervalis* Ell. & Ev.

On leaves of *Quercus coccinea* Muench. with *Taphrina caerulescens* (Mont. & Desm.) Tul., Newfield, N. J., in Ellis & Everhart, N. Am. Fungi No. 2179 sub *P. taphrinicola* Ell. & Ev.

On leaves of *Quercus ilex* L., Montand-les-Miramas, France, in herb. Roussel, leg. Castagne, Mus. d'Hist. Nat., Paris, sub *P. monochaeta* Desm.; ex. herb. Desm. in herb. Curtis in herb. Farlow, and Coll. Desmazières 1863, Nos. 8 and 283, sub *P. monochaeta* Desm. (syn., *Hendersonia acuminata* Lév.); Florence, Italy, 1860, L. Caldesi in Erbar. Critt. Ital. 652, fasc. 13, 14, 1861, sub *P. monochaeta* Desm.; *ibid.* Rabenhorst, Fungi europ., No. 1043; Arco, Trentino, Italy, Sept. 1874, in herb. mycol. P. A. Saccardo, and Saccardo Mycotheca Veneta, No. 327, 1876, as *P. ilicina* Sacc. (type); Lenormand Montand, Marseille, France, in herb. Curtis in herb. Farlow; herb. de Notaris (Italia), misit Sprague, in herb. Curtis in herb. Farlow, sub *P. monochaeta* Desm.; Bologna, Italy, Oct. 30, 1953, G. Goidanich; France, M. Castagne, No. 742, sub *Hendersonia acuminata* Lév.; Arco, Tirolia, May 1915, Diettrich-Kalkhoff, sub *Hyaloceras pachysporum* Bubak var. *brevicorne* Bubak.

On leaves of *Quercus palustris* Muench., associated with injuries caused by *Taphrina caerulescens* (Mont. & Desm.) Tul., Columbia, Kan.

On leaves of *Quercus pedunculata* Ehrh. [= *Q. robur* L.] in Roumeguère Fungi Gallici Exs. 6160, Sainte-Isabelle (Côte d'Or), Sept. 1891. F. Fautrey sub *P. monochaeta* Desm.; on dry galls in leaves (*Andricus fecundator*), Mantua, Italy, sub *Monochaetia monochaeta* (Desm.) Allescher var. *gallicola* Trotter.

On dry wood of *Quercus pontica* K. Koch, Berlin Bot. Gard. No. 3190, Aug. 1928.

On leaves of *Quercus rubra* L., Vosges, France, leg. Mangin, in herb. Mus. d'Hist. Nat., Paris.

On dead leaves of *Quercus tinctoria* [= *Q. velutina* Lam.], Newfield, N. J., May 1898, in Ellis & Everhart, Fung. Col. No. 1353 (label also cites Ellis & Everhart, N. Am. Fungi No. 1624, sub *P. monochaeta* Desm.); St. George, Kan., June 1888, Kellerman and Swingle, No. 1269, sub *P. uncinata* Ell. & Kellerm. with *Chaetophoma maculosa* Ell. & Morgan.

On fallen leaves of *Quercus variabilis* Bl., Nanking, China, April 18, 1930, S. C. Teng, No. 610, sub *Monochaetia saccardoi* (Speg.) Allesch.

On fallen leaves of *Quercus velutina* Lam., Tisbury, Mass., July 27, 1930, A. Kevorkian, herb. Farlow.

On leaves of *Quercus virens* Ait. [= *Q. virginiana* Mill.], Gainesville, Fla., in Ravenel, Fungi Am. 36, sub *P. concentrica* Berk. & Br.

On fallen leaves of Japan chestnut *Castanea crenata* Sieb. & Zucc., Flora Ludoviciana No. 1665, Lafayette, La., Mar. 21, 1888, A. B. Langlois in herb. N. Y. Bot. Gard., sub *Pestalotia affinis* Ell. & Ev. [= *Monochaetia everhartii* Sacc.]. The species is not to be confused with *P. affinis* Sacc. & Vogl. described earlier on *Juglans* and *Vitis*.

On brown weathered leaves of *Rhododendron maximum* L., Burbank, Tenn., R. Thaxter, in herb. Farlow.

On dead areas on living leaves of *Rhododendron linearifolium* Sieb. & Zucc. var. *macrosepalum* (Maxim.) Makino, Matsuyama, Ehime, Japan, H. Yoshii, July 20, 1947; also H. Yoshii and K. Fukuda, July 10, 1948, sub *Monochaetia rhododendri* Yoshii. This species name is a homonym and the characters furnished in the original description are the same as for *M. desmazierii* Sacc.

Mycologists have confused *M. desmazierii* [= *M. monochaeta*] with *M. mucronata*, which has 4-celled conidia. Saccardo described *M. desmazierii* with 4-celled conidia. The specimen on dry leaves of *Quercus pedunculata* Ehrh. described by Saccardo (Atti Soc. Ven.-Trent. Sci. Nat.

Padova 2:198,1873, pl. 17, fig. 25) with 4-celled conidia (2 dark cells) and short setulae, 6 μ long, is *Monochaetia saccardiana* (Vogl.) Sacc. Voglino described conidia with 5 cells (Atti Soc. Ven.-Trent Sc. Nat. Padova 9, 2:235 (reprint, p. 29), 1885, pl. 10, fig. 27). Diedicke described 4-celled conidia, but his figure 9 (p. 870) shows 5 cells. The chestnut and oak large leaf spot fungus described by Graves (Mycologia 4:170–174,1912) and Hedgcock (Mycologia 21:324–325, 1929) and named *M. desmazierii* Sacc. is more properly *M. kansensis* (Ell. & Barthol.) Sacc. *Monochaetia desmazierii* will not rot apples (Wollenweber and Hochapfel, Z. Pflanzenkr. 46:403–404, 1936).

The large leaf spot of chestnut is the subject of a paper by Nisikado and Watanabe in Japan (Ber. Ohara Inst. Land. u. Forschw. 10:1:9–16, Mar. 1953). The disease and pathogen are described at length. Significance is given to the variation of the fungus on the host and on nutrient culture media.

12. **Monochaetia alnea** (Hariot & Briard) Allescher, Rabh. Krypt. Flora 1: Abt. 7, 666, 1902; Syll. Fung. 18:485,1906.
   Pestalotia alnea Hariot & Briard, Jour. Bot. Fr. 5:172,1891; Syll. Fung. 10:494,1892.

Spots dried out, gray-brown, circular, on both leaf surfaces, 5–7 mm in diam, surrounded by a brown, indefinite line. Pustules epiphyllous, punctiform, subepidermal, erumpent, globose, 200–250 μ in diam. Conidia ovate-elongate, pointed at both ends, 16–20 × 6–8 μ with 3–4 septa, intermediate cells brown, exterior cells hyaline, apical cells with a hyaline, often curved setula, 12–16 μ long. Pedicels filiform, 12–16 μ.

On dry leaves of *Alnus glutinosa* Gaertn., Ville-sur-Terre, France, P. Hariot.

13. **Monochaetia osyrella** (Tassi) Sacc. & D. Sacc., Syll. Fung. 18:486,1906.
   Pestalotia osyridella Tassi, Boll. Lab. Ort. Bot. R. Univ. Siena 6:127,1904.

Pustules at first subcutaneous, then erumpent, varying in size, solitary or somewhat gregarious. Conidia fusiform, 5-celled, 18–20 × 7–8 μ; exterior cells hyaline, the 3 intermediate cells yellowish; setulae erect, rarely oblique, 14–15 μ long; pedicels usually equalling the length of conidium.

On dead twigs of *Osyris alba* L., S. Colomba, Siena, Italy, Sept. 1903. Saccardo and D. Saccardo (Syll. Fung. 18:486,1906) adopted the spelling *M. osyrella* (Tassi) Sacc. & D. Sacc.

14. **Monochaetia rosae-caninae** Unamuno, Bol. R. Soc. Española Hist. Nat. 29:123,1929, fig. 4.

Spots round, 3–4 mm diam, brown, surrounded by violet zone. Acervuli subepidermal, epiphyllous, sparse, pale brown, 80–85 × 30–40 μ. Conidia oblong, 5-celled, not constricted at septa, $16-18 \times 5-7 \mu$, the three intermediate cells fuliginous, exterior cells hyaline; setulae filiform, curved or somewhat hooked; pedicels about equalling length of conidia, apical cells conic, narrowed at the base.

On living leaves of *Rosa canina* L., Izurza, near Durango (Vizcaya), Mexico, Sept. 1928, associated with *Septoria rosae* Desm., and *Cercospora* sp.

15. **Monochaetia phyllostictea** (Sacc.) Allescher, Rabh. Krypt. Flora 1: Abt.
    7, 674, 1902; Syll. Fung. 18:485,1906.

   Pestalotia phyllostictea Sacc., Atti R. Ist. Ven.-Sci. lett. arti VI:3:736
   (reprint, p. 25), 1885, pl. XI, fig. 32; Syll. Fung. 10:493,1892.

   Monochaetia cydoniae P. Evans & Doidge, Bull. Misc. Inform. Kew,
   no. 9:428,1908; Syll. Fung. 25:610,1931.

Spots brown, weathered or bleached on drying, variable. Pustules punctiform, $75-125 \mu$ diam, erumpent. Conidia 5-celled, elliptic fusoid, erect or slightly curved, $19-22 \times 6-8 \mu$; intermediate colored cells umber, equally colored, $14-16 \mu$ long, guttulate; setulae straight, sharply curved to one side, or at right angles to the axis of the conidia, up to 5μ long; exterior hyaline cells short, obtuse or broad conoid; pedicels short.

On spots on living leaves of *Rubus fruticosus* L., France, leg. Roumeguère in herb. P. A. Saccardo. The pedicel is stated to measure $15-20 \times 1.5 \mu$.

Monochaetia cydoniae P. Evans & Doidge, on living twigs of *Cydonia vulgaris* Pers. [= *C. oblonga* Mill.] from Transvaal, South Africa, and collected by I. B. Pole Evans, appears to be the same as *M. phyllostictea*. This fungus was described with 3 to 4 septate conidia, $18-24 \times 6 \mu$, crowned with oblique setulae.

16. **Monochaetia schini** Lucas & Camara, Agron, Lusit. 16:103, 1954, tab. 3
    fig. 11–12.

Acervuli subconoid, immersed, chestnut-brown, somewhat large, $170-230 \times 115-200 \mu$; conidiophores somewhat filiform-conoid, slender, colorless, minute, $4.5-5 \times 1.3 \mu$. Conidia $20-23 \times 8-9.5 \mu$, numerous, more or less ellipsoid, erect, curved, 5-celled, not or only slightly constricted at septa; intermediate colored cells brown, exterior cells hyaline; setulae $8-9.5 \times 1.2-2 \mu$.

On twigs of *Schinus molle* L., Sacavem Hort. Sta. Agron. Nat., Portugal, Maria Tereza Lucas, April 1953, associated with other fungi.

17. **Monochaetia berberidis** Lind, in Rostrup, Danish Fungi, 1913, pp. 489–
    490, pl. 8, fig. 104; Syll. Fung. 25:610,1931.

Spots epiphyllous, orbicular, dry, brown-margined; pustules sparse, epiphyllous, black, subcutaneous, later erumpent, $120-165 \mu$ diam. Conidia fusoid, curved, 4-septate, not constricted at septa, 20–27 × 6–9 μ; intermediate cells dark, exterior cells minute, hyaline; apical setulae 10 μ long, curved; pedicels 20 μ long.

On living leaves of *Berberis buxifolia* Lam., J. Gaardbogaard, Dec. 1897, J. Larsen.

18. **Monochaetia concentrica** (Berk. & Br.) Sacc., Syll. Fung. 18:485,1906.

> *Pestalozzia concentrica* Berk & Br., M. A. Curtis Geol. Nat. Hist. Survey, North Carolina, pt. 3 (Botany) 1867, p. 118, nom. nud.; Grevillea 2:156,1874; Syll. Fung. 3:797,1884.
>
> *P. coryli* Rostr., Bot. Tidsskr. 19:211,1895; Syll. Fung. 14:1027,1899.
>
> *Monochaetia coryli* (Rostr.) Allescher, Rabh. Krypt. Flora 1: Abt. 7, 669, 1902.
>
> *Monochaetia lentisci* Gonz.-Frag., Bol. R. Soc. Española Hist. Nat. 24: 450,1923–1924.

Similar to *Monochaetia desmazierii* except that the conidia are larger, 20–26 × 6.5–8.5 μ, and the 3 intermediate colored cells are darker or umber, 15–19 μ long. The setulae are characteristically short, not exceeding 15 μ. The pustules are concentrically disposed, and many of the specimens exhibit concentrically zoned spots or areas of different shades of brown color, but the zonation may be entirely absent.

On brown or ash-colored spots or generally distributed on dead weathered leaves of *Castanea*, *Quercus*, and *Corylus*.

The original description of the fungus cites Berkeley and Broome as the authorities for the name. This was later changed (Grevillea 6:135,1878) to Berkeley and Ravenel and this is the combination of authors accompanying the original specimen. The type description is vague and inaccurate, but nevertheless, Berkeley considered his fungus closely allied to *P. monochaeta* Desm., a 5-celled conidial form with a single setula. Berkeley described 3-septate conidia with a single setula and, more rarely, conidia with 3 setulae. The description becomes more confusing by including in the type concept a 6-celled conidial form of *Monochaetia* on *Pyrus*, *Malus* and *Crataegus* as follows: "*P. concentrica* Berk. & Br. Pustules concentrically arranged on pallid or white spots. Spores 3 septate, 25 μ long, with a single oblique or sometimes horizontal process at apex, more rarely with a 3-threaded crest. Nearly allied to *P. monochaeta* Desm. On leaves of *Pyrus*, South Carolina (Ravenel); leaves of apple, Hendersonville, N. C.; on *Crataegus*, Tuskegee, Alabama (Beaumont); on *Castanea pumila* (Beaumont)."

All but the fungus on *Castanea* have 6-celled conidia. They belong to the species *Monochaetia unicornis* (Cooke & Ell.) Sacc. and *M. turgida* (Atk.) Sacc., forms common to the *Rosales*. The form on *Castanea* has 5-celled conidia, and although it is the last one among the host plants mentioned in the type description, it carries the name *P. concentrica* Berk. & Rav. in Berkeley's handwriting and may be regarded as the type.

P. coryli Rostr. on leaves of *Corylus avellana* L., Viemose, near Petersvaerft, Denmark. Conidia 5-celled, $23-25 \times 6-7 \mu$, setulae $11-13 \mu$. The fungus was reported developing on brown leaf spots.

Specimens examined: On leaves of *Castanea pumila* (L.) Mill., Alabama, Beaumont, in herb. Kew. No. 5094 (type); on leaves of *Quercus*, Aiken, S. C., in Ravenal, Fungi Am. No. 34; on leaves of *Quercus coccinea* Muench., Islip, Long Island, N. Y., Oct. 2, 1914, R. C. Livington in herb. Forest Path. U.S.D.A., No. 20399 sub *Monochaetia desmazierii* Sacc., saprophytic following *Taphrina caerulescens*; on leaves of *Quercus coccinea* Muench. var. *tinctoria* DC. [= *Q. velutina* Lam.], Newfield, N. J., in Ellis & Everhart, N. Am. Fungi, 2nd Ser., No. 3563, sub *P. hysteriiformis* Berk. & Curt. On leaves and twigs of *Pistacia lentiscus* L. Segorbe (Castellón), Spain, 1922, Dr. C. Pau, sub *Monochaetia lentisci* Gonz.-Frag. Acervuli small: conidia $20-24 \times 6.8 \mu$, setulae $10-15 \mu$. There is nothing in the original description of *M. lentisci* to warrant a new species.

19. **Monochaetia kansensis** (Ell. & Barthol.) Sacc., Syll. Fung. 18:485,1906.
   Pestalotia monochaeta Desm. var. *quercus-pedunculatae* Sacc. nom. nud., Saccardo Mycotheca Veneta No. 324, 1876, and Rabenhorst, Fungi europ. No. 2119, 1876.
   P. monochaeta Desm. var. *castaneae-vescae* Sacc., nom. nud., Saccardo, Mycotheca Veneta No. 325, 1876.
   P. kansensis Ell. & Barthol., Erythea 4:26, 1896; Syll. Fung. 14:1028,1899.
   P. flagellata Earle, Bull. Torrey Bot. Club 24:30,1897; Syll. Fung. 14:1027, 1899.
   Monochaetia flagellata (Earle) Sacc., Syll. Fung. 18:485,1906.
   Monochaetia pachyspora Bubak, Oest. Bot. Z. 54:185,1904; Syll. Fung. 18:486,1906.

Pustules globose to lenticular, epiphyllous or hypophyllous on irregular brown spots and pale areas, arranged in broad concentric bands or generally distributed, black, dense, punctiform, solitary or densely gregarious, sometimes confluent, $100-250 \mu$ in diam, erumpent at maturity, rimosely dehiscent, sooty and blackening the matrix. Conidia 5-celled, erect, or sometimes slightly curved, tapering at both ends, $18-26 \times 6-8 \mu$, hardly constricted at the septa; intermediate colored cells olivaceous or umber, concolorous, pellucid, guttulate, $12-17 \mu$ long; exterior cells long conic, apical cells attenuated into a long, flexuous filiform setula bent abruptly sideward, $10-38 \mu$ or usually $15-26 \mu$ long; basal hyaline cells attenuated; pedicels $3-15 \mu$ long.

On leaves of *Castanea* and *Quercus*, usually associated with definitely bordered, concentrically zoned brown areas or spots, sometimes extending across or involving the entire leaf.

Specimens examined: On dead leaves of *Quercus macrocarpa* Michx., Rockport, Kan., Jan. 1894, E. Bartholomew in Ellis & Everhart Fungi Col. No. 785 and Ellis & Everhart N. Am. Fungi No. 3281, sub *Pestalotia kansensis* Ell. & Barthol.; on *Quercus alba* L., Aiken, S. C., H. W. Ravenel in Ravenel, Fungi Am. No. 35 and Ellis & Everhart, N. Am. Fungi No. 1624, sub *P. monochaeta* Desm.; on wilting leaves of *Quercus pedunculata* Ehrh. [*Q. robur* L.], Montello Forest near Treviso, Italy, Sept. 1874, P. A. Saccardo in Saccardo Mycotheca Veneta No. 324 (1876) and Rabenhorst, Fungi europ. No. 2119 (1876) sub *P. monochaeta* Desm. var. *quercus pedunculatae* Sacc. and similar material in herb. P. A. Saccardo (1873) and in Thuemen Myc. Univ. No. 84 (1875) sub *P. monochaeta* Desm.; on leaves of *Quercus rubra* L., Vosges Mts., France, Sept. 1910, Mangin; Bethlehem, Pa., June, C. H. Peck sub *P. monochaeta* in herb. N. Y. State Mus.; Auburn, Ala., Aug. and Sept. 1891, B. M. Duggar, sub *P. flagellata* Earle.

On leaves of *Castanea dentata* (Marsh.) Borkh., Leicester, N. C., July 23, 1909, B. B. Higgins, sub *P. concentrica* Berk. & Br.; Mingo, W. Va., Aug. 1902, W. A. Kellerman in Nat. Fungi Coll., U.S.D.A. No. 61133; Pisgah Forest, N. C., Aug. 10, 1910, A. W. Groves sub *Monochaetia desmazierii* Sacc.; on leaves of *Castanea* sp., northern Alabama, Peters, No. 410, herb. Curtis in herb. Farlow, sub *P. mutica* Berk. & Curt. (herb. name); on languishing leaves of *Castanea vesca* Gaertn. [= *C. sativa* Mill.] Bosco, Montello near Treviso, Italy, Sept. 1874, Saccardo Mycotheca Veneta No. 325 (1876) sub *P. monochaeta* Desm. var. *castaneae vescae* Sacc.

Graves (Mycologia 4:170–174,1912) studied this fungus on leaves of *Castanea dentata* (Marsh.) Borkh. and *Quercus rubra* L. He described spots concentrically zoned and reaching a diameter of 5–6 cm. Wounding of leaves and insertion of conidia into wounds were required for successful infection. The fungus was identified by W. G. Farlow as *Monochaetia desmazierii*, although it was asserted that the measurements did not conform closely with early material distributed by Desmazières. The fungus studied by Graves has setulae more than 15 μ long, in contrast to *Monochaetia desmazierii* which has setulae less than 15 μ long. The earliest specimens of the fungus were collected by Peters on leaves of *Castanea* in northern Alabama and named *Pestalotia mutica* Berk. & Curt. There is no published record of this name.

Monochaetia pachyspora Bubak is a synonym. The fungus was described on living leaves of *Quercus ilex* L., Tirol, Austria, Sept. 21, 1903. The setulae measure 15–25 μ long and conidia 7–9 μ wide (Ann. Mycol. 14: 154–155,1916).

Hedgcock (Mycologia 21:324–325,1929) reported this large concentric leaf spot fungus as *M. desmazierii*, on a wide range of hosts in numerous southern states as follows: *Acer rubrum, Castanea dentata, Hamamelis virginiana, Hicoria alba, H. glabra, H. laciniosa, H. ovata, Quercus alba, Q. borealis, Q. coccinea, Q. marilandica, Q. montana, Q. myrtifolia, Q. rubra, Q. stellata, Q. velutina, Q. virginiana,* and *Ulmus alata.*

20. **Monochaetia hysteriiformis** (Berk. & Curt.) Guba, comb. nov.

> *Pestalotia hysteriiformis* Berk. & Curt. in Curtis, Geol. & Nat. Hist. Survey, North Carolina, pt. III (Bot.) 118, 1867, nom. nud.; Grevillea 2:155,1874; Syll. Fung. 3:793,1884; Voglino, Atti Soc. Ven.-Trent. Sci. Nat. Padova 9:2,235,1885, pl. 10, fig. 30.

Pustules globose-hemispherical, distinct, dense punctiform, scattered or gregarious, 75–200 μ in diam, amphigenous, innate-erumpent. Conidia 5-celled, 25–35 × 6.5–9.5 μ, usually somewhat curved, long fusiform, only slightly constricted at the septa, intermediate colored cells umber or darker, hardly olivaceous and equally colored, the walls darker, 19–24 μ long or less; exterior cells hyaline, conic; setulae 9–13 μ long, more or less curved or obliquely disposed; pedicels 3–10 μ, curved, usually shorter than the setulae.

On dead leaves or brown or ash-colored concentrically zoned spots or areas with sharp borders on living leaves of *Quercus.*

Specimens examined; on leaves of *Quercus nigra* L., Aiken, S. C., in Ravenel Fungi Am. No. 33 (type) and similar specimens in herb. Mus. d'Hist. Nat., Paris, donated by Berkeley and Ravenel in 1856; also herb. Berkeley No. 1516, 1879; Nantucket Fungi No. 159 in herb. Guba, on leaves of *Quercus velutina* Lam., Sept. 30, 1937, E. F. Guba.

The type in Berkeley's herbarium at Kew is accompanied by a drawing of the conidia showing 3 cells and 3 setulae and a long pedicel. The specimens show 3 colored cells (all that is recognized by the original description), exterior hyaline cells, long pedicels and short setulae. The inscription accompanying the specimen in Ellis & Everhart, N. Am. Fungi No. 3563 bearing the name *P. hysteriiformis* Berk. & Curt. states that the fungus is like the specimen in Ravenel, Fungi Am. No. 33 and descriptions in Voglino (Atti Soc. Ven.-Trent. Sci. Nat. Padova 9:235,1885) but not like the original description in Grevillea 2:115,1874. This specimen (Ellis & Everhart, N. Am. Fungi No. 3563) is *M. concentrica* (Berk. & Br.) Sacc., not *P. hysterii-formis* Berk. & Curt.

21. **Monochaetia miersii** Speg., Bol. Acad. Nac. Ci. Cordoba (Argent.) 25: 113,1921.

Acervuli somewhat lenticular, black, slightly innate-erumpent, at first covered by the epidermis, then more or less exposed, numerous, gregarious in places, brownish-black, 200–350 μ in diam. Conidia fusiform, clavate fusiform, sessile or subpedicellate, 5-celled, 30–35 × 7–10 μ; 3 intermediate colored cells equal in size, dark, pellucid; exterior cells small, hyaline, basal cell elongate-turbinate, tapering, apical cell short conoid, abruptly terminating into a short somewhat lateral or oblique setula, 8–10 × 1 μ; pedicel short and delicate.

On rind of fruits of *Bellota miersii* C. Gay, in the woods near Los Perales, Chile, spring season of 1918, Spegazzini.

22. **Monochaetia macropoda** (Speg.) Allescher, Rabh. Krypt. Flora 1: Abt. 7, 671, 1902.
   Pestalotia macropoda Speg., Michelia 1:480,1879; Syll. Fung. 3:800,1884.

Pustules epiphyllous at first covered, then erumpent, conoid, minute, grayish to fuliginous. Conidia fusiform, 35–38 × 7 μ, 4-septate, slightly constricted at septa, the 3 intermediate cells olivaceous, exterior cells hyaline; setulae oblique or erect, up to 15 μ long, abruptly and shortly recurved or hooked; inferior cell pedicellate, 45–50 μ.

On dead fronds of *Pteridium aquilinum* (L.) Kuhn, Conegliano, Italy, 1877.

23. **Monochaetia russeliae** Guba sp. nov.

Pustulae subepidermicali-erumpentes, globoso-lenticulares, magnitudine variabiles, plerumque 100–150 × 100 μ, punctiformes, carbonaceae, maturae fuligineae; conidia 5-cellularia, elliptico-fusoidea, 20–23 × 6–9.5 μ, erecta, ad septa vix constricta, cellulis mediis concoloribus, fuligineis vel cacainis, guttulatis, opacis, 15.5–19 μ longis; cellulis extrimis obtusis, hyalinis, setulis 9–13 μ longis, subcurvatis; pedicellis brevibus, erectis.

Pustules subepidermal-erumpent, globose lenticular, usually 100–150 × 100 μ, smaller or larger, punctiform, carbonaceous, sooty at maturity. Conidia 5-celled, elliptic-fusoid, 20–23 × 8–9.5 μ, erect, hardly constricted at septa; intermediate colored cells fuliginous, chocolate-colored, guttulate, opaque, equally colored, 15.5–19 μ long; exterior cells obtuse, hyaline, the basal cell with hyaline contents; setulae 9–13 μ, slightly curved; pedicels short, erect.

On dead stems of *Russelia equisetiformis* Schl. & Cham., Paget, Bermuda, Dec. 2, 1921, H. H. Whetzel, No. 143.

24. **Monochaetia osyridella** Bubak, Bull. Herb. Boiss. (Ser. II) 6:484–485, 1906, pl. 15, fig. 5; Syll. Fung. 22:1228,1913.

Pustules subepidermal, 120–150 μ wide, round in circumference, black, finally tearing epidermis. Conidia 5-celled, long-fusiform, 18–29 × 5.5–6.5 μ, equilateral, bent above, the 3 intermediate colored (rarely only 2) cells, chestnut brown, middle cell the smallest; exterior cells hyaline, with erect or laterally directed hyaline setulae, 12–15.5 μ; pedicels cylindric, 15–18 × 2–2.5 μ.

On dry stems of *Osyris alba* L. near Ulcinj, Montenegro. The species is only slightly different, if at all, from *Monochaetia osyrella* (Tassi) Sacc. & D. Sacc., according to Saccardo (Syll. Fung. 22:1228,1913). The change in the name might appear desirable to avoid conflict with *M. osyrella* (Tassi) Sacc. & D. Sacc. (Syll. Fung. 18:486,1906) formerly *Pestalotia osyridella* Tassi, Boll. Lab. Ort. Bot. R. Univ. Siena 6:127,1904.

25. **Monochaetia cryptomeriae** M. Wilson, Trans. Brit. Mycol. Soc. 9:192, 1924, pl. 8, fig. 1–7; Grove, British Stem and Leaf Fungi II: 344, 1937, fig. 128.

Pustules amphigenous, scattered, immersed, then erumpent, circular or ovoid, blackish, 0.75–1 mm diam. Conidia fusoid, rather acute at both ends, 4-septate, slightly constricted at septa, 22–30 × 7.5–10 μ; exterior cells hyaline, intermediate colored cells chocolate brown, central cell darker than the other two; apical setulae 20–32 μ, filiform, oblique at base, straight in the upper part; pedicels hyaline, 4–20 × 1–2 μ.

On dead fallen leaves of *Cryptomeria japonica* (L.f.) D. Don, Raith, Fife-shire, Scotland (Wilson).

Section *Sexloculatae*
Species Nos. 26–41

26. **Monochaetia terebinthi** (Brizi) Allescher, Rabh. Krypt. Flora 1: Abt. 7, 671, 1902; not *M. terebinthi* (Brizi) Sacc., Syll. Fung. 18, 485, 1906. *Pestalotia terebinthi* Brizi, Boll. Soc. Bot. Ital. 2 (n.s.):81–82,1895; Syll. Fung. 14:1025,1899.

Pustules small, at first immersed, then erumpent, black. Conidia obovate-fusoid, 18–22 × 9–11 μ, 6-celled with broad cell walls, the four inter-mediate cells fuliginous, the exterior cells conoid, hyaline; apical setulae 8–10 μ; pedicels sometimes curved, hyaline.

On dead abnormal twigs of *Pistacia terebinthus* L. near Mompeo, Sabina, Italy, C. Cuboni.

27. **Monochaetia curtisii** Guba sp. nov.

Acervuli in maculis griseis in marginibus et extremitatibus foliorum brunneorum emortuorum, atri, punctiformes, gregarii, plerumque epiphylli, globoso–lenticulares, erumpentes 150–300 μ in diam, conidia 6-cellularia, 19–23 × 6–7 μ; cellulae 4 mediae coloratae olivaceae, 15–16 μ longae; setulae 12–16 μ longae, flexuosae; pedicellus circa 10 μ longus.

Discolored gray spots or areas along margins and extremities of brown dead matrix; acervuli black punctiform, gregarious, generally distributed, mostly epiphyllous, globose–lenticular, depressed, 150–300 μ diam, erumpent, the sooty contents blackening the matrix. Conidia 6-celled, 19–23 × 6–7 μ; four intermediate colored cells olivaceous, 15–16 μ long; setulae 12–16 μ long, flexuous; pedicels about 10 μ long.

On dead leaves of *Rhododendron catawbiense* Michx., Mt. Nigro, N. C., Sept. 1854, herb. Curtis No. 4482 in herb. Farlow.

28. **Monochaetia breviaristata** (Tracy & Earle) Sacc., Syll. Fung. 18:485,1906.
Pestalotia breviaristata Tracy & Earle, Bull. Torrey Bot. Club 22:178,1895.

Pustules punctiform or scattered, globose-lenticular, erumpent, conoid, black, surrounded by the torn epidermis, 75–200 μ diameter. Conidia 6-celled, curved, elliptical, 20–23 × 7.5–8.5 μ (25–27 × 7–8 μ, per Tracy and Earle); four intermediate colored cells umber, 15–19 μ, the septa often diagonal; setulae strongly oblique, 6–10 μ long; exterior hyaline cells obtuse; pedicels half the length of the conidia, often deciduous, somewhat swollen at the base or broken, a small portion attached to the conidia.

On living stems of *Tecoma radicans* Juss. [= *Campsis radicans* (L.) Seem.], with *Diplodia minuta* Ell. & Tracy, Starkville, Miss., March 21, 1895, S. M. Tracy.

On dead twigs of *Lyonia ligustrina* (L.)DC. Rochester, N. Y. April 15, 1877, W. S. Little.

29. **Monochaetia juniperi** (Rostr.) Allescher, Rabh. Krypt. Flora 1: Abt. 7, 670, 1902; Syll. Fung. 18:485,1906.
Pestalotia juniperi Rostr., Bot. Tidisskr. 19:211–212,1895; Syll. Fung. 14:1029,1899.

Pustules epiphyllous, gregarious, black. Conidia fusoid, 6-celled, all cells dark brown, 21–22 × 7–8 μ; superior setulae oblique; pedicels long, stipitate.

On needles of *Juniperus communis* L., Hofmans-gave, Denmark. According to the description all cells are colored, indicating that the exterior cells are dilutely colored.

30. **Monochaetia diospyri** Yoshii, Rep. Matsuyama Agr. Col. 13:27–37,1954.

Pale brown spots at first 0.5 mm diam, then larger and confluent forming irregular dead areas with conspicuous dark borders, reddish brown above, dotted with black fruiting bodies. Pustules largely epiphyllous, covered, erumpent at maturity, 108–180 μ diam, black. Conidia 6-celled, usually curved, broad fusiform to oblong cylindric, 16–35 μ (mean 28.5 μ) × 7–12 μ (mean 9.3 μ); four intermediate cells brown olivaceous, exterior cells hyaline;

setulae short, usually curved, 2–8 μ long (mean 3.9 μ); pedicels 14–38 × 2–4 μ.

In spots in living leaves of *Diospyros kaki* L.f. Morioka, Iwate, Japan, H. Yoshii, July 20, 1937. This is the cause of the large leaf spot disease of *Diospyros kaki* L. in Japan.

31. **Monochaetia unicornis** (Cooke & Ell.) Sacc., Syll. Fung. 18:485,1906.
  Hyaloceras parmense Pass. Real Accad. Lincei Sci. fisiche, mat. nat. 6:469,1890; Syll. Fung. 10:484,1892.
  H. hamamelidis Dearn. Mycologia 16:171, 1924.
  Monochaetia fibriseda (Ell. & Barthol.) Sacc., Syll. Fung. 18:485, 1906.
  M. mali. (Ell. & Ev.) Sacc., Syll. Fung. 18:485–486, 1906.
  M. uniseta (Tracy & Earle) Sacc., Syll. Fung. 18:485, 1906.
  Pestalotia fibriseda Ell. & Barthol., Erythea 4:27,1896; Syll. Fung. 14:1025,1899.
  P. mali Ell. & Ev., Jour. Mycol. 8:13:1902.
  P. rostrata Zabr. in Peck, Rep. Bot. N. Y. State Mus. 28:59,1876; Syll. Fung. 3:788,1884.
  P. unicornis Cooke & Ell. Grevillea 7:6,1878.
  P. uniseta Tracy & Earle, Bull. Torrey Bot. Club 23:209,1896; Syll. Fung. 14:1025,1899.

Pustules narrow elliptic to linear, punctiform, black, 300–800 × 150 μ, growing between the bark fibers, solitary, sometimes coalescing, sooty on maturity.

Conidia 6-celled, 22–27 × 7.5–9.5 μ, intermediate colored cells olivaceous, umber or somewhat darker, concolorous, 16–21 μ long, transparent, the walls darker; exterior hyaline cells obtuse, the apical cells crowned with curved, flexuous, oblique setulae, 6–13 μ long; pedicels erect, 3–10 μ long.

On wood of *Chamaecyparis thyoides* (L.) B.S.P., Newfield, N. J., Apr. 11, 1878, No. 2924 in herb. Ellis, N. Y. Bot. Gard. [Fig. 5a]. *Pestalotia unicornis* Cooke & Ell. was vaguely described with 6-celled conidia, 35 × 8 μ, long pedicels, hyaline exterior cells and brown intermediate cells. The published description states "on white cedar wood" but Ellis wrote with specimen "on red cedar bark." The matrix is white cedar.

On *Crataegus* (leaves); Tuskegee, Ala., Beaumont No. 283, sub *P. concentrica* Berk. & Br. in herb. Curtis No. 4607 in herb. Farlow.

On bark of dead trunks of *Hamamelis virginiana* L. near London, Ontario, Canada, May 1912, Dearness No. 3971, sub *Hyaloceras hamamelidis* Dearn. Conidia 25–29 × 8–9.5 μ, slightly curved; four intermediate colored cells umber, walls fuliginous, 22–26 μ long; setulae usually 4–10 μ, sometimes up to 22 μ, turned to one side; exterior cells pale yellow or hyaline, obtuse; pedicels 4–10 μ long or longer and coarse. Notes by Dearness and H. D.

FIG. 5 [31].   (*a, b*) *Monochaetia unicornis* (Cooke & Ell.) Sacc. (*c, d, e*) *Cryptostictis cupressi* Guba.

House are deposited with the type specimen and similarity with *H. parmense* Pass. is implied.

On bark of *Juniperus virginiana* L. Hillsborough, N. C., April 1867, sub *Pestalotia unicolor* Berk. & Curt., herb. Curtis in herb. Farlow [Fig. 5b]. *Coryneum* is written in pencil over *Pestalotia* and a pencil drawing of a 6-celled *Coryneum* conidium is shown. The name *Coryneum unicolor* Curtis nom. nud. (Geol. and Nat. Hist. Surv. North Carolina Bot. III, 120, 1867) was given to this specimen. Similarly, Bennett (Catalogue of Plants of Rhode Island, 1888, p. 87) listed *Coryneum unicolor* on decorticated wood of *Juniperus*, but the Bennett specimen is *Pestalotia unicolor* Berk. & Curt., which was named in 1869 and described in 1874. This specimen in the Curtis herbarium reads "*P. unicolor* B. & C. vid. *Coryneum.*" The fungus is now *Pestalozzina unicolor* (Berk. & Curt.) Sacc.

On bark of *Lonicera* sp., New Baltimore, N. Y., Feb. 27, 1872, G. L. Zabriskie in herb. N. Y. State Mus., Albany, sub *Pestalotia rostrata* Zabr. Pustules 100–250 μ diam, globose lenticular; conidia 6-celled, 20–26 × 7.5–9.5 μ, intermediate cells olivaceous or umber, 17–21 μ long; setulae oblique, 3–10 μ long; pedicels 3–6 μ, erect or oblique. Cotype material on bark of apple is missing. Ellis and Everhart, in N. Am. Fungi No. 2536, stated that the fungus belonged to *Monochaetia*, but the combination was never made.

On leaves of *Pyrus malus* L. [= *Malus sylvestris* Mill.] in Ellis & Everhart Fungi Col. No. 1630, Newfield, N. J., Aug. 20, 1900, J. B. Ellis, sub *Pestalotia mali* Ell. & Ev. Spots circular, pustules punctiform; conidia 6-celled, 22–24 × 7.5–8.5 μ; setulae 3–7 μ. According to the type description the conidia are 20–25 × 6–7 μ, setulae 6–8 μ, oblique; pedicels 20–25 μ. On bark and leaves of *Pyrus malus* L. [= *Malus sylvestris* Mill.], herb. Curtis, No. 4497 in herb. Farlow, Hendersonville, N. C., Sept. 1854 sub *P. concentrica* Berk. & Br. (type); Durham, N. C., F. A. Wolf in herb. Farlow and herb. Guba; Vincennes, Indiana, June 9, 1934, L. Pierce sub *Monochaetia mali* (Ell. & Ev.) Sacc.; Ellis & Everhart, N. Am. Fungi No. 9836, Stockton, Kan., July 5, 1927, E. Bartholomew; Herb. Dept. Plant Path. No. 822, Cornell University; Quincy, Pa., Aug. 5, 1906, D. M. Wertz; Auburn, Ala., May 22, 1912, F. A. Wolf, in herb. Farlow; Newfield, N. J., April 1885, J. B. Ellis, sub *Pestalotia pseudopeziza* Ell. (herb. name) and sub *P. unicornis* Cooke & Ell., Nat. Fungus Coll., U.S.D.A., and herb. N. Y. Bot. Gard.

On *Rosa* (leaves), Tuskegee, Ala., Aug. 20, 1900, G. W. Carver, No. 499, sub *P. seiridioides* Sacc., in herb. Farlow.

On weathered wood of *Rhus glabra* L., Rockport, Kan., Sept. 12, 1895, E. Bartholomew, Kansas Fungi No. 1931, in herb. Farlow, sub *Pestalotia fibriseda* Ell. & Barthol. Pustules innate-erumpent, globose-lenticular to sub-hysteriform, 0.5–1 mm long; conidia 6-celled, 22–26 × 7.5–9.5 μ; intermediate colored cells 19–22 μ; setulae 6–13 μ, oblique; pedicels coarse, 6–10 μ.

The type description states: "conidia 15–20 × 8 μ, appendages 10–20 μ; pedicels 25 μ long."

On branches of *Tamarix gallica* L., Bot. Gard., Parma, Italy, sub *Hyaloceras parmense* Pass. Conidia slightly curved, 6-celled, 22–25 × 8–10 μ; setulae oblique, 8–10 μ long; pedicels filiform, as long as conidia.

On bark of *Vitis* (Prof. Gulley grape), Starkville, Miss., March 16, 1896, sub *Pestalotia uniseta* Tracy & Earle. Pustules 50–100 × 100–200 μ, elliptical, scattered; conidia 6-celled, 25–30 × 7–8 μ; setulae 8–10 μ long, abruptly bent; pedicels very short, bent in same direction.

A new canker disease of *Cupressus macrocarpa* Gord. was observed by Wimbush in Kenya, Africa, in 1942 (Emp. For. Rev. 23:74,1944). Nattrass, in a study of the disease (East Africa Agr. Jour. 11:82,1945), designated the fungus *Monochaetia unicornis* (Cooke & Ell.) Sacc. Further studies were reported by Nattrass and Ciccarone (Emp. For. Rev. 26:289–290,1947), Ciccarone (Ann. Sper. Agraria Roma 3:1,1–58,1949) and Jones (Ann. Appl. Biol. 40:323–343,1953; 41:325–335,1954; Trans. Brit. Mycol. Soc. 37:286–305,1954). *Cupressus lusitanica* Mill. is less susceptible. *Juniperus procera* Hochst. is an indigenous host.

Ciccarone contributed an extensive report on the cypress canker in the plantations of Kenya. He described the histology of the cankers, the development of the fungus, and the morphology of acervuli and conidia. Similarity with the cypress canker in California caused by *Coryneum cardinale* Wagener is shown. One variant strain of the fungus was nonpathogenic. Infection is through breaks in the periderm of the host and by invasion of the main stem from infected lateral branches or twigs. A detailed emended description of the fungus asserted as *Monochaetia unicornis* (Cooke & Ell.) Sacc., and considered as the pathogen, is reported as follows:

Monochaetia unicornis (Cooke & Ell.) Sacc., em. Ciccarone, Ann. Sper.
    Agraria Roma 3:1,20,1949, figs. 1–5.

Acervuli subepidermal or subperidermal, scattered, sometimes seriate in transverse lines, occasionally confluent, often seated in loculate stromata, varying in form and size, usually lenticular, depressed or conical, at first covered by epidermis or periderm, erumpent, breaking the periderm into transverse narrow lip-like fissures, finally widely exposed and limited by the revolute and irregular laciniate margins. The pustules are black, contorted, carbonaceous, usually 0.2–1 cm long and 0.15–0.2 mm in width; stromata up to 250 μ, 40–70 μ thick below the locules with context irregularly angulate and internally almost colorless, the outer layers microparenchymatous, 20–25 μ thick, clear and pale brown.

Conidia elongate fusoid, sublanceolate, straight or inequilateral, not or rarely gibbous, 5-septate, 22–34 × 6–10 μ, not or hardly constricted at septa, 4 intermediate cells 15–23 μ long, rusty-yellow or pale brown, inner septae often darker: setula at apex hyaline, for most part straight, obliquely projected, 10×0.8 μ, inferior concolorous stalk exactly similar to setula and $1.5–11 \times 0.8$ μ; conidiophores septate, torulose, usually branched, brownish at base, upper part hyaline or grayish, gradually tapering, $8–100 \times 1.4–2.5$ μ, paraphyses thinner, flexuous, branched, hyaline, $30–95 \times 1–2.5$ μ.

Habitat. In live bark of *Cupressus thyoides* L. [= *Chamaccyparis thyoides* (L.) B.S.P.], *C. macrocarpa* Gord. also *C. lusitanica* Mill. (and *C. sempervirens* L.), in which the fungus induces cankers of brick red and sooty blackish color. Cankers at first thick, then depressed or sunken in the middle, elongated in the direction of the branch, sometimes closely fissured in the same direction, the fissures issuing resin. Canker girdles the branch; in thick branches it occupies only one side and has prominent rust-colored wavy margins.

New Jersey, North America, also Kenya, British East Africa.

Jones recognized three strains of the pathogen A,B,D, showing form distinctions in acervuli, conidia, mycelial growth and germination of the conidia, and significant differences in the biology of their parasitism. Strains A and B might be considered as biotypes of one species and D as a separate species or variety, that is, var. *juniperi* D. R. Jones. *Cupressus macrocarpa* Gord. being very susceptible, the removal of trees of this species in plantation areas in Kenya, East Africa, has led to a reduction of disease in neighboring *C. lusitanica* plantations.

According to Nattrass (correspondence, Aug. 4, 1953) the perfect stage of *M. unicornis* is a species of *Rhynchosphaeria* (*Phaeophragmiae, Sphaeriales*). The imperfect form of the cypress canker pathogen on the basis of cultures and natural specimens from Kenya, Africa, is not typical of the genus *Monochaetia*. The conidia have in addition to one apical setula or attenuated beak, an oblique setula projecting from the base of the lowest cell adjoining the long, thick pedicel. The conidia, when detached from the pedicels, have a truncate base (Jones, Trans. Brit. Mycol. Soc. 37:286–305,1954, pl. 11, fig. 4). The basal and apical setulae are of the same length. The four intermediate cells are thick-walled and dark-colored. The exterior cells are pale yellow or subhyaline with contents. Jones stated (see above, p. 290) that the conidia break away from the pedicels to which they are attached "or a portion of the pedicel may remain attached to an end cell. The other end cell bears a single setula, or occasionally two in collections of strain B."

Fuller and Newhook (New Zealand Jour. Agr. 88:3,211,213,215,217,219–220,1954) described the serious nature of cypress canker in New Zealand. The disease was attributed to the pathogen *Monochaetia unicornis* (Cooke & Ell.) Sacc. My study of specimens from New Zealand shows that the fungus is identical with the one in Kenya, Africa. The following material was studied: on branches of *Chamaecyparis lawsoniana* (Murr.) Parl. Auckland City, N. Z., Feb. 12, 1954, F. J. Newhook, No. 12893 [fig. 5c]. Conidia

21–26 × 8–9.5 μ; intermediate colored cells 15.5–19 μ long, olivaceous or umber, walls and septa darker; setulae 6–10 μ long, oblique, attenuated and beak-like; pedicels 3–5 μ, erect, central; oblique setulae sometimes adjoining the pedicels.

A similar disease of cypresses in California with identical pathology is caused by the closely related fungus *Coryneum cardinale* Wagener (Science 67:584,1928; Jour. Agr. Research 58:1–46,1939; New World Cypresses II, Anaheim, Cal. 1:255,1948). The same infection phenomena and degrees of susceptibility among different species of *Cupressus* featuring *M. unicornis* characterize *Coryneum cardinale* Wagener. Variants of *C. cardinale* comparable with differences manifested by strains of *M. unicornis* under different environmental conditions, are also reported. Type material was examined as follows: on bark of branches of *Cupressus macrocarpa* Gord., Atherton, Cal., March 16, 1934, W. W. Wagener, and Lafayette, Cal., March 20, 1952, W. W. Wagener.

According to Hansen *et al.* (Phytopathology 46:636–637,1956) the perfect stage of the *Coryneum* fungus is a *Leptosphaeria*, but under conditions of high humidity a beaked perithecium is produced, like *Rhynchosphaeria* as reported by Nattrass.

The genera *Monochaetia*, *Coryneum* and *Cryptostictis* have similar spore forms except for the setulate attachments. Pure cultures of the cypress canker fungus from Kenya, Africa, reveal conidia with hyaline attenuated beaks surmounting the colored cells characteristic of certain forms of *Coryneum*, for example, *C. delleanii* Servazzi and others cited by Servazzi (Boll. Lab. Sper. R. Osserv. Fitopat. Torino 12:4,1934). Natural specimens of the fungus in cankers in *Cupressus macrocarpa* from Kenya show both this feature and the apical hyaline conical cells with setulae characteristic of *Monochaetia*. We have here, if we include 'Wagener's *Coryneum*, three distinct conidial forms representing as many related genera with similar host and pathological relationships.

The cypress canker fungus in Kenya and New Zealand is not *Monochaetia unicornis* (Cooke & Ell.) Sacc. It does not belong to the genus *Coryneum*. The extremities of the conidia of the pathogen are not precisely indicated by Ciccarone (Ann. Sper. Agraria Roma 31:1,20,1949, fig. 4). The attenuation of the apical hyaline cell into a long beak or appendage and the oblique basal setula projecting from basal hyaline cell are missing. These are normal features of the conidia of the Kenya cypress canker fungus. The same features characterize the conidia of specimens from New Zealand. These features are lacking in the conidia of the type specimen of *Monochaetia unicornis* (Cooke & Ell.) Sacc. on cedar wood, *Chamaecyparis thyoides*, collected in New Jersey. There are other differences. The cypress canker fungus is distinct and is considered a new species belonging to the genus *Cryptostictis*.

Cryptostictis cupressi Guba sp. nov.

Acervuli punctiformes, coalescentes vel liberi, globosolenticulares vel lato-lineares, primum tecti, dein erumpentes et corticem irregulariter vel rima lineari fissentes, cortice desciscente et massam atram subcircularem sporarum, fragmentis laceratis epidermidis cinctam detegente, 150–300 μ in diam. vel majores; conidia plerumque 6-cellularia, cylindrico-fusoidea, 22–32 × 6.5–9.5 μ, ad septa vix constricta, cellulis mediis flavidulis usque fusco-brunneis, concolores, tunica obscuriori; cellula apicalis in rostrum 7–15 μ longum attenuata, flavidula vel hyalina, vacua vel impleta, interdum conica et appendice brevi obliqua usque 10 μ longa instructa; cellula basalis flavidula vel hyalina, vacua vel impleta, appendice obliqua lateraliter inserta, 7–16 μ longa; pedicellus longus, crassus, deciduus; cellula basalis infra truncata.

Acervuli simple or compound, enveloped in stromata, punctiform, coalescing or free, globose-lenticular or broad lineate, at first covered, erumpent and tearing bark in an irregular manner or by a linear crevice, bark falling away and exposing the black irregularly circular spore mass, surrounded by torn shreds of the epidermis, 150–300 μ in diam. or larger. Conidia usually 6-celled, cylindric-fusoid, 22–32 × 6.5–9.5 μ, hardly or only slightly constricted at the septa, usually 4 intermediate colored cells. 19–27 μ long, pale yellow to dark brown, concolorous, walls darker; apical cells attenuated into an appendage-like beak, 7–16 μ long, yellowish or hyaline with or without contents, sometimes conic and surmounted by a short divergent appendage up to 10 μ long; basal cell yellowish or hyaline with or without contents; oblique appendage at base affixed laterally, 7–16 μ long; pedicels long, thick, deciduous, the basal cells truncate below.

In cankers in branches of *Cupressus macrocarpa* Gord., Nairobi, Kenya, Africa, R. M. Nattrass, Dec. 1949 [fig. 5d]; cultures from cankers in branches of *Cupressus* and *Juniperus*, Strains A, B, C and D, Kenya, Africa, D. R. Jones, Sept. 1953 [fig. 5e]. On *Cupressus macrocarpa* Gord. with ascus stage, *Rhynchosphaeria* sp., Uplands, Kenya, Dec. 1949 (Nattrass).

32. **Monochaetia turgida** (Atk.) Sacc., Syll. Fung. 18:485,1906.
    Pestalotia turgida Atk., Bull. Cornell University 3: no. 1,37–38,1897; Syll. Fung. 14:1026,1899.
    P. crataegi Ell. & Ev., Bull. Torrey Bot. Club 27:58,1900; Syll. Fung. 16:1015,1902.

    Monochaetia crataegi (Ell. & Ev.) Sacc., Syll. Fung. 18:485,1906.

Spots on leaves circular, confluent up to 1 cm in diam, usually zoned above, pale or brown beneath, resembling a frog eye and dropping out, resembling shot holes; associated with dead areas or cankers. Pustules black, punctiform, sparse or gregarious, often concentrically disposed, globose, discoid, largely epiphyllous, 125–200 μ diam, erumpent in a stellate manner, convex and surrounded by the torn shreds of the epidermis. Conidia broad elliptic to oblong cylindric, 6-celled, curved, 22–32 × 7.5–10 μ, not constricted at septa; intermediate colored cells olivaceous to fuliginous, equally colored, 16–24 μ long; exterior hyaline cells broad conoid, hemispherical, sometimes slightly attenuated; septa and walls thick and darker than the cells; setulae oblique or sometimes horizontal, 6–16 μ long; pedicels curved in same direction as setulae and up to 23 μ long, usually 3–12 μ long.

On leaves of *Crataegus* sp., Auburn, Ala., Nov. 1, 1891 (type).

The species is characterized by larger conidia and longer setulae than in *Monochaetia unicornis*. According to the description, the conidia are 22–28 × 8–12 μ, intermediate-colored cells brown or fuliginous, setulae 8–15 μ; pedicels 6–12 μ.

On leaves of *Crataegus parvifolia* Ait., Hume, Fungi Florida No. 26, Lake City, Fla., Nov. 22, 1899, H. H. Hume; Ellis & Everhart Fungi Col. No. 1453, Lake County, Fla., Oct. 22, 1899, H. H. Hume, sub *P. crataegi* Ell. & Ev. The description mentions oblong cylindrical conidia, 20–23 × 7–8 μ, oblique setulae 4–5 μ and pedicels 12–15 μ.

On leaves of *Pyrus communis* L., Ravenel, No. 1354, South Carolina, sub *Pestalotia concentrica* Berk. & Br. [= *Monochaetia concentrica*] (Berk. & Br.) Sacc., in herb. Kew. Study shows 6-celled conidia, 22–29 × 9–10 μ, setulae 9–19 μ; pedicels 3–16 μ.

On dead bark and twigs of *Ulmus* sp., Ellis & Everhart, N. Am. Fungi, 2nd ser., No. 2536, London, Ontario, May 1890, Dearness; similar material in Canadian Fungi, March 24, 1890; in herb. Farlow, sub *Pestalotia rostrata* Zabr.

33. **Monochaetia tecomae** (Niessl) Allescher, Rabh. Krypt. Flora 1: Abt. 7.
     675,1902; Syll. Fung. 18:485,1906.
    Pestalotia tecomae Niessl, Hedwigia 22:188,1883; Syll. Fung. 3:799,1884.
    P. bignoniae Camara, Boll. Soc. Broteriana 25:23,1910; Syll. Fung.
     22:1224,1913.

Pustules punctiform, lenticular, depressed, immersed and covered, then rupturing epidermis, irregularly indented, brown to black. Conidia 6-celled, 28–32 × 9–10 μ, fusiform, erect or slightly curved; 4 intermediate colored cells umber, 22–24 μ long; one setula, 9–12 μ long, curved; pedicels 3–7 μ long, rope-like.

On dried stems of *Tecoma radicans* Juss. [= *Campsis radicans* (L.) Seem.], Bot. Gard., Coimbra, Portugal, A. Moller, No. 1180 (type of *P. tecomae* Niessl); on branches of *Bignonia jasminifolia* H.B.K., Bot. Gard., Coimbra, Portugal, A. Moller, April, 1909 (type of *P. bignoniae* Camara).

P. tecomae Niessl was described with 4-celled, dark brown conidia, 20–24 × 7–8 μ. The hyaline exterior cells were not considered. The type description of *P. bignoniae* Camara, which is the same fungus, mentions 6-celled conidia, 27–32 × 10 μ, setulae 5–8 μ long, exterior hyaline cells; rope-like pedicels, 12–20 μ long.

34. **Monochaetia veneta** (Sacc.) Allescher, Rabh. Krypt. Flora 1: Abt. 7,668, 1902; Syll. Fung. 18:485,1906.

Pestalotia veneta Sacc., Michelia 1:92,1879; Saccardo, Fungi Ital. tab. 83, 1877; Syll. Fung. 3:799,1884.

Pustules punctiform, gregarious, sub-cutaneous, later erumpent, globose-lenticular, black, 125–300 μ diam. Conidia 6-celled, oblong-fusoid, 21–28 × 7–8.5 μ, not constricted at septa; four intermediate cells guttulate, 15–20 μ long, fuliginous, equally colored, the walls black; exterior cells small, hyaline; apical setulae 8–18 μ long, curved, flexuous; pedicels filiform, up to 40 μ long, fasciculate, descending into a yellowish pseudo-stroma.

On twigs of *Cornus sanguinea* L., Selva, Italy, Sept. 1873; Conegliano, Italy, April, 1876, leg. Spegazzini; Roumeguère, Fungi Gallica Exs. No. 7246, France, Jan., 1897, leg. F. Fautrey; herb. Grove, Witley, England, Nov. 26, 1928, Grove and Rhodes.

Saccardo's original description states that conidia measure 30–34 μ the apical setulae 15–18 μ, and the pedicels 40–45 μ long.

35. **Monochaetia rhododendri** Woronichin, Trud. Bot. Musea Akad. Nauk U.S.S.R. 21:202,1927; Vassiljevsky and Karakulin, Fungi Imperf. Par. 2:467,1950.

Spots violet, black, brown in the centers, 2–3 × 1.5 mm, dispersed in middle section of the leaves or usually present along the margins and 15 × 6 mm, often involving the entire leaf. Acervuli black, sparse, amphigenous, small. Conidia subfusoid, straight, acute at the ends, 6-celled, 23–27 × 6–7 μ; exterior cells hyaline, intermediate colored cells brown; setula 23–25 μ long, curved; pedicel filiform up to 15 μ long.

On living leaves of *Rhododendron caucasicum* Pall., Tiflis, Transcaucasia Dist. Gori, near Bakurjani, June 26, 1914 and Kvischeti, Aug. 23, 1914, leg. Kuske.

The original description specifies 6-celled conidia but the later compilation by Vassiljevsky and Karakulin mentions 5-celled conidia.

36. **Monochaetia jefferisii** (Ell.) Sacc., Syll. Fung. 18:485,1906.

Pestalotia jefferisii Ell., Bull. Torrey Bot. Club 9:133,1883; Syll. Fung. 3:798,1884.

Pustules globose, punctiform, gregarious or scattered, generally distributed, black and sooty. Conidia large, 6-celled, 25–29 × 8–10 μ; four intermediate cells umber to fuliginous somewhat obscuring the septa, 20–24 μ long; setulae 30–45 μ long; exterior cells hyaline, obtuse, basal one often conic, attenuated; pedicels 12–22 μ long.

On dead branches of *Viburnum prunifolium* L., Westchester, Pa., June, 1882, leg. Everhart, Haines, Jefferis and Gray in Ellis, N. Am. Fungi No. 953.

The original description states that the conidia measure 18–20 × 7.5–9 μ; pedicels long; setulae oblique, 5.5–7 μ long.

A similar 6-celled conidial form designated *Pestalotia veneta* Sacc. was issued in Ellis & Everhart, N. Am. Fungi No. 2577, on twigs of *Viburnum lentago* L., London, Ontario, Canada, May 1890, leg. J. Dearness, but the conidia are larger, 28–35 × 10–11 μ, the colored part 23.5–28 μ, umber to fuliginous, the walls and septa black; exterior cells hyaline, apical cells obtuse, basal cells long conic; setulae oblique, 16–31 μ long; pedicels 12–22 μ long.

37. **Monochaetia crataegina** Syd., Ann. Mycol. 18:160,1920; Syll. Fung. 25: 610,1931.

Spots amphigenous, irregular, about 1 cm or more in diam, zoned and yellow-brown above, pale brown beneath. Pustules epiphyllous, loosely or densely dispersed, irregular, 200–400 μ, in diam, often angulate, covered by dark epidermis, finally uncovered, black. Conidia broad fusoid, sometimes slightly curved, 5-septate, 25–35 × 7–9 μ; intermediate cells yellow brown, the exterior cells hyaline; apical setulae up to 22 μ long; basal cells tapering into hyaline pedicels, 20–35 μ long.

On leaves of *Crataegus melanocarpa* Bieb. var. *hyrcanica* Bornm. near Poltavskojé, Abchasia, Caucasia, G. Woronow, submitted by J. Bornmüller.

38. **Monochaetia ceratospora** (de Not.) Guba comb. nov.

    Seiridium notarisii (Dur. & Mont.), Hoehnel, Sitzb. Akad. K. Wiss. Wien Math.-Naturw. Kl. Abt. 1:125:29–33,1916.

    Stilbospora ceratospora de Not., Micro. Ital. 10:67–68,1839, fig. 10; Syll. Fung. 3:783,1884.

    Hyaloceras notarisii Dur. & Mont., in Durieu, Flore d'Algerie Crypt. I; 587,1846; Thuemen, Boll. Soc. Adri. Sci. Nat. Trieste 8:(reprint, p. 28), 1883; Hoehnel, Sitzb. Akad. K. Wiss. Wien, Math.-Naturw. Kl. 119, 663,1910.

    H. ceratospora (de Not.) Hoehn., Sitzb. Akad. K. Wiss. Wien, Math.-Naturw. Kl. 119:663–664,1910.

Pustules 225–300 × 200 μ, punctiform, scattered over the matrix, at first subepidermal, then erumpent, rising like a cone well above the epidermis, convex, with well-developed stroma above and below, the conidial contents enveloped in a firm carbonaceous tissue, rupturing on maturity and liberating the sooty mass. Conidia 6-celled, usually curved, slightly attenuated at both extremities, 25–32 μ long; 4 intermediate colored cells umber, the walls darker or fuliginous, 22–25 × 9–12.5 μ; exterior cells hyaline, obtuse, comparatively small, the apical cell abruptly descending into an oblique setula, 6–10 μ long; pedicels similarly oblique, 6–10 μ long.

On dead withered twigs of *Olea sylvestris* Mill. [= *O. europaea* L.], Sassari, Island of Sardinia, 1835, in herb. C. Montagne, Mus. d'Hist. Nat. Paris; herb. Hoehnel No. 4101 in herb. Farlow, sub *Hyaloceras notarisii* Dur. & Mont. Montagne's drawings accompanying the specimens show 4-celled colored conidia with setulae and pedicels and no hyaline exterior cells. The fruiting pustules originate under the bark and the diagrammatic drawings suggest the presence of well developed stromatic tissue.

39. **Monochaetia plagiochaetia** (Sacc.), Allescher., Rabh. Krypt. Flora 1: Abt. 7,670,1902, not (Sacc.) Sacc., Syll. Fung. 18:485,1906.
Pestalotia plagiochaetia Sacc., Michelia 1:533,1879; Saccardo, Fungi Ital., 1881, tab. 1118.

Pustules globose-lenticular, innate-erumpent, at length cup-shaped, black. Conidia 6-celled, oblong cylindric, somewhat inequilateral, $38–40 \times 9 \mu$; exterior cells hyaline, intermediate cells fuliginous; apical cell obtuse, setulae oblique, 8μ long, arising at the side of the apex of the superior cell; basal cell attenuated into pedicel, $6–8 \mu$ long.

On stems of *Laurus nobilis* L., France, Brunaud. The conidium appears to be drawn in reverse (tab. 1118) and thus the truncate apex is the base, lacking pedicel, with a setula projecting from the base of the hyaline cell. This character features the genus *Cryptostictis*.

40. **Monochaetia seiridioides** (Sacc.) Allescher, Rabh. Krypt. Flora 1: Abt. 7,673,1902; Syll. Fung. 18:485,1906.
Pestalotia seiridioides Sacc., Syll. Fung. 3:799,1884; 15:329,1901.
Coryneum marginatum Hazl., Verh. K. zool.-bot. Ges. Wien 20,213,1870, pl. 4, fig. 29–37 (not Fries).
Hyaloceras seiridioides (Sacc.) Died., Ann. Mycol. 2:544,1913.
Seiridium marginatum Nees, Syst. Pilze, Schwamme. Wurzburg, pp. 22–23, 1817, tab. 1, fig. 19; Syll. Fung. 3:783,1884.
Pestalotia compta Sacc. var. *ramicola* Berl. & Bres. Ann. Soc. Alpinisti Tridentini 14:81,1887–88 (publ. 1889), pl. 6, fig. 9; Syll. Fung. 10:493, 1892.
Monochaetia compta (Sacc.) Allescher var. *ramicola* Berl. & Bres., Rabh. Krypt. Flora 1: Abt. 7,673,1902.
Hyaloceras comptum (Sacc.) Died. var. *ramicola* Berl. & Bres., Krypt. Flora Mark Brandenb. 9:879,1915.

Pustules black, carbonaceous, discoid, globose to oblong, punctiform, $150–300 \mu$ in diam, borne in the cortex, finally erumpent, provided with a thick parenchymatic or stromatic wall, the cavity crowded with simple hyaline conidiophores arising from base and sides, the thick cover tearing away and freeing the sooty conidia.

Conidia 6-celled, long cylindric, fusiform, tapering toward the ends, erect or slightly curved, 30–40 × 7.5–9.5 μ; four intermediate cells umber or olivaceous, equally colored, 23–30 μ long, the walls and septa usually darker; exterior hyaline cells conoid, attenuated or acute; setulae 9–35 μ, curved; pedicels 15–32 μ long.

On stems of *Rosa canina* L., Rothenburg near Nuremberg, Germany (Hochstetter). Specimens examined; herb. Barbey-Boissier No. 2491 and Fuckel, Fungi Rhenani No. 2136, Jura, Switzerland (Du Morthier); herb. Hoehnel No. 4173, Tirol, Austria, July 1903 (Hoehnel).

Nees named this fungus on dog rose "der gerandete Kettenstaub." The fungus was vaguely illustrated by the artist employed by Nees. Dark spores are shown bridged together in pairs by threads or filaments, also individual spores with an appendage at each end. The original figures were copied and reproduced by Krombholz (Abbild. Beschr. essb., schäd., verd. Schwämme, Prague, 1831, tab. 6, fig. 41); Bonorden (Handbuch Allg. Myk. 1851, tab. IV, fig. 88); Corda (Anleit. z. Stud. Myk. 1842, tab. B., fig. 5); and Bischoff (Allg. Ubers. Org. Phan. Krypt. Pflanenkr., 1860, tab. 77, fig. 3864).

Diedicke (Krypt. Flora Mark Brandenb. 9:877,1915) reported that specimens on *Rosa* from Neufchâtel collected by Du Morthier and from Brünn by Niessl bearing the name *S. marginatum* Nees belong to *Hyaloceras seiridioides* (Sacc.) Died. The 5-septate conidia are not bridged together and measure 35–40 × 7–9 μ. Diedicke (pp. 879–880) regarded both *S. marginatum* Fckl. (Symb. Mycol., 1869, p. 391, tab. II, fig. 31), and *Coryneum marginatum* Haszl. (Verh. K. zool.-bot. Ges., Wien 20:213,1870, pl. IV, 29–37) as synonyms. *Monochaetia seiridioides* Sacc. in herb. Hoehnel No. 4173 in herb. Farlow is the same as *Seiridium marginatum* Nees. This fungus occurs in association with *Massaria marginata* Fckl. The ascus stage, according to Hoehnel, occurs in material from Tirol collected by Hoehnel and from Jura by du Morthier (Sitzb. K. Akad. Wiss. Wien Math.-Naturw. Kl. Abt. 1: 125,1916). The connection is also reported by Fuckel (Symb. Mycol. II, 1873, Nachtr., p. 28).

Pestalotia compta Sacc. var. *ramicola* Berl. & Bres. described on *Rosa canina* L., collected at Trento, Italy, is the same as *Monochaetia seiridioides* (Sacc.) Allescher. The type description mentions 3-septate conidia, 3 intermediate colored cells and exterior hyaline cells, but pl. 6, fig. 9, shows a 6-celled *Monochaetia* conidium with 4 intermediate colored cells and exterior hyaline cells. Saccardo (Syll. Fung. 10:493) refers to this fungus as *P. seiridioides* Sacc. Diedicke (Krypt. Flora Mark Brandenb. 9: p. 870, fig. 8) erroneously represented the fungus with 4-celled conidia, the 2 intermediate cells colored, exterior cells hyaline, with one apical setula. He named it *Hyaloceras comptum* (Sacc.) Died. var. *ramicola* Berl. & Bres.

Saccardo (Syll. Fung. 3:444) considered *Sporocadus caudata* Preuss on rose canes (Hoyerswerda No. 153) a species of *Cryptostictis* and designated it *C. caudata* (Preuss) Sacc., but Hoehnel (Sitzb. K. Akad. Wiss. Wien, Math.-Naturw. Kl. Abt. 1:125,29–33,1916) regarded the fungus as *S. marginatum* Nees. On the basis of the original description of *Sporocadus caudata* Preuss (Linnea 24:146,1851), no accurate disposition of the fungus is possible. Cooke (Nuovo Gior. Bot. Ital. 10:27,1878) placed the fungus in the genus *Pestalotia*.

Schweinitz (Trans. Am. Philos. Soc. IV (n. s.) 306, No. 3084, 1834) gave the name *Seiridium marginatum* Link (Handbuch Erk. Gewachse, Berlin, 1833, p. 426), to a fungus on *Rosa corymbosa* Ehrh. (= R. palustris Marsh) from Bethlehem, Pa. Saccardo (Syll. Fung. 15:329) stated that *S. marginatum* Schw. (also Nees) is *Phragmidium speciosum* Fries. Fries (Summa Veg. Scand. 1846, p. 474) asserted that *S. marginatum* Schw. in America is a species of *Phragmidium*, and Fries (Syst. Mycol. 3:496,1829) designated it *Aregma speciosa* Fries. Cooke (Grevillea 3:171,1875) named it *Phragmidium speciosum* (Fries) Cooke. Later, Arthur (Rés. Sci. Congr. Bot. Vienna 1906, p. 341) named the fungus *Earlea speciosa* Arth.

Schweinitz (Trans. Am. Philos. Soc. IV (n. s.) 306, 1834 and Syll. Fung. 3:783) described the fungus *Seiridium smilacis* Schw. on *Rosa* sp. not *Smilax*. Arthur (N. Am. Flora 7: pt. 3, Apr. 1912, 175–176) placed all these names in synonymy under *Earlea speciosa* (Fries) Arth., but Bartholomew (Handbook N. Am. Uredinales, 2nd ed. 1933, p. 37) placed them all, including *E. speciosa*, in synonymy under *Phragmidium speciosum* (Fries) Cooke, and this is the accepted name today (Arthur, Manual of Rusts, 1934, p. 88).

41. **Monochaetia coryneoidea** (Harkn.) Sacc., Syll. Fung. 18:485,1906.
   Pestalotia coryneoidea Harkn., Bull. Cal. Acad. Sci. 1:33,1884; Syll. Fung. 3:799,1884.

Pustules flattened, black, oblong or oval, 0.1 mm broad, at length depressed and opening by irregular apertures. Conidia 35–37 × 12 μ, fusiform, curved, 5-septate, intermediate cells greenish black, exterior cells hyaline, small, often nearly obsolete; apices with 1 oblique setula, 12 μ long.

On dead twigs of *Umbellularia californica* (Hook. & Arnold), Nutt., Mt. Tamalpais, Cal.

According to Harkness, the fungus differs from *P. plagiochaetia* Sacc. in the greater relative width of the conidia and much smaller size of the exterior hyaline cells.

PESTALOTIA

Melanconiales, Melanconiaceae, Phaeophragmiae

Pestalotia de Not., Microm. Ital., 2:28, Fig. 9, in Mem. R. Accad. Sci. Torino. II:3,80–81,1839.
 Labridella Brenckle, Fungi Dakotenses, No. 663, Oct. 1929. Mycologia 22:160–161,1930.
 Truncatella Steyaert, Bull. Jard. Bot. État Bruxelles 19(3),293,1949.
 Pestalotiopsis Steyaert, Bull. Jard. Bot. État Bruxelles 19(3),300,1949.

Fruiting bodies black, carbonaceous, varying from simple acervuli without stromatic area to stromatic apothecioid structures, pycnidia and pseudopycnidia, rarely with a true ostiole and rarely as loose fertile hyphae without a distinct stratum or stroma. Conidia fusiform, straight or curved, 4- to 6-celled or loculate and crowned with 2 or more, rarely 1 and more simple or branched setulae, their extremities sometimes spatulate or knobbed, sometimes arising from the slope or base of the apical cells; exterior cells hyaline or rarely dilutely colored, rarely with contents; intermediate cells equally or variably colored pale brown to almost black, guttulate; pedicels hyaline, simple, rarely branched, attached to the base of the conidia.

Section *Quadriloculatae*

Conidia 4-celled; two intermediate colored cells

Species Nos. 42–75

a. Setulae simple or branched like a staghorn, sometimes 1 and branched; exterior hyaline cells and attachments deciduous with age.
 b. Conidia 12–16 × 5–7 μ
  e. Setulae 1–3, 10–32 μ long ....   42. *P. epilobii*
                  43. *P. nuciseda*
 b. Conidia 15–22 × 6–8 μ ....   44. *P. aesculi*
  e. Setulae 2, 16 μ long ....   45. *P. chamaeropis*
  e. Setulae 2–3, 8–21 μ long ....   46. *P. betulae*
  e. Setulae 1–4, rarely 5, usually up to
    20 μ, sometimes up to 30–40 μ....   47. *P. truncata*
                  48. *P. laurocerasi*
                  49. *P. hartigii*

        e. Setulae 4–6, 12–23 μ . . . .   50. *P. caulicola*
                                                              51. *P. affinis*
                                                              52. *P. chrysanthemi*

b. Conidia 22–26 × 7–8 μ
        e. Setulae 3–5, 6–31 μ . . . .   53. *P. citrina*
a. Setulae simple or rarely branched; exterior hyaline
cells and setulae usually persisting.
    b. Conidia 12–16 μ long
        c. Conidia 5–6 μ wide
            d. Colored cells olivaceous or pale brown
                e. Setulae 2–3, rarely 4, 8–18 μ long.   54. *P. casuarinae*
                                                  55. *P. besseyi*

            d. Colored cells fuliginous
                e. Setulae 4, 18–20 μ long . . . .   56. *P. gastrolobii*
        c. Conidia 6–8 μ wide
            d. Colored cells umber to fuliginous,
                almost opaque: exterior hyaline cells
                obscure, minute
                e. Setulae 3 up to 8 μ long. . . . .   57. *P. puyae*
                e. Setulae 3, 15–20 μ long . . . .   58. *P. maura*
    b. Conidia 16–22 μ long or in a narrower range.
        c. Conidia 5.5–7.5 μ wide
            d. Colored cells olivaceous or pale brown
                e. Setulae 3, 5–7 μ . . . .   59. *P. camphori*
                e. Setulae 2–4, usually 3, 7–25 μ long.   60. *P. stevensonii*
                                                  61. *P. maculicola*

        c. Conidia 7.5–8.5 μ wide
            d. Colored cells fuliginous, walls thick
                dark; apical cells obscure, basal cells
                cylindric
                e. Setulae 3–4, 15–29 μ long. . . . .   62. *P. jacksoniae*
        c. Conidia 8–10 μ wide
            d. Colored cells brown to fuliginous
                e. Setulae 3, 13–16 μ . . . .   63. *P. pitospora*
                e. Setulae 4 up to 14 μ long. . . . .   64. *P. teucrii*
                e. Setulae 4–5, 15–30 μ long. . . . .   65. *P. watsoniae*
    b. Conidia 18–26 μ
        c. Conidia 6–8 μ wide
                e. Setulae 2, 26–30 μ long . . . .   66. *P. jaczewskii*
                e. Setulae 3, 20 μ long . . . .   67. *P. hordeidestrua*
                e. Setulae 4–5, 20–27 μ long . . . .   68. *P. penzigii*
        c. Conidia 6–10 μ wide
                e. Setulae 2–6, 8–20 μ long . . . .   69. *P. insueta*

  c. Conidia 7.5–10 μ wide
   d. Colored cells olivaceous or umber
    e. Setulae 2–5, usually 3, 19–37 μ long 70. *P. berberidis*
 b. Conidia 22–27 μ long
  c. Conidia 3–5 μ wide, colored cells dark
    e. Setulae 2, 9 μ long . . . . 71. *P. siliquastri*
                var. *italica*
  c. Conidia 6–7 μ wide; interior cells fuliginous
    e. Setulae 5, 30–40 μ long. . . . . : 72. *P. eupyrena*
  c. Conidia 7.5–9 μ wide
   d. Colored cells olivaceous
    e. Setulae 4, sometimes 3, 30–52 μ
     long . . . . 73. *P. moorei*
  c. Conidia 9–10 μ wide
   d. Colored cells fuliginous
    e. Setulae 5, 18–35 μ long . . . . 74. *P. helichrysii*
 b. Conidia 27–30 × 10–11 μ
   d. Colored cells brown, large and cuboid
    e. Setulae 3, rarely 2, 30–40 μ long. . . 75. *P. torrendii*

Section *Quinqueloculatae*

Conidia 5-celled; three intermediate colored cells

Species Nos. 76–258

a. Setulae knobbed at the extremities (Spathulatae), Nos. 76–90
 b. Colored cells brown, or yellow brown, concolorous
  c. Conidia 16–22 × 5–7 μ
   d. Conidia hardly constricted at septa
    e. Setulae usually 3, 7–22 μ, usually
     up to 15 μ long . . . . 76. *P. phoenicis*
   d. Conidia strongly constricted at septa
    e. Setulae 2–3, 30–32 μ long. . . . . 77. *P. javanica*
  c. Conidia 19–26 × 5–7 μ
    e. Setulae 2–4, usually 3, 9–20 μ long 78. *P. fici*
  c. Conidia 22–32 μ long
   d. Conidia narrow, 5–8 μ wide
    e. Setulae 3, 18–35 μ . . . . 79. *P. elastica*
    e. Setulae 2–4, 25–50 μ, sometimes up
     to 60 μ. . . . . 80. *P. theae*
   d. Conidia broad, 6.5–9.5 μ wide
    e. Setulae usually 3, up to 25 μ . . . . . 81. *P. annulata*
                  82. *P. clavata*
                  83. *P. capitata*

c. Conidia 28–38 μ long
  d. Conidia 6–8 μ wide
    e. Setulae usually 3, 18–38 μ long. . . . 84. *P. aeruginea*
  d. Conidia 7–9 μ wide
    e. Setulae usually 3, stout with wide
      lumen, 45–60 μ long . . . . 85. *P. trichocladi*
b. Upper 2 colored cells umber, the lowest
  olivaceous, or central one darker
  c. Conidia 18–27 μ
    d. Conidia 4–8 μ wide
      e. Setulae 2–3, 6–16 μ long. . . . . 86. *P. gossypii*
  c. Conidia ovate-fusiform, 24–29 μ long
    d. Conidia 7–9.5 μ wide
      e. Setulae usually 3, 12–22 μ long. . . 87. *P. lapageriae*
  c. Conidia 21–37 μ long
    d. Conidia 7–9 μ wide
      e. Setulae 3, 13–50 μ long, subapical. 88. *P. antennaeformis*
b. Upper 2 colored cells fuliginous, lowest olivaceous; setulae coarse
  c. Conidia 22–30 μ long, pedicels often knobbed
    d. Conidia 7–10.5 μ wide
      e. Setulae 3, 20–40 μ . . . . 89. *P. ilicis*
      e. Setulae 2–4, usually 3, 30–60 μ. . . . 90. *P. gibbosa*
a. Setulae not knobbed at the extremities (Non-Spathulatae), Nos. 91–258
  b. Intermediate colored cells concolorous, olivaceous or pale brown,
    some of the conidia sometimes with faintly contrasted colored cells;
    No. 20, umber brown; No. 8, fuliginous, concolorous (Concolorae,
    Olivae-Pallidae), Nos. 91–160
    c. Conidia 12–18 × 4–6 μ
      e. Setulae 2, 6–7 μ . . . . 91. *P. toxica*
      e. Setulae 2–3, up to 16 μ . . . . 92. *P. espaillatii*
      e. Setulae mostly 2, 10–19 μ, acro-
        pleurogenous, branched . . . . 93. *P. fibricola*
      e. Setulae 2–4, usually 3, 15–20 μ. . . . 94. *P. senegalensis*
      e. Setulae 3–4, 10–20 μ . . . . 95. *P. citri*
    c. Conidia 14–18 × 6.5–8.5 μ
      e. Setulae 3–9, up to 10 μ, apical
        hyaline cells obscure . . . . 96. *P. distincta*
    c. Conidia 15–21 × 4.5–7 μ
      e. Setulae 1–3, rarely 4, often branched
        Setulae 6–16 μ . . . . 97. *P. fuchsiae*
        Setulae 10–24 μ sometimes faintly
          knobbed . . . . 98. *P. guepini*

e. Setulae 2 or usually 2, 4–11 μ

    Setulae 4–8 μ ....   99. *P. quercicola*
                         100. *P. bromeliicola*
    Setulae 6–11 μ .... 101. *P. aletridis*
                         102. *P. sorbi*

e. Setulae 2–3, usually 3, 4–16 μ

    Conidia hardly constricted at septa 103. *P. calabae*
                         104. *P. cryptomeriae*
                         105. *P. siliquastri*
                         106. *P. adusta*
                         107. *P. virginiana*

    Conidia strongly constricted at septa .... 108. *P. torulosa*

e. Setulae 3, 10–20 μ .... 109. *P. flavidula*

c. Conidia 18–26 × 4–5 μ

    e. Setulae 3, 5–10 μ.............. 110. *P. kawakami*

c. Conidia 18–26 × 5–8 μ

    e. Setulae 1–3, up to 16 μ, when 3 up to 10 μ .... 111. *P. algeriensis*

    e. Setulae similar, 9–22 μ, one attenuated .... 112. *P. heterocornis*

    e. Setulae 2

        Setulae 8–15 μ .... 113. *P. bicilia*
              8–21 μ .... 114. *P. lawsoniae*
           10–23 μ .... 115. *P. vismiae*
           12–26 μ .... 116. *P. carveri*

    e. Setulae usually 3, 6–15 μ

        Conidia narrow .... 117. *P. eugeniae*
                        118. *P. ilicicola*
                        119. *P. microspora*
                        120. *P. podocarpi*
        Conidia elliptic................ 121. *P. breviseta*
                        122. *P. sinensis*

    e. Setulae usually 3, 8–23 μ

        Conidia narrow .... 123. *P. uvicola*
                        124. *P. neglecta*
        Conidia elliptic................ 125. *P. disseminata*

    e. Setulae usually 3, 14–32 μ

        Conidia narrow .... 126. *P. carissae*
         Conidia elliptic................ 127. *P. olivacea*

    e. Setulae 3–4 often branched, acrogenous .... 128. *P. bicolor*

e. Setulae 3–4, simple, acropleurogenous
  Setulae up to 11 μ . . . . 129. *P. gravesii*
  Setulae 12–26 μ . . . . 130. *P. montellica*
e. Setulae usually 4, irregularly exert-
  ed, 6–19 μ. 131. *P. gaurae*
e. Setulae 4, apical, up to 15 μ. . . . . . . 132. *P. eleagni*
e. Setulae 3–5, 10–22 μ. . . . . 133. *P. weinmanniae*
c. Conidia 18–26 × 7–9.5 μ
  e. Setulae usually 3, 15–24 μ. . . . . 134. *P. lespedezae*
  e. Setulae 4, 9–17 μ. . . . . 135. *P. quadriciliata*
c. Conidia 22–30 × 5–8 μ
  e. Setulae 2–3, 10–13 μ, irregularly
    exerted . . . . 136. *P. rhamni*
  e. Setulae usually 3, apical, up to 14 μ
    Conidia narrow . . . . 137. *P. osyridis*
    Conidia elliptic. . . . . 138. *P. mayumbensis*
  e. Setulae similar, 10–25 μ
    Conidia narrow . . . . 139. *P. cocculi*
    Conidia elliptic. . . . . . •. . . . . 140. *P. mangifolia*
  e. Setulae 3, sometimes 4, 15–38 μ
    Conidia narrow . . . . 141. *P. suffocata*
    Conidia elliptic. . . . . 142. *P. galactis*
                                      143. *P. caroliniana*
  e. Setulae 2–5, 10–15 μ. . . . . 144. *P. conglomerata*
  e. Setulae 3–5, stout, with lumen
    13–25 μ. . . . . 145. *P. baarnensis*
  e. Setulae 3–6, filiform, 6–20 μ. . . . . . 146. *P. rosae*
c. Conidia 22–30 × 7–10 μ wide or more
  e. Setulae 1–4, usually 2, up to 40 μ,
    when 1 up to 70 μ. . . . . 147. *P. monochaetioides*
  e. Setulae 3, up to 20 μ . . . . 148. *P. subsessilis*
    Setulae 15–32 μ . . . . 149. *P. macrochaeta*
  e. Setulae 3–6, usually 4–5, 6–20 μ or slightly longer,
    acrogenous
    Setulae simple. . . . . 150. *P. funerea*
    Setulae partly branched . . . . 151. *P. multiseta*
  e. Setulae similar, acropleurogenous. 152. *P. thujae*
c. Conidia 25–35 × 6–7 μ
  d. Conidia monomorphic
    e. Setulae usually 3, 19–24 μ . . . . 153. *P. caudata*
  d. Conidia polymorphic
    e. Setulae usually 4 . . . . 154. *P. heterospora*

   c. Conidia 25–35 × 7–10 μ

     e. Setulae 1–4, branched, 24–44..... 155. *P. nattrassii*

     e. Setulae 3, 19–38 μ.............. 156. *P. betazamiae*

     e. Setulae 3, 20–45 μ.............. 157. *P. oryzae*

   c. Conidia 25–35 × 9–12 μ, fuliginous...... 158. *P. trevoae*

   c. Conidia 30–40 × 7–9 μ

     e. Setulae usually 4–5, distinct or
       paired, often branched, 15–22 μ.. 159. *P. macrospora*

   c. Conidia 35–45 × 7–11 μ

     e. Setulae 2–3, stout, with lumen
       9–29 μ....................... 160. *P. hughesii*

b. Intermediate colored cells contrasted, the upper two umber, brown, lowest yellow brown, olivaceous (Versicolorae, Umberae-Olivae), Nos. 161–201.

   c. Conidia 16–22 μ long.

     d. Conidia 5–7 μ wide.

       e. Setulae 2–3, stout, 5–10 μ .... 161. *P. paraguayensis*

       e. Setulae usually 3, filiform, usually
        up to 16 μ .... 162. *P. palmarum*

     d. Conidia 6–9 μ wide

       e. Setulae 3 up to 14 μ............ 163. *P. stellata*

       e. Setulae 3, filiform, 12–20 μ ...... 164. *P. langloisii*

   c. Conidia 18–26 μ long

     d. Conidia 5–7 μ wide

       e. Setulae 1–3, rudimentary, abortive,
        2–9 μ........................ 165. *P. westerdijkii*

       e. Setulae 1–4, usually 2–3, 10–20 μ.. 166. *P. cruenta*

       e. Setulae 3, 6–18 μ.............. 167. *P. foedans*

       e. Setulae 3–4, usually 3, 6–16 μ..... 168. *P. gaultheriae*

       e. Setulae 3, 12–20 μ.............. 169. *P. coffeae*

                                170. *P. eusora*

       e. Setulae 2–4, usually, 3, 13–25 μ .. 171. *P. gracilis* ·

       e. Setulae 2–3, usually 3, 21–32 μ... 172. *P. pauciseta*

       e. Setulae 3, 20–34 μ.............. 173. *P. vaccinii*

     d. Conidia 6–9 μ wide

       e. Setulae 2, 12–16 μ.............. 174. *P. lambertiae*

       e. Setulae 2–3, usually 3, 5–16 μ.... 175. *P. canangae*

                                176. *P. oleandri*

       e. Setulae 3, 12–22 μ.............. 177. *P. acaciae*

       e. Setulae 3–4, usually 3,4–22 μ .... 178. *P. zahlbruckneriana*

       e. Setulae 3, 10–20 μ stout......... 179. *P. aquatica*

       e. Setulae 2–3, usually 3,13–32 μ ... 180. *P. crassiuscula*

       e. Setula 2–5, usually 3,12–48 μ .... 181. *P. conigena*

    d. Conidia 7.5–10 μ wide
       e. Setulae 3, stout, 9–16 μ .... 182. *P. vismifolia*
       e. Setulae 3–4, 12–20 μ .... 183. *P. japonica*
       e. Setula 2–3, 17–27 μ .... 184. *P. eriobotrifolia*
       e. Setulae 2–5, usually 4,15–32 μ.... 185. *P. natalensis*
       e. Setulae 3, stout, 18–38 μ .... 186. *P. longiseta*
  c. Conidia 20–30 μ long
    d. Conidia 5–8 μ wide
       e. Setulae 3, 7–16 μ .... 187. *P. batatae*
       e. Setulae 2–3, usually 3, 13–22 μ... 188. *P. matildea*
       e. Setulae 2–4, usually 3, 16–26 μ... 189. *P. paeoniae*
       e. Setulae 2–4, usually 3, 6–35 μ.... 190. *P. oxyanthi*
       e. Setulae 2–5, usually 3, 20–33 μ... 191. *P. leucothoës*
                                 192. *P. subcuticularis*
       e. Setulae 2–5, usually 4, 6–28 μ.... 193. *P. cibotii*
    d. Conidia 7–10 μ wide
       e. Setulae usually 3, 3–13 μ .... 194. *P. aceris*
       e. Setulae usually 3, 9–20 μ .... 195. *P. maculiformans*
       e. Setulae usually 3, 25–35 μ .... 196. *P. populi-nigrae*
       e. Setulae usually 3, 23–40 μ........ 197. *P. sydowiana*
    d. Conidia 8–12 μ wide
       e. Setulae 3, 20–26 μ .... 198. *P. caffrae*
       e. Setulae usually 3, 26–33 μ........ 199. *P. staticis*
  c. Conidia 25–31 μ long
    d. Conidia 8–10 μ wide
       e. Setulae 3, 15–30 μ .... 200. *P. ardisiae*
  c. Conidia 28–38 μ long
    d. Conidia 7–10 μ wide
       e. Setulae 2–3, 15–40 μ .... 201. *P. planimi*
b. Intermediate colored cells strongly contrasted, the upper two of them fuliginous (chestnut brown to black), often swollen and opaque, the lowest colored cell light brown (Versicolorae, Fuliginae-Olivae), Nos. 202–258.
  c. Conidia 13–22 μ long
    d. Conidia 5–7 μ wide
       e. Setulae 2, 8–10 μ .... 202. *P. pandani*
       e. Setulae 3, 6 μ ....:..... 203. *P. saccardensis*
       e. Setulae 10–16 μ .... 204. *P. theobromae*
                                   205. *P. coptospermae*
       e. Setulae 13–23 μ .... 206. *P. briosiana*
    d. Conidia 6.5–9.5 μ wide, elliptic to gibbous

e. Setulae 3 or 3 and sometimes 2 and 4

    Setulae 6–11 μ .... 207. *P. pampeana*

    Setulae 8–17 μ .... 208. *P. gibberosa*

    Setulae 12–22 μ, stout .... 209. *P. albo-maculans*

    Setulae 20–25 μ .... 210. *P. conceptionis*

    Setulae 20–31 μ .... 211. *P. stictica*

    Setulae 33–45 μ .... 212. *P. cryptomericola*

c. Conidia 17–23 μ long

  d. Conidia 6–8 μ wide

    e. Setulae usually 3

      Setulae slender, 10–15 μ ..... 213. *P. milletiae*

      Setulae stout, 12–26 μ .... 214. *P. virgatula*

  d. Conidia 7–9.5 μ wide

    e. Setulae usually 3

      Setulae 6–16 μ, stout .... 215. *P. heucherae*

      Setulae 9–22 μ .... 216. *P. versicolor var.*
                                                  polygoni

      Setulae 9–26 μ, stout .... 217. *P. malicola*

      Setulae 15–27 μ, slender ..... 218. *P. leprogena*

c. Conidia 19–26 μ long

  d. Conidia 6–8.5 μ wide

    e. Setulae 2, 8–10 μ .... 219. *P. ventricosa*

    e. Setulae 3, 6–8 μ, filiform .... 220. *P. peyronelii*

    e. Setulae 2 and 3, usually 3

      Setulae 8–16 μ .... 221. *P. ixorae*

      Setulae 10–15 μ .... 222. *P. pycnoides*

      Setulae 9–25 μ .... 223. *P. zonata*

      Setulae 17–25 μ .... 224. *P. alöes*

      Setulae 20–30 μ .... 225. *P. cinchonae*

      Setulae 9–31 μ .... 226. *P. menezesiana*

      Setulae 17–31 μ .... 227. *P. clavispora*

      Setulae 16–33 μ .... 228. *P. photinae*

      Setulae 23–39 μ .... 229. *P. laricicola*

      Setulae 20–45 μ .... 230. *P. longisetula*

  d. Conidia 7–10 μ wide

    e. Setulae 2–4, usually 3

      Setulae 9–20 μ .... 231. *P. glandicola*

      Setulae 12–25 μ, flagellate.... 232. *P. flagisetula*

      Setulae 15–30 μ, filiform ..... 233. *P. clusiae*

                            234. *P. paeoniicola*

                            235. *P. sphaerelloides*

Setulae 15–30 μ, coarse . . . . . . 236. *P. diospyri*

237. *P. versicolor*

238. *P. scirpina*

Setulae 24–45 μ . . . . 239. *P. filisetula*

   e. Setulae 4–5, up to 40 μ . . . . 240. *P. magoscyi*

d. Conidia 8–12 μ wide

   e. Setulae 2, coarse, up to 20 μ . . . . . 241. *P. guaranitica*

   e. Setulae, usually 3

      Setulae 12–16 μ . . . . 242. *P. rapaneae*

      Setulae 6–22 μ . . . . 243. *P. congensis*

      Setulae 19–26 μ, coarse . . . . . . 244. *P. mangiferae*

      Setulae 20–25 μ . . . .,. . . 245. *P. laughtonae*

      Setulae 16–34 μ . . . . 246. *P. curta*

c. Conidia 25–30 μ long

  d. Conidia 7–10 μ wide

    e. Setulae 3, sometimes 2–4

      Setulae 13–16 μ . . . . 247. *P. dianellae*

      Setulae 12–22 μ . . . . 248. *P. elasticola*

      Setulae 9–23 μ, slender . . . . . . 249. *P. scirrofaciens*

      Setulae 15–34, rather coarse.. 250. *P. rhododendri*

      Setulae 24–35 μ . . . . 251. *P. paraguariensis*

      Setulae 25–40 μ . . . . 252. *P. longi-aristata*

      Setulae 30–40 μ, coarse with
lumen . . . . 253. *P. triseta*

    3. Setulae 4–5, sometimes 6, filiform,
20–35 μ . . . . 254. *P. brassicae*

  d. Conidia 9–12 μ wide

    e. Setulae usually 3

      Setulae 16–33 μ . . . . 255. *P. sonsensis*

      Setulae 19–29 μ . . . . 256. *P. calophylli*

      Setulae 18–27 μ, coarse . . . . . . 257. *P. tiliae*

      Setulae 20–60 μ, coarse . . . . . . 258. *P. conspicua*

Section *Sexloculatae*

Conidia 6-celled; four intermediate brown colored cells;
exterior cells hyaline or subhyaline (No. 4 with brown coloured
basal cells)

Species Nos. 259–262

a. Conidia 20 × 8 μ

  b. Setulae 3, up to 10 μ . . . . 259. *P. valdiviana*

a. Conidia 24–30 × 8–10 μ
  b. Setulae dichotomously branched or 2–3
    parted . . . . 260. *P. corni*
a. Conidia 27–36 × 6–9 μ
  b. Setulae usually 2–5, simple or branched,
    6–18 μ . . . . 261. *P. pezizoides*
a. Conidia 30–35 × 8–11 μ
  b. Setulae 6–12 μ long, projecting from apical
    attenuated beak . . . . 262. *P. cornu-cervae*

Species Descriptions
Section *Quadriloculatae*
Species Nos. 42–75

42. **Pestalotia epilobii** Rolland & Fautrey, Rev. Mycol. Fr. 16:10,1894; Syll. Fung. 11:578,1895.

Pustules erumpent, coniform.　Conidia 4-celled, 14–16 × 5–6 μ, the two colored cells brown, 14 × 8 μ; setulae 2–3, divergent, branched, 20–25 μ; pedicels 8–10 × 2 μ, coarse; hyaline exterior cells deciduous with age.

On dried stems of *Epilobium hirsutum* L., June 1893, Côte d'Or, France, F. Fautrey.　Specimens are distributed in Roumeguère, Fungi Galliae Exs. No. 6458, but the author has had no success finding the fungus.

43. **Pestalotia nuciseda** Fairman, Proc. Rochester Acad. Sci. 6:88,1921, pl. 16, fig. 5.

Pustules gregarious, sub-globose, black, subepidermal, later erumpent and superficial, dense, carbonaceous.　Conidia erect, elliptic fusoid, 4-celled, 12.5–16 × 6–7 μ (Fairman, 12–18 × 7–8 μ); 2 colored cells umber or darker, equally colored, usually 10–13 μ long, globulate; basal cells subhyaline, minute, obtuse, hemispherical, the pedicels deciduous, apical hyaline cells attenuated, hidden or stalk-like, armed with a crest of 1–3 simple and branched setulae, 10–32 μ long, the branches curved and diverging nearly or at right angles to the conidia.

On nuts and nut shucks of *Hicoria* (= *Carya*, Nutt.), Lyndonville, N. Y. in Mycol. Fairmanii No. 5264, May, 1919, Fairman; No. 5265, L. B. Wright and Clara Gray.

44. **Pestalotia aesculi** Fautrey, Rev. Mycol. Fr. 11:153,1889; Syll. Fung. 10:485,1892.

Pustules scattered, subcutaneous, then erumpent, oblong, remaining in part covered by the torn epidermis.　Conidia numerous, ovate-oblong,

3-septate, 16–20 × 8 μ, almost sessile; intermediate colored cells brown; exterior cells hyaline coniform, the apical cells with 2 diverging setulae, 16 μ long.

On *Aesculus hippocastanum* L. Noidan, Côte d'Or, France, April, 1889.

45. **Pestalotia chamaeropis** Pass., Rend. R. Accad. Lincei 4:104,1888; Syll. Fung. 10:492,1892.

Acervuli scattered or gregarious, punctiform, black. Conidia fusiform-clavate, 2- to 3-septate, apex crowned with 2 diverging setulae; pedicels short; colored part 15 × 5 μ; uppermost cells falling off with setulae.

On wilted petioles of *Chamaerops humilis* L. Parma, Italy. Spots are lacking and in the opinion of the author the conidia are smaller than those of *P. phoenicis* Vize and differ from *P. palmarum* Cooke in having 2 setulae. The identity of this species requires clarification. The two species mentioned have 5-celled conidia.

46. **Pestalotia betulae** Moroczkovsky, Jour. Bot. Acad. Sci. (Ukraine) 2:3–4, 183,1941–45,1946.

Acervuli epiphyllous, sparse, immersed, brown, minute, up to 100 μ diameter. Conidia 4-celled, cylindric, sometimes unequilateral, 15–22 × 5.5–8 μ, hardly constricted at the septa dividing the two intermediate brown cells, terminal cells hyaline minute, conoid, the apical cell crowned with 2 to 3 filiform, recurved setulae, 8–21 μ long. Conidiophores hyaline, filiform, for the most part deciduous.

On dying leaves of *Betula alba* L. near Malin, Prov. Zhytomyriens, Ukraine, U.S.S.R., July 19, 1939, Sidorenko.

47. **Pestalotia truncata** Lév., Ann. Sci. Nat. Bot. 3.5:285,1846; Syll. Fung. 3:794,1884.
    Didymosporium truncatulum Cda., Icon. Fung. 6:5,1854, tab. 1, fig. 16; Syll. Fung 3:794,1884.
    Pestalotia choenostroma Lacroix, Ann. Soc. Linn. Angers 2:10–16,1856.
    P. polygoni Wint., Hedwigia 10:162,1871; Syll. Fung. 18:483,1906.
    P. truncatula Fckl., Symb. Mycol. 1869, p. 391, tab. 1, fig. 43a, b; not (Cda.) Fckl. in Syll. Fung. 3:794,1884.
    P. lignicola Cooke, Handbook of British Fungi, 1871, 471; Syll. Fung. 3:794,1884.
    P. nummularia Hariot & Briard, Jour. Bot. Fr. 5:172,1891; Syll. Fung. 10:496,1892.
    P. lepidospermatis P. Henn. Hedwigia 40:355,1901; Syll. Fung. 18:484, 1906.
    Pestalotia hartigii Tubeuf var. *betulae* Laub., Arb. Kaiserl. Anstalt. Land. u. Forstw. 5:210,1906, fig. 5a,b; Centralbl. Bakt., Abt. 2:19,619,1907; Syll. Fung. 22:1225,1913.

P. chartarum Bres., Ann. Mycol. 13:105,1915; Syll. Fung. 25:609,1931.
P. menthicola, Urries, Bol. Soc. Española Hist. Nat. 32:227,1932.
P. truncata Lév. var. *lignicola* Grove, British Stem and Leaf Fungi II, 1937, p. 346.
Phragmotrichum lignicola Cda, Icon. Fung. 2:9,1838, tab. 9: fig. 46.
Seiridium lignicola (Cda.) Sacc., Syll. Fung. 3:783,1884.
Truncatella truncata (Lév.) Stey., Bull. Jard. Bot. État Bruxelles 19:295–296,1949, pl. VIII, fig. A.

Pustules, acervuli or pseudopycnidia, one or sometimes many loculate, without true ostiole, globose-lenticular, 200–700 μ in diam, or oblong to long hysteriform, 200–800 × 100–250 μ, or otherwise 150–600 × 100–200 μ, with a thin stroma, immersed at first, erumpent at maturity, scattered or gregarious and confluent, carbonaceous, blackening the matrix. Conidia 4-celled, elliptic-fusoid, 14–20 × 6–8 μ, erect, usually not constricted at the septa, intermediate colored cells cask-shaped, olivaceous or darker, the walls sometimes darker, guttulate, 11–15 μ long, usually 11–14 μ, enveloped in a clearly differentiated epispore, with age truncate and without the exterior hyaline parts; basal hyaline cells hemispherical, papillaeform or obtuse, deciduous with age or persistent and deflated; apical hyaline cells hidden, minute, subulate, filiform, attenuated frequently into 1 simple setula or forked along the axis near or distant from the apical cells, often 2 setulae, one of which is forked, sometimes 2 or rarely 3 or 4 simple or branched setulae like a stag-horn, 6–32 μ long, usually 10–20 μ and sometimes up to 40 μ long; pedicels coarse and long, 20–40 μ, sometimes up to 50 μ long; hyaline extremities at length deciduous, the remains brown, 1-septate, truncate.

On prostrate twigs of *Populus fastigiata* Poir, near Paris, France.
Specimens examined: On *Populus* (prostrate wood), Meloduno, France, Nov. 28, 1851, Dr. Roussel in herb. Mus. d'Hist. Nat. Paris and reported by Tulasne, Sel. Fung. Carp. II, 202,1863; *ibid* Jan. 10, 1852, in herb. Patouillard (herb. Farlow) Harvard University and herb. Mus. d'Hist. Nat. Paris, Champ. du Mus. No. 418 [Fig. 6a]. On dry wood strips of *Fagus*, Prague, 1845, sub *Didymosporium truncatulum* Cda. The fungus is identical with *Pestalotia truncatula* Fckl. (Symb. Myc., 1869, p. 391, tab. 1, fig. 43a,b) on twigs of *Salix aurita* L., Austria [=*P. truncata* Lév.] according to Saccardo (Syll. Fung. 3:794,1884 and 15:242,1901). On cut wood pieces of *Betula*, Lyndonville, N. Y., July 9, 1918, C. E. Fairman, sub *P. lignicola* Cooke in Mycol. Fairmanii No. 5178. On dry leaves of *Lepidosperma angustatum* R. Br., Bridgetown, West Australia, leg. Nelson, April, 1901, sub *P. lepidospermatis* P. Henn. On roots of *Mentha rotundifolia* (L.) Huds., Barbunales, Spain, Sept. 1931, sub *P. menthicola* Urries. On dry stems of *Polygonum aviculare* L., Grünau, Germany, July 1871, G. Winter, sub *P. polygoni* Wint. in herb. Berlin Bot. Mus. On wood chips of *Quercus pedunculata* Ehrh.

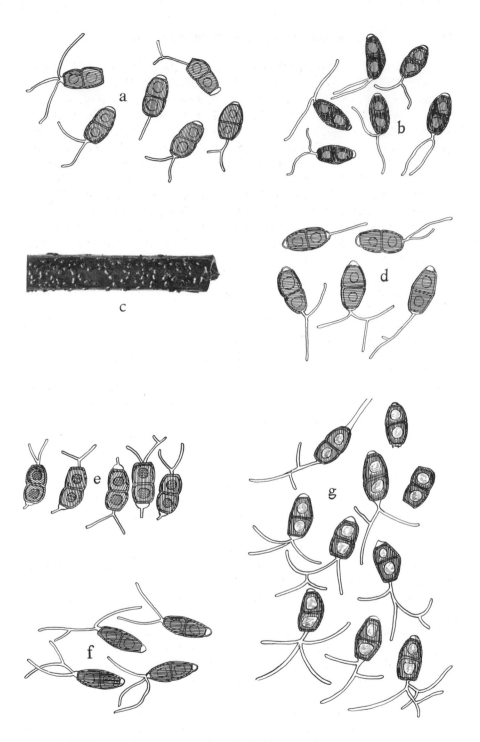

Fig. 6 [47]. *Pestalotia truncata* Lév. (*c*) fruiting pustules.

[=Q. robur L.], Monkwood, Worcestershire, England, Oct. 11, 1927, in herb. Grove. On *Salix aurita* L. (twigs), Austria (Nassau), 1868, leg. Fuckel in Fungi Rhenani Nos. 2137 and 2494 as *P. truncatula* Fckl. [Fig. 6b]. On *Salix purpurea* L. (twigs), Sitka, Alaska, Feb. 1915, J. P. Anderson, Alaska Fung. No. 105 in Nat. Fungus Coll., U.S.D.A. [Figs. 6c,d, 13]. On *Salix* (wood pieces) Lyon (Rhone), France, 1886, in Roumeguère, Fungi Galliae Exs. No. 4475 [Fig. 6e]. On *Salix herbacea* L. (leaves), Cape Dorset, Canada, Aug. 28, 1934, N. Polunin, Flora Canad. East Arctic No. 2381, a–51. On cardboard in forest, Königstein, Saxony, Germany, June and July 1900, sub *P. chartarum* Bres. in Krieger, Fungi Saxonici No. 2397 [Fig. 6f].

P. truncata has a wide host range among many orders of the plant kingdom. Pertinent information relating to all of the synonymous species except those reported on host plants in the orders Rosales and Coniferales is as follows:

Didymosporium truncatulum Cda. On dry wood strips of *Fagus* (Fagales), Prague, Bohemia, 1845.

Pestalotia polygoni Wint. On stems of *Polygonum aviculare* L. (Polygonales), Grünau, Germany, July 1871.

P. truncatula Fckl. On twigs of *Salix aurita* L. (Salicales), Austria.

P. lignicola Cooke. On wood chips, England. Regarded as a wood inhabiting form of *P. truncata* Lév. var. *lignicola* Grove (British Stem and Leaf Fungi II, 346, 1937). Grove stated that the variety is hardly worth distinguishing from *P. truncata* Lév.

P. nummularia Hariot and Briard. On diseased leaves of *Lysimachia nummularia* L. (Primulales), Chartres, near Mery-sur-Seine (Aube), France, Sept. 1890. P. Hariot.

P. lepidospermatis P. Henn. On dry leaves of *Lepidosperma angustatum* R. Br. (Graminales) near Bridgetown, West Australia, leg. Nelson, April 1901.

P. hartigii Tubuef var. *betulae* Laub. On bark of stems of *Betula* (Fagales), Kreis Jerichow, Saxony, Germany, Aug. 1905. This fungus differs from *P. hartigii* according to Laubert, by longer setulae and somewhat shorter hyaline terminal cells. He found other fungi in constricted stems of young birches and discredited Tubeuf's allegation of the parasitic habit of these fungi and instead regarded them as secondary invaders following frost damage.

P. chartarum Bres. On cardboard, Königstein, Saxony, Germany, 1900.

P. menthicola Urries. On roots of *Mentha rotundifolia* (L.) Huds. (Polemoniales), Barbunales, Spain, Sept. 1931 [Fig. 6g].

Phragmotrichum lignicola Cda. On dead willow twigs (Salicales), Prague, Bohemia, 1837.

Hazslinsky (Verh. K. K. zool.-bot. Ges. Wien 20:211–218,1870) described the development of a fungus with brown-colored 2-celled conidia arising acrogenously and chained together by a narrow colorless connecting member.   The conidial extremities are colorless and taper into long tails resembling a 4-celled spored *Monochaetia*.   To this poorly described fungus Hazslinsky gave the name *Seiridium marginatum* Nees & Henry, a bad error which furthered the misunderstanding of an already uncertain fungus.   Without the extremities the conidia are 2-celled, truncate (Hazslinsky, see above, fig. 25) and analogous to *P. truncata* Lév. (Syn. *P. truncatula* Fckl., Symb. Mycol., tab. I, fig. 43b, 1869, and Tubeuf, Beitr. Kennt. Baumkr. 1888, pl. 5).   This is the same fungus described by Corda (Icon. Fung. II: 9,1838, tab. 9, fig. 46) as *Phragmotrichum lignicola* on dead twigs of *Salix*, Prague, 1837.   While Corda's illustrations of the fungus show conidia chained together with a bridging filament there is no doubt that his fungus is *Pestalotia truncata* Lév. because the conidia are 4-celled, including the 2 hyaline exterior cells and the specimen is on *Salix* from Bohemia, a common matrix and source of *P. truncata* Lév.   Considerable imagination was applied by Zobel, Corda's artist, to show the pedicels and setulae as links uniting the conidia in chains.   Corda's original illustrations were reproduced by Lindau (Engler and Prantl, Die natürlichen Pflanzenfamilien I: I** 1900, p. 411, fig. 214) and by Allescher (Rabh. Krypt.–Flora 1: Abt. 7,633,1902) but both authors employed the new name, *Seiridium lignicola* (Cda.) Sacc., to agree with Saccardo's earlier disposition of it (Syll. Fung. 3:783).

Voglino (Atti. Soc. Ven.-Trent, Sci. Nat. Padova 9:209–243,1885) referred to the figures of *P. truncata* Lév. by Corda (Icon. Fung. 5, tab. I, fig. 16) and Fuckel (Symb. Mycol. 1869, p. 391, pl. 1, fig. 43a,b).   His description of the species made no reference to branched setulae but they are shown in pl. 8, fig. 4 of his paper.   Saccardo (Syll. Fung. 3:794,1884) regarded *Didymosporium truncatulum* Cda. (Icon. Fung., vol. 6, tab. 1, fig. 16, 1854) and *P. truncatula* (Cda.) Fckl. (Symb. Mycol., 1869, p. 391, tab. 1, fig, 43a,b) and *P. lignicola* Cooke (Handbook of British Fungi, 1871, No. 1403. p. 472) as synonyms of *P. truncata* Lév.   This was doubted by Tubeuf (Beitr, Kennt. Baumkr. 1880).   Saccardo reported the fungus on wood of *Quercus*. *Salix*, *Populus*, *Padus*, *Eucalyptus*, *Fagus*, cones of *Abies*, stems of *Hypericum*, etc., in France, Bohemia, Italy, Germany and California.

Corda (Icon. Fung. 5, p. 4, Anleit, p. 14) reported the hyaline apex of the conidia tapered into 2–4 setulae or "germ tubes with branches."   Other conidia are illustrated with a hemispherical hyaline cell at each end; the two central cells guttulate, colored and truncate, and the exterior hyaline cells finally deciduous.   Corda's misunderstanding of the character of the conidia led to the error in assigning the fungus to *Didymosporium truncatulum* Cda. Tubeuf (Beitr. Kennt. Baumkr., pp. 40–51´, 1880) called attention to the errors in Corda's figures asserting that the drawings showed more than was observed.   Zobel, the artist, showed the setulae as germ tubes.   The failure to recognize exterior cells gave the conidia of Léveillé and Corda a truncate form and both chose the expression *truncata* and *truncatulum*; in 1869 Fuckel introduced the name *P. truncatula*. Both Corda and Fuckel attached specific value to the guttulate middle cells. Corda, Léveillé, and Fuckel all overlooked either both or one of the exterior cells, when, as a matter of fact, the forms they considered were 4-celled and not 2-celled. Tubeuf noted that the conidia of *P. truncatula* (Cda.) Fckl. in Fungi Rhenani No. 2137 are very similar to *Didymosporium truncatulum* Cda. and *P. hartigii* Tubeuf, but he was not convinced of their similarity in the absence of "pycnidia."

According to Hoehnel (Fragm. Myk., 1030,1917) the perfect stage of *P. truncata* Lév. is *Ceratostoma vitis* Fckl. (Symb. Mycol., p. 129, 1860). Both occur on all kinds of host plants and he regarded both as the same fungus. Both occur together in Krieger, Fungi Saxonici No. 580, named *Ceratostoma vitis* on *Humulus lupulus* L. *P. truncata* Lév. was collected on twigs of the same plant in Yokohama, Japan, March, 1940, by T. Kawamura and apparently it is the only host in the order *Urticales* for this species.

48. **Pestalotia laurocerasi** Westd., Bull. Acad. Roy. Belg. Ser. II:2,556, fig. 1, 579, 1857; Syll. Fung. 3:786,1884; Steyaert, Bull. Jard. Bot. Ètat Bruxelles 19:70–72,1948, pl. I, II.

   Truncatella laurocerasi (Westd.) Stey., Bull. Jard. Bot. État Bruxelles 19: 298,1949.

   Pestalotia ramulosa van Beyma, Centralbl. Bakt. Abt. 2:88:140,1933.

   Truncatella ramulosa (van Beyma) Stey., Bull. Jard. Bot. État Bruxelles 19:296–298,1949, pl. 8, fig. B.

   Pestalotia potentillae Rich., Soc. Sci. Arts, Vitry-le-François 15:409, 1887–88 (publ. 1889); Syll. Fung. 10:491,1892.

   Pestalotia sarothamni Allescher, Bot. Centralbl. 42:106,1890. Bot. Ver. in Landshut 12:82,1892; Syll. Fung. 10:485,1892.

   Monochaetia rosenwaldii Khaz., Jour. Agr. Research 26:45–59, 1923, pl. 1–13.

   P. eriobotryae McAlp., Agr. Gaz., New South Wales 6:856,1895, figs. 33–34; Syll. Fung. 14:1026,1899.

   P. platani Fautrey, Rev. Mycol. Fr. 18:70,1896; Syll. Fung. 14:1028,1899.

   P. lignicola Cooke var. *fragariae* Roum., Fungi Galliae Exs. 5486, 1890.

   P. malorum Elenk. & Ohl, Giur. Boliesni Rastenii 6:5–6,77–112,1912; Syll. Fung. 25:605,1931.

   P. truncatula Fckl. var. *corticola* Roum., Fungi Galliae Exs. 1760, 1881. Reliq. Libert.

   P. truncata Lév. var. *rubi* Karst., Hedwigia 35:48,1896.

Pustules hypophyllous, sparse, globose-lenticular, circular, 225–450 μ in diam. Conidia ellipsoid, 4-celled, 17–22 × 6–8 μ, the two intermediate cells guttulate, chestnut brown, opaque, 9–19 μ long, surrounded by a hyaline membrane; exterior cells hyaline, hemispherical, small, the apex with 1–3 simple or branched setulae, like a staghorn; pedicels of variable length, 30–40 × 2–3 μ, deciduous.

On dead fallen leaves of *Prunus laurocerasus* L. with other fungi. Belgium, Clem. Dumont, No. 1533.

Westendorp described *P. laurocerasi* with 3-celled conidia, the lowest cell hyaline and the colored superior cell with two diverging setulae arising together from the truncate cell. Actually the spores are 4-celled and the superior cell is hyaline and crowned with a single branched setula. According to Steyaert, *P. laurocerasi* is like *P. truncata* Lév., yet he has kept them distinct. Two specimens in the herbarium of the Jardin Botanique, Bruxelles, by Mlle. Libert designated "*P. spireae* Nobis and *P. strobilina* Nobis" with the inscriptions "sur *Spirea salicifolia* Aestate" and "in squamis strobilinum *Pini abietis* Aestate" [= Picea abies (L.) Karst.] are the same as *P. laurocerasi*. The pustules of the fungus on *Spirea* measure 450–1000 × 300–625 μ. Since these are unpublished herbarium names they have no valid place in literature.

Specimens examined: On dry petioles of *Fragaria vesca* L., near Rouen, France (Seine Inf.), Reliq. Letend. E. Niel. Roumeguère, Fungi Galliae Exs. 5486, 1890, sub *P. lignicola* Cooke var. *fragariae* Roum. On *Prunus padus* L. (bark), Malmédy, Belgium, in Roumeguère Fungi Galliae Exs. 1760, 1881 (Reliq. Libert) sub *P. truncatula* (Cda.) Fckl. var. *corticola* Roum. On *Pyrus communis* L. (cankers in twigs), Ist. Pat. Veg., Bologna, Italy, May 1951, G. Goidanich. On *Pyrus malus* L. [= *Malus sylvestris* Mill.] (twigs) Provadia, Bulgaria, July 18, 1932. A. Christoff, sub *P. malorum* Elenk. & Ohl.; Magdeburg, Germany, July 1935, culture from Wollenweber, No. 5716; on roots of nursery tree, California, Feb. 28, 1935, G. L. Stout. On *Rubus* (black raspberry canes), culture on stems of sweet clover, Oregon, March 27, 1935, S. M. Zeller.

Pertinent information relating to all of the synonymous species of *P. truncata* Lév. reported on host plants in the Order Rosales is as follows:

Pestalotia malorum Elenk. & Ohl. On leaves of *Pyrus malus* L. [= Malus sylvestris Mill.], Soczy, Caucasia, Russia, 1912, U. P. Savicz. Species according to authors is like *P. truncata* Lév. but the exterior cells of the conidia are larger and not deciduous. This is doubtful.

P. truncata Lév. var. *rubi* Karst. On dry canes of *Rubus*, Aboom, Finland, 1895.

P. eriobotryae McAlp. On dead leaves of *Eriobotrya japonica* Lindl., Melbourne, Australia.

P. truncatula Fckl. var. *corticola* Roum. On bark of branches of *Prunus padus* L., Malmédy, Belgium.

P. lignicola Cooke var. *fragariae* Roum. On dry petioles of *Fragaria vesca* L., Rouen (Seine Inf.) France.

Monochaetia rosenwaldii Khaz. In galls in trunks and branches of apricot, *Prunus armeniaca* L. Reported as the cause of galls yet artificial inoculations of fungus in branches of young trees were not successful.

Pestalotia platani Fautrey. On leaves of *Platanus orientalis* L. France.

P. potentillae Richon. On dry stems of *Potentilla reptans* L. St. Armand near Lumier, France.

P. ramulosa van Beyma. On leaves of *Lupinus*, Baarn, Holland, 1932. Van Beyma thoe Kingma.

P. sarothamni Allesch. On wilted twigs of *Sarothamnus scoparius* Koch [= *Cytisus scoparius* Link], near Dachau, Germany.

Pestalotia hartigii Tubeuf was originally described on *Abies* and *Picea*. It has a wide host range among members of the Coniferales. It is similar to *P. truncata* Lév. and for the record its extensive literature and synonymy are kept distinct.

49. **Pestalotia hartigii** Tubeuf, Beitr. Kenntn. Baumkr. 1888, pp. 40–51, pl. 5; Bot. Centralbl. 39:134,1889; Syll. Fung. 10:490,1892.

    P. sabinae Fautrey, Rev. Mycol. Fr. 13:171,1891; Roumeguère, Fungi Galliae Exs. 5884, 1891; Syll. Fung. 10:491,1892.

    P. tumefaciens P. Henn, Verh. Bot. Ver. Prov. Brandenb. 37:XXVI–XXVIII,1895 (publ. 1896); Syll. Fung. 14:1029,1899.

    P. truncatula Fckl. var. *conigena* Roum., Fungi Galliae Exs. 1759, 1881, nom. nud.

    P. dryina Auers. nom. nud., herb. Bot. Mus. Berlin.

    Truncatella hartigii (Tubeuf) Stey. Bull. Jard. Bot. État Bruxelles 19:298–299,1949, pl. 8, fig. c.

Pustules like pycnidia with thin stroma and without true ostioles. Conidia ovoid-elongate, 18–20 × 6 μ; intermediate cells 12–14 μ; apical cells with 1–4 setulae or growing out into a thread divided by two equal branches and branching again, 20 μ long; pedicels 30–50 μ long; hyaline extremities finally dropping away or basal cells remaining and deflated.

On stems of *Picea excelsa* Link. [= *P. abies* (L.) Karst.], and *Abies pectinata* DC. [= *A. alba* Mill.], and related species, Spessart, Germany, and elsewhere in Germany and Bohemia.

P. sabinae Fautrey. On twigs of *Juniperus sabina* L., Côte d'Or., France.

P. tumefaciens P. Henn. On galls on branches of *Abies nobilis* Lindl. [= *A. procera* Rehd.], *A. balsamea* (L.) Mill., *A. subalpina* Engelm. [= *A. lasiocarpa* (Hook.) Nutt.], *A. pichta* Forb. [= *A. sibirica* Ledeb.], Berlin, 1895.

Grove (British Stem and Leaf Fungi II, 1937, p. 349) asserted that *P. tumefaciens* is merely a form of *P. truncata*.

Specimens examined: On *Abies alba* Mill. (stems) in herb. Tubeuf, Bavarian Forest, Germany, 1886, as *P. hartigii* Tubeuf; Roumeguère, Fungi Galliae Exs. 1227, Lyon, France, Jan., 1880, Therry, sub *P. lignicola* Cooke. On galls on twigs and branches of *Abies nobilis* [= *A. procera* Rehd.], *A.*

balsamea (L.) Mill., *A. subalpina* [= *A. lasiocarpa* (Hook.) Nutt.], *A. pichta* [= *A. sibirica* Ledeb.], Bot. Gard., Berlin, May 1895, leg. P. Hennings sub *P. tumefaciens* P. Henn. in herb. Berlin Bot. Mus. (type). On *Juniperis sabina* L., Noidan, Côte d'Or, France, March 1891, leg. Fautrey in Roumeguère, Fungi Galliae Exs. 5884, sub *P. truncata* Lév. On *Picea excelsa* Link [= *P. abies* (L.) Karst.] wood pieces, Leipzig, Germany, July 4, 1886, sub *P. dryina* Auers. nom. nud. in herb. Berlin Bot. Museum; (decorticated wood), Redfield, New York, July, C. H. Peck, sub *P. lignicola* Cooke in herb. N. Y. State Mus. [Fig. 7a]. On *Pinus sylvestris* L., Lyon, France, Apr. 1880, Therry, sub *P. lignicola* (herb. Thuemen) in herb. N. Y. State Mus. [Fig. 7b]; same specimens in Thuemen, Myc. Univ. No. 1778 (on naked wood) and according to Tubeuf (Beitr. Kenntn. Baumkr.) the substratum is *Abies pectinata* DC. [= *A. alba* Mill.]. On cone scales, Roumeguère, Fungi Galliae Exs. 1759, Malmédy, Belgium, sub *P. truncatula* Fckl. var. *conigena* Roum.; on *Pinus* sp. (culture), Berlin, Germany, June 1927, H. W. Wollenweber.

The fungus is close to *P. truncata* Lév. which was reported on dead wood, but because Tubeuf thought *P. hartigii* was parasitic he regarded it as a different species. The conidia issue from pycnidia in black droplets, the stroma is formed of hyaline pseudoparenchyma and conidia are produced near and close to stroma to account for differences in the length of the pedicels. Tubeuf recognized differences between his fungus and *Didymosporium truncatulum* Cda., *P. truncatula* Fckl. and *P. truncata* Lév., all of which he regarded as different. Saccardo regarded these species as well as *P. lignicola* Cooke (Handbook of British Fungi, No. 1403, p. 472) and *P. hartigii* synonyms of *P. truncata* Lév. (Syll. Fung. 3:794,1884).

Some alleged differences between *P. truncata* Lév. and subsequent species have already been cited. There are others. Urries characterized *P. menthicola* Urries as having many chambered pseudo-pycnidia without true ostioles. *P. malorum* Elenk. & Ohl. has pseudo-pycnidia and minutely erumpent

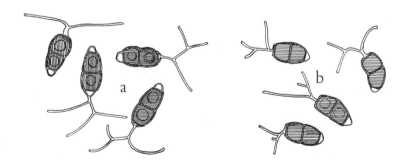

FIG. 7 [49]. *Pestalotia hartigii* Tubeuf.

ostioles. *P. truncata* Lév. var. *rubi* has smaller and narrower conidia. Van Beyma distinguished *P. ramulosa* van Beyma by conidia with more visible epispore, more developed and branched setulae and but a slight constriction at the central septum of the conidia. These characters are general among all of the species on different substrata and nutrient media. We have in *P. truncata* a widely cosmopolitan and flexible species showing variations under different conditions and which may be demonstrated in pure culture as physiologic strains or varieties.

The stem constriction disease (Einschnürungskrankheit) of forest tree seedlings in Europe precipitated a controversy in the latter quarter of the 19th century. This alleged fatal disease of fir and pine was originally noted by Hartig (Allgem. Forestw. u. Jagd. Ztg., 1883, p. 406) in a nursery at Spessart, Germany. The disease was manifested as a constriction of the stems near the ground level, a weakly developed root and a swelling of the stem above the constriction. This condition Hartig believed was due to the crushing of the cambium by mechanical action of freezing, but he felt uncertain of his hypothesis. Tubeuf was given the problem for study. In his collections of specimens he noted the presence of black pustules of a fungus associated with the disease, to which he assigned the name *P. hartigii* Tubeuf, and which together with other observations led him to accept it as the cause of the disease. He regarded it as a distinct species chiefly because of its occurrence in living tissue in contrast to the dead substratum of *P. truncata* Lév., which it approaches closely. He associated the organism with the one causing a similar disease of beech, oak, and ash seedlings, and in spite of the constant association of the fungus he failed to establish its parasitism.

Occurrences of the fungus and the disease were reported by Rostrup on young beech trees in Denmark, by Pfizenmayer on fir seedlings at Heiligkreuzthal, Germany, by Lagerberg on silver fir in nurseries in Sweden, and by Henry on beech seedlings at elevations of 1350 meters in France, the death of as great as 30 per cent of the stand of seedlings being reported under some conditions. Aumann attributed the disease to rapidly alternating extreme temperatures such as would result from snow and sunshine. Münch claimed that the disease was due to the heat of the sun raising the temperature of the ground surface far above the degree of tolerance of the plant cells and that the fungus is absent in stems showing the first signs of the disease. Fischer was unable to produce the disease by artificial methods of inoculation with spores through wounds or otherwise, which thus definitely disproved the parasitism of the fungus. Tubeuf finally reconciled himself to the climatic aspect of the disease and regarded Münch's explanation as the most satisfactory one.

Trotter (Riv. Pat. Veg. (n.s.) 12:1922) noted *P. hartigii* as a saprophyte following the blighting of pine needles (*Pinus pinea* L.) due to *Cladosporium laricis* Sacc. Trotter claimed distinctions between *P. hartigii* and *P. truncata* and between *P. mycophaga, P. tumefaciens* and *P. sabinae*, and between *P. strobilicola, P. lignicola, P. abietina* and *P. conorum-piceae.* Vincens (Bull. Soc. Path. Veg. Fr. 5:27–31,1918) observed yellowing and necrosis of pine needles and death of twig terminals associated with *P. hartigii.* His effort to obtain infection by artificial methods failed. He regarded *P. hartigii* and *P. truncata* synonymous.

Hotson and Stuntz (Phytopathology 24:1145–1146,1934) reported heavy losses among nursery plantings of *Chamaecyparis lawsoniana* Parl. in the Seattle, Washington, district by stem canker occurring from wound infections by apparently a species of *Monochaetia.* Numerous seedlings of *C. lawsoniana* were inoculated with positive results. The fungus is more likely *P. truncata* Lév. which often has a preponderance of monochaetioid conidia.

Cultures of *P. truncata* Lév. from pear canker, apple bark and pine wood caused a rot of apple fruits through wounds and the fungus attacked apple as rapidly as *Gloeosporium, Phoma, Fusarium* and *Cylindrocarpon* according to Wollenweber and Hochapfel (Z. Pflanzenkr. 46:404–406,1936). The fungus is also reported by Kidd and Beaumont (Trans. Brit. Mycol. Soc. 10:109, 1924) and Heald and Ruehle (Washington Agr. Exp. Sta. Bull. 253:33,1931) as the cause of decay in apples but as *P. hartigii* Tubeuf. Bjorling (Svenska Skogsv F. Tidsskr. 35:250–258,1937) isolated *P. hartigii* from pine, birch, and beech, and inoculations on pine produced only a superficial black spotting. Vaataja (Bi-Mo. Progr. Rep. Div. For. Biol. Dept. Agr. Canada 12:4,3,1956) reported the constant association of *P. hartigii* with diseased needles of *Picea glauca* (Moench) Voss. and with the red patch disease and snow mold of seedlings in seed beds. Brewer (Canad. Jour. Bot. 36: 941–946,1958) recovered the fungus, determined as *Truncatella ramulosa*, from accumulations in pulp and paper mills in Nova Scotia, Canada.

Steyaert (Bull. Jard. Bot. État Bruxelles 19:285–354,1949) proposed the new genus *Truncatella* to embrace this species, but the writer prefers not to segregate these 4-celled spore types from the genus *Pestalotia.*

The great prevalence of *Pestalotia truncata* Lév. on host plants of the Orders Coniferales, Rosales and Salicales is surprising. Also the absence of this species in the tropics may have some significance. The fungus is an inhabitant of plant roots and is widely prevalent in the Arctic and Temperate climatic zones to which most members of the Coniferales and Salicales are native.

50. **Pestalotia caulicola** Lév., Ann. Sci. Nat. Bot. III, 5:285–286,1846; Syll. Fung. 3:795,1884.

Pustules cushion-like, circular, gregarious and confluent, small, at length erumpent and rather superficial. Conidia 4-celled, $15.5–20 \times 6–7 \mu$; two intermediate cells umber or darker, sometimes fuliginous, $12–16 \mu$ long; exterior hyaline cells small, relatively inconspicuous, the apical cells hidden or narrow and attenuated; crest of 4–6 simple or branched, filamentous setulae 12–23 μ long or one setula either simple or branched; basal cells papillaeform or hemispherical; pedicels deciduous.

On dead withered, stems of *Cirsium lanceolatum* (L.) Hill [= *C. vulgare* (Savi) Tenore], Ville-d'Avray, near Paris, France, leg. Léveillé in herb. Mus. d'Hist. Nat., Paris, France [Fig. 8].

The type description mentioned acervuli protruding by a slightly erumpent ostiole, 3-4-celled conidia with 4 or 5 simple or branched setulae.

51. **Pestalotia affinis** Sacc. & Vogl., Atti Soc. Ven.-Trent. Sci. Nat. Padova
     9:2:216,1885; tab. VIII, fig. 6; Syll. Fung. 10:488,1892.

Acervuli punctiform, loosely gregarious, small, later erumpent, black, subglobose.   Conidia 3-septate, ovate, 14–20 × 6–8 μ, two intermediate cells dark colored, setulae 4–5, filiform, divergent, branched, 18–25 μ long; pedicels 30–50 × 2 μ, rarely up to 70 μ.

On canes of *Vitis*, Gallia, near Malmédy, Belgium.   Libert, No. 346 in herb. P. A. Saccardo, Padua.   The type description also includes the same fungus on pieces of *Juglans* wood, Lyons, France, April, 1880 (Crypt. Lyonnais, J. J. Therry, No. 4810) in herb. P. A. Saccardo.

Another *P. affinis* Ell. & Ev. (1889) on *Castanea*, was replaced by the name *P. everhartii* Sacc. (Syll. Fung. 10:492,1892) then changed again to *Monochaetia everhartii* (Sacc.) Sacc. (Syll. Fung. 18:485,1906).

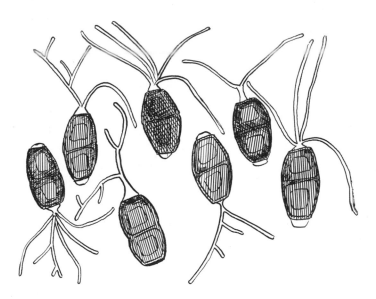

Fig. 8 [50].   *Pestalotia caulicola* Lév.

52. **Pestalotia chrysanthemi** Hóllos, Ann. Mus. Nat. Hungarici 4: pt. 2,369, 1906, tab. 9, fig. 27; Syll. Fung. 22:1224,1913.

Acervuli covered by the epidermis, erumpent, depressed-globose, black, about 0.5 mm diam. Conidia oblong-ellipsoid, 4-celled, not constricted at septa, 16–22 × 7–9 μ; 2 intermediate cells large, dark, guttulate, exterior cells small, hyaline, deciduous, the basal cells tapering into hyaline pedicels; setulae 2–5; unequal in length, divergent, sometimes forked.

On dead stems of *Chrysanthemum indicum* L. Kecskemet, Hungary.

53. **Pestalotia citrina** McAlp., Proc. Linn. Soc., New South Wales, Ser. I, 28:556,1903; Syll. Fung. 18:482,1906.

Pustules borne under the epidermis, subglobose or lenticular, convex, scattered or punctiform, 75–225 μ diam. Conidia 4-celled, clavate-fusiform, tapering to the base, erect or usually curved, hardly constricted at septa, 22–26 × 7–8 μ; 2 intermediate colored cells 12–16 μ long, olivaceous, equally colored; exterior cells hyaline, acute, the apical cells sometimes conic, the basal cells pointed; setulae 3–5, simple or frequently branched, arising from the tip of the apical cells, 6–31 μ, often 15–25 μ long; pedicels 4–9 μ, slender.

On stems of *Lobelia gibbosa* Labill, Sandringham, Victoria, Australia, C. French, Dec. 1902, in herb. Dept. Agr., Victoria, Australia.

McAlpine reported conidia 24–28 × 7–8.5 μ with 3 to 4 and occasionally 5 septa, 1 to 3 setulae up to 21 μ long, pedicels up to 28 μ long and acervuli 250–330 μ in diam.

54. **Pestalotia casuarinae** Cooke & Mass., Grevillea 16:114,1888; Syll. Fung. 10:490,1892.

Acervuli scattered, or gregarious and confluent pustulaeform, black, elongate-lenticular, subepidermal then erumpent, tearing the epidermis longitudinally. Conidia 4-celled, erect, elliptic-fusoid, 14.5–15.5 μ long; median cells olivaceous, oblong, guttulate, slightly constricted at septa, 9.5–11 × 5–6 μ; exterior cells hyaline, subglobose or short conic; the apical cells bearing 2–3, usually 3, short, curved, widely divergent setulae, 8–18 μ long, arising from different points around the crest of the apical cells; pedicels short, stout, broadened upward.

On twigs of *Casuarina* sp., Melbourne, Australia, No. 402 (Campbell), in herb. Kew [Fig. 9]. The fungus is characterized by 4-celled conidia, 3 laterally divergent setulae and clear brown colored, guttulate, intermediate cells. The measurements by Cooke and Massee are: colored cells 10–12 × 6–7 μ, conidia and setulae combined 45–50 μ long.

55. **Pestalotia besseyi** Guba sp. nov.

Pustulae depresso-globosae, sparsae vel gregariae, plerumque supra matricem emortuam dispersae, punctiformes, subepidermicales, erumpentes,

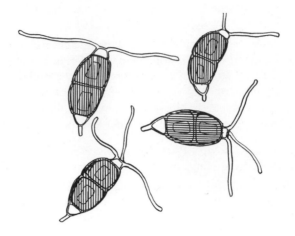

Fig. 9 [54].   *Pestalotia casuarinae* Cooke & Mass.

epidermidem elevantes fissentesque et massam atram fragmentis laceratis cinctam detegentes, 125–250 μ in diam.; conidia 4-cellularia, elliptico-fusoidea, 12.6–16 × 5–6 μ, ad septum inter cellulas coloratas sub-constricta; cellulae duae mediae concolores, olivaceae, guttulatae, 8–10 μ longae; cellulae extimae conicae; setulae 3, rare 4, simplices, numquam ramosae, 9–16 μ, plerumque 12 μ longae, ex apice conidii oriundae; pedicellus deciduus.

Pustules globose-depressed, punctiform, scattered or gregarious, generally distributed over the dead brown matrix, subepidermal, erumpent in a circular manner, lifting and tearing the epidermis and surrounded by the torn shreds, 125–250 μ diam, exposing the black contents.

Conidia 4-celled, elliptic fusoid, 12.6–16 × 5–6 μ, slightly constricted at septa dividing the colored cells, two intermediate colored cells olivaceous, guttulate, equally colored, guttules paler than cell color, 8–10 μ long: setulae 3, simple, rarely 4, never branched, 9–16 μ long mostly about 12 μ, borne at the apex of the conidia; exterior cells hyaline, conoid; pedicels deciduous.

On dry pods of *Acacia koa* Gray, Kolekola Pass, Oahu, Hawaii, E. A. Bessey, Jan. 24, 1940 in herb. Michigan State College, No. 592.

56. **Pestalotia gastrolobii** Fl. Tassi, Boll. Lab. Ort. Bot. R. Univ. Siena 3:101, 1900; Syll. Fung. 16:1015,1902.

Pustules scattered, gregarious, small, black, erumpent.   Conidia 15–16 × 6 μ, elliptic-fusoid, 4-celled, not constricted at septa, the two intermediate cells sooty colored, exterior cells small, hyaline; setulae 4, 18–20 μ long; pedicels deciduous.

On dead or withering legumes of *Gastrolobium boormanii* Maid. & Betche, New South Wales, Australia.

57. Pestalotia puyae P. Henn.

Pustules epiphyllous, subepidermal, subglobose or lenticular, erumpent, carbonaceous, gregarious, on raised, elliptic, yellowish-brown spots, 100–150 μ diam. Conidia 4-celled, elliptic or ovoid, rounded at the ends, 12.5–16 μ long; two colored cells umber or fuliginous, the walls slightly darker, 10–13 × 6.5–8 μ, the basal cells hyaline, short, broad obtuse or papillaeform, the apical hyaline cells similar, bearing 3 straight setulae, 3–8 μ long; pedicels long and coarse, 6–22 μ long.

On leaves of *Puya coarctata* Fisch. [=*P. chilensis* Mol.] Penco, Chile, Sept. 1906, herb. Berlin Bot. Mus., associated with spots and forming black crusty cushions beneath the epidermis [Fig. 10]. The species is distinct. According to Hennings' brief description deposited with the specimen, the conidia measure 10–13 × 5–6 μ, the setulae 10–12 μ and the pedicels 10 × 2 μ. A broader characterization of the fungus based on the writer's study is offered in the emended description.

58. Pestalotia maura Ell. & Ev., Jour. Mycol. 4:123,1888; Syll. Fung. 10: 489,1892.

Pustules amphigenous, somewhat prominent, black, minute, on round reddish-brown spots, 2–3 mm in diam. Conidia obovate, acute below, 4-celled, dark and almost opaque, 12–15 × 6–8 μ with a crest of 3 horizontally spreading setulae, 15–20 μ, arising without distinct hyaline apical cells from the obtuse apices; basal hyaline cells small, acute, terminating in a hyaline pedicel, shorter than the conidia.

On leaves of *Psychotria rufescens* H.B.K., Halifax River, Florida (A. H. Curtis, No. 1121, A. Commons, No. 881).

Ellis and Everhart (Jour. Mycol. 5:157,1889) reported the fungus on dead

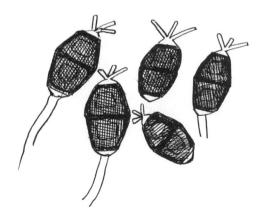

Fig. 10 [57]. *Pestalotia puyae* P. Henn.

leaves of *Persea carolinensis* Nees [=*P. borbonia* (L.) Spreng.], *Quercus virens* Ait. [=*Q. virginiana* Mill.], and *Q. palustris* Muench submitted by A. B. Langlois, St. Martinsville, La. The innate erumpent acervuli are scattered irregularly over the matrix. This species according to Ellis is well characterized by obconic conidia, the two cells next below the upper cell almost black.

The type specimen deposited in the N. Y. Bot. Gard. is blank. The specimen designated *P. maura* Ell. & Ev. on oak leaves, 3, IX–8 and 3–(784), Nat. Fungus Coll., U.S.D.A., has 5-celled clavate fusiform conidia, 20–24 × 6.5–9 μ, the colored cells 14–18 μ long, the 2 upper colored cells umber to fuliginous and setulae 3, 15 μ long. This is more properly *Pestalotia glandicola* (Cast.) Guba. Another specimen, IV–88, with the same designation on red oak leaves (*Quercus rubra* L.), with 5-celled spores, one short appendage and pale brown intermediate cells, is *Monochaetia monochaeta* (Desm.) Allescher. The form on *Persea carolinensis* is also *Pestalotia glandicola*.

59. **Pestalotia camphori** Kurosawa, Bot. Mag. Tokyo 22: no. 253, (53)–(55), 1908 (Japanese). Miyabe Festschrift, Tokyo, 49–51, 1911 (English).

Spots brown, elliptic, 4 mm in diam, becoming black and larger, the blackened bark cracking in several places. Conidia 4-celled, club-shaped, 18.2 × 5.2 μ, apical hyaline cells bearing 3 setulae, 5.2–6.4 μ long, the other cells faintly colored.

On black spots in bark of *Cinnamomum camphora* Nees & Eber., Japan.

The author, by inoculation experiments, confirmed his contention that the black bark spot disease of camphor trees is predisposed by injuries caused by the insect *Phleothrips nigra* Sasaki. *Pestalotia camphori* Kurosawa and *Glomerella cinnamomi* grow on the affected portion of the bark and hasten the progress of the disease, often causing the death of the young branches.

60. **Pestalotia stevensonii** Peck, Bull. Torrey Bot. Club 6:135,1877; Syll. Fung. 3:792,1884.

> *P. strobilicola* Speg., Michelia 1:479,1879; Syll. Fung. 3:792,1884.
>
> *P. conigena* Lév. var. *abietis* Roum., Fungi Galliae Exs. 2338, 1883, nom. nud.
>
> *P. abietina* Vogl., Atti Soc. Ven.-Trent. Sci. Nat. Padova, 9:1885, tab. 8, fig. 3; Syll. Fung. 10:490,1892.
>
> *P. conorum-piceae* Tubeuf, Beitr. Kenntn. Baumkr., 1888, pp. 40–51; Syll. Fung. 10:490,1882.
>
> *Truncatella conorum-piceae* (Tubeuf) Stey., Bull. Jard. Bot. État Bruxelles 19:299,1949, pl. 8, fig. D.

Pustules oblong, elongate, hysteriform or globose-lenticular, 200–1000 × 125–350 μ, black, gregarious or scattered, innate-erumpent, closely surrounded by the torn epidermis. Conidia 4-celled, 16–22 × 5.5–7.5 μ, erect, elliptic fusoid or oblong fusoid; two intermediate colored cells olivaceous or umber, equally colored, enveloped by a hyaline epispore, guttulate, 11–15 μ, the guttules pale olivaceous; apical hyaline cells prominent, conoid or conic-cylindric bearing 2–4 usually 3 simple, divergent setulae, rarely if at all branched, 7–25 μ long; basal hyaline cells long conic or cylindric; pedicels long and coarse, easily separating, equal to or exceeding the length of the conidia, 10–50 μ long, the exterior hyaline cells persisting.

On dead or blighted cone scales and needles of *Abies, Picea, Pinus* and related genera.

Specimens examined: On *Picea excelsa* Link [=*P. abies* (L.) Karst.] (dead cone scales): Roumeguère, Fungi Galliae Exs. 2338, Collechio Forest, Parma, Italy, G. Passerini sub *P. conigena* Lév. var. *abietis* Roum.; *ibid*. Rabenhorst, Fungi eur. 2462 sub *P. conigena* Lév.; herb. N. Y. State Mus., Westchester, Pa., June 2, 1876, W. C. Stevenson, Jr. (type); Ellis & Evershart, Fungi Col. No. 82, Newfield, N. J., May 1893; Ellis & Everhart Fungi Col. No. 349, Newton, Mass., W. G. Farlow sub *P. truncatula* Fckl.; herb. N. Y. State Mus., C. H. Peck, September; herb. Grove, Italy, sub *P. truncata* Lév.   On *Abies nigra* [=*Picea mariana* (L.) Britt.] (dead cone scales), Massachusetts, Russell No. 567 in herb. Curtis, herb. Farlow, Harvard University, sub *Seiridium* sp.   On *Abies pectinata* DC. [= *Q. alba* Mill.] (dead cone scales), Roumequère, Fungi Galliae Exs. 5883, Côte d'Or, France, April 1891, F. Fautrey, sub *P. abietina* Vogl.; Albany, N. Y., March 31, 1912, S. J. Burnham sub *P. truncata* Lév.; herb. N. Y. State Mus., Menands, N. Y., September, C. H. Peck.

On *Pinus edulis* Engelm. [=*P. cembroides* Zucc. var. *edulis* (Engelm.) Voss]; herb. Forest Path., U.S.D.A., No. 24941, Stonewall, Col., June 18, 1917, Hedgcock and Johnston.   On *Pinus ponderosa* Lawson (needles), Groom Creek Canyon, Prescott National Forest, Prescott, Ariz., Dec. 18, 1956, P. D. Keener.   On *Pinus rigida* Mill. (needles), in herb. Dept. Plant Path. Cornell University, No. 2401, P. B. Fletcher, Oct. 19, 1906.   On *Pinus strobus* L. (needles) in herb. Dept. Plant Path., Cornell University, No. 2405, Mohawk Lake, N. Y., Oct. 1906, A. K. Smiley.   On *Pinus* sp. (cone scales), Myc. Fairmanii No. 5001, Shadigee, shore of Lake Ontario, Yates, N. Y., March 3, 1927, C. E. Fairman sub *P. hartigii* Tubeuf.

Saccardo (Syll. Fung. 3:792,1884; 15:242,1901) regarded *P. stevensonii* Peck (1877) as a synonym of *P. strobilicola* Speg. (1879) but Ellis (Ellis & Everhart, Fungi Col., No. 82, Oct. 1893) indicated that the synonymy should be reversed.   Tubeuf (Beitr. Kenntn. Baumkr. 1888, 40–51) recognized that this species was different from *P. truncata* Lév. and *P. truncatula* Fckl.   Both *P. conorum-piceae* Tubeuf (1888) and *P. abietina* Vogl. (1885) were described on dead cone scales of *Abies excelsa* DC. [=*A. alba* Mill.] collected by Passerini in the Collechio Forest, northern Italy, and distributed in Rabenhorst, Fungi europ., No. 2462 as *P. conigena* Lév. [Fig. 11a] and on material

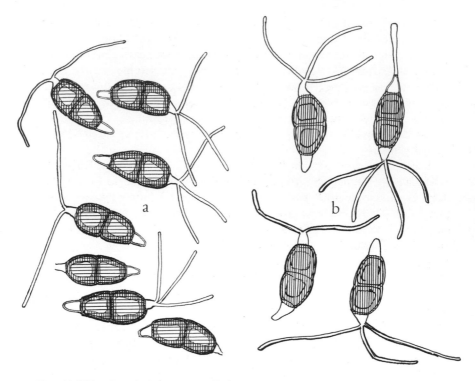

FIG. 11 [60].   *Pestalotia stevensonii* Peck.

collected by Farlow and Trelease in Newton, Mass., and distributed in Ellis & Everhart, Fungi Col. No. 349 as *P. truncatula* Fckl. [Fig. 11b].   The former material was also distributed in Roumeguère, Fungi Galliae Exs. 2338 as *P. conigena* Lév. var. *abietis* Roum., but without description.   Klebahn (Myc. Centralbl. 4:19,1914) stated that *P. abietina* Vogl. is closely related to *P. truncata*, *P. hartigii*, *P. tumefaciens*, *P. lignicola*, *P. aesculi*, *P. camelliae*, *P. chamaeropis*, *P. epilobii*, *P. genistae*, *P. ilicis*, *P. affinis*, and *P. sabinae*. According to my studies, these forms are like *P. truncata* Lév., not like *P. abietina* Vogl.   Allescher (Rabh. Krypt. Flora, 1: Abt. 7,677–678,1902), not being aware of the similarity of *P. abietina* and *P. conorum-piceae*, published both names with distinct descriptions.

Pertinent information relating to the following synonyms are:

P. strobilicola Speg.   On decaying cones of *Pinus sylvestris* L. Susegana, Italy, Nov. 1876.

P. abietina Vogl.   On cones of *Abies excelsa* DC. [= *A. alba* Mill.], Parma, Italy, and Newton, Mass.

P. conorum piceae Tubeuf.   On fallen cones of *Picea excelsa* Link [= *P. abies* (L.) Karst.], Parma, Italy, and Newton, Mass.

61. **Pestalotia maculicola** Rostr., Bot. Tidsskr. 10:210–212,1895; Syll. Fung.
14:1024,1899; 25:607,1931.

Spots orbicular, 3–4 mm in diam, white, amphigenous, surrounded by a
dark border line. Pustules small, black. Conidia oblong-fusoid, 4-celled,
-16–20 × 6–7 μ, the 2 intermediate cells dark; the apices awned with 3 setulae.

On leaves of *Ulmus montana* With., Silkeborg and Lyngby, Denmark,
causing round colorless spots on both surfaces according to the author.

62. **Pestalotia jacksoniae** P. Henn, Hedwigia 40:97,1901; Syll. Fung. 18:480,
1906.

Pustules black, subglobose, subcorticate, then erumpent, splitting the
epidermis. Conidia erect or curved, 4-celled, 19–22.5 × 7.5–8.5 μ; intermediate colored cells globose, chocolate brown or umber with thick dark
walls, enveloped by a fragile hyaline membrane, constricted at the septa, the
contents granular, 12–14.5 μ long; basal hyaline cells long cylindric or oblong;
apical hyaline cells obtuse, hidden, bearing usually 3–4 long setulae, 15–29 μ
long.

On stems of *Jacksonia macrocalyx* Meissn., near Perth, West Australia,
1900, Diels, No. 2098a in herb. Berlin Bot. Mus. [Fig. 12]. According to the
original description the colored cells measure 10–15 × 8–10 μ, the apex is
papillaeform, the setulae 20–35 μ long. The two colored cells and the walls
are strongly developed, while the hyaline exterior cells are rudimentary and
papilla-like.

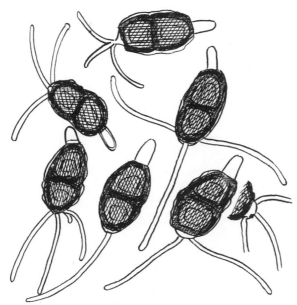

FIG. 12 [62]. *Pestalotia jacksoniae* P. Henn.

63. **Pestalotia pitospora** Costa & Camara, Acta Biol. Portugal 4:173–174, 1953.

Acervuli more or less triangular, black, 342–365 × 114–170 μ. Conidiophores filiform, pale-yellow, 19–39 × 2–2.5 μ. Conidia cask-shaped, 4-celled, exterior cells hyaline, intermediate cells dark brown, 16–23 × 7–11 μ; pedicel 11 × 1.5 μ; apical setulae 3, curved, colorless, 13–15.5 × 0.8 μ.

On canes of *Vitis vinifera* L., Arrifana, Vale do Vonga, Portugal, Maria Eugenia, April 1952. Named after the swollen, bulging character of the conidium. The fungus occurs in association with *Phoma uvicola* B. & C. and *Phomopsis viticola* Sacc.

64. **Pestalotia teucrii** Gonz.-Frag., Trab. Mus. Nac. Ci. Nat. Madrid. Ser. Bot. 10:170,1916; Syll. Fung. 25:602,1931.

Pustules scattered, subcorticate, depressed, then erumpent, surrounded by the broken epidermis, context at the base fuliginous. Conidia elongate-ellipsoid, 4-celled, 18–24 × 9–10 μ, exterior cells hyaline, conoid, small; intermediate cells yellowish-fuliginous, somewhat constricted at middle septa, somewhat broad, apices for the most part with 4 setulae up to 14 μ long; pedicels yellowish or hyaline, up to 7 × 3 μ.

On dead branches of *Teucrium fruticans* L., near Pedrosso de la Sierra, Spain, May 1914, associated with *Pleospora herbarum* (Pers.) Rabh.

65. **Pestalotia watsoniae** Verwoerd & Dippenaar. South African Jour. Sci. 27:327–328,1930; Laughton, Bothalia 4:830,1948.

Spots roundish, 4–7 cm or irregularly extended, light gray with a reddish brown margin, becoming paler with age. Acervuli 120–150 μ diam, 120–200 μ high, amphigenous, scattered, punctiform, cupulate, black, subepidermal, erumpent, depressed or shallow when situated over the veins. Conidia 19.5–22.5 × 7.5–9.5 μ, ellipsoid fusoid, shortly pedicellate, 4-celled, not constricted at the septa, the 2 intermediate cells brown and equal in size, thick walled, 12.5–16 μ long, the exterior cells hyaline, conic, the apical cells obtuse bearing usually 4–5 setulae, sometimes branched, 15–30 μ long; pedicels short, 1.5 μ in diam.

On leaves of *Watsonia rosea* Ker. and varieties, Bot. Gard., University of Stellenbosch, No. 297, Stellenbosch, South Africa. Laughton published a good description of the fungus and reported its occurrence on several varieties of the host plant species.

66. **Pestalotia jaczewskii** Morotschk., Leningrad Akad. Nauk Botanicheskii Inst. Acta Inst. bot. Acad. scientiarum Ser. 2; Plantes Crypt. 1:276, 1933.

Acervuli convex, erumpent, brown, often gregarious. Conidiophores filiform, hyaline, 26–40 × 0.5–2 μ. Conidia cylindric or ovoid, 18–26 × 6–8 μ,

3-septate, not or slightly constricted at the septa: intermediate cells brown, guttulate; exterior hyaline cells minute, often deciduous with age, apical cells with 2 setulae, filiform, recurved, 26.5–30 μ long, at length deciduous.

On dead stalks of *Sorghum* sp., in garden of Institute Polytechnic, Kiev, Russia, April 23, 1929.

67. **Pestalotia hordeidestrua** Denhardt, Ber. Deut. Bot. Ges. 22:175–176,1904
Syll. Fung. 18:484,1906.

Pustules black, 1.5 mm long, similar to black sori of *Puccinia graminis*. Conidia 4-celled, $19 \times 9.5 \mu$, 3 setulae, about twice as long.

On living stalks of *Hordeum vulgare* L. (Graminales). Summer of 1900, Berlin, Germany.

Author claimed that fungus is similar to *P. hartigii* Tubeuf. He successfully infected young barley plants with conidia from pure culture, resulting in their early death. A microphotograph of the conidia of this species was published in Lindner, Atlas d. mikroskopischen Grundlagen d. Gärungskunde, table 44, Berlin (P. Parey), 1903.

Lindner's table 44 provides a much better understanding of the fungus than the description. The conidia appear to measure 19×6–7μ, 2 intermediate cells dark brown, somewhat constricted at the septa, apical hyaline cells long conic-cylindric, basal hyaline cells narrow conic; setulae 3, divergent, as long as conidia, equal in length, borne at the apex, none of them branched; pedicels short. Table 44 shows conidia and setulae of the same length. The fungus is not like *P. hartigii*.

68. **Pestalotia penzigii** Boyer & Jacz., Bull. Soc. Bot. 40:296,1893 (1894).
Ann. École Nat. Agr. Montpellier 8:222, fig. 8, 1893 (1894); Syll. Fung. 11:578,1895.
P. nicolai Bubak, Bull. Herb. Boiss., Ser. 2, 6:485,1906, tab. 14, figs, 14–15; Syll. Fung. 22:1223,1913.

Acervuli scattered, subepidermal or innate, at first covered them erumpent, tearing open the epidermis or bark, black, globose depressed, cushionlike, 180–270 μ wide. Conidia 4-celled (3-celled, Boyer & Jacz., Bubak) oblong or elongate-ellipsoid, 18–26.5×6.5–8.5μ, basal cell hyaline, small, conoid, the two cells above 16–18 μ, chestnut brown; apical cell ramoseawned, hyaline; setulae 5, rarely 4, 20–27 μ long, divergent, filiform, joined to a short awn crowning the colored cells; pedicels usually thicker than setulae, up to 15 μ long $\times 2 \mu$ wide, hyaline.

On dry stems of *Genista scorpius* DC. Montpellier, France [Fig. 13a].

On dry stems of *Salvia officinalis* L. in association with *Pleospora vulgaris* Niessl, Dobrsko near Rijeka, Montenegro, sub *P. nicolai* Bubak [Fig. 13b].

The conidia are 3-celled with an obscure or rudimentary apical awlshaped hyaline cell.

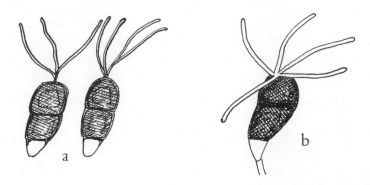

FIG. 13 [68].   (*a*) *Pestalotia penzigii* Boyer & Jacz.   Ann École Nat. Agr. Montpellier 8: 1893, fig. 8.   (*b*) *P. nicolai* Bubak, Bull. Herb. Boiss., ser. II, 6: 1906, tab. 14.

69. Pestalotia insueta Petr., Sydowia (Ann. Mycol.), 1; 5–8,1947.

Pustules irregular and loosely distributed, usually singular, globose, broad ellipsoid, erumpent, 180–250 μ diam, rarely up to 300 μ. Conidia 4-celled, 19–25 × 6.5–10 μ, long fusiform or somewhat club-shaped, tapering to the base, only slightly curved; exterior cells small; two intermediate cells 7–10 μ long, olive brown, each with epispore; lowest hyaline cells pointed, 2.5–5 μ long; upper hyaline cells 2–5 μ long with 3–5, rarely 6 setulae, 8–30 μ long, curved simple, rarely branched; pedicels 2.5–7 × 1 μ.

On dead stems of *Phlomis brevilabris* Ehrenb., Syria, Libani, July 21, 1897, J. Bornmüller. Fungus is described with pycnidia occurring in association with the ascomycete *Neobroomella ciliata* Petr. Petrak considers *Pestalotia* its imperfect form.

70. Pestalotia berberidis Guba sp. nov.

Pustulae globoso-lenticulares usque oblongae, numerosae, punctiformes, 75–375 × 75–150 μ, maturae erumpentes, epidermidem in rima lineari fissentes et massam atram detegentes; conidia 4-cellularia, 19–25 × 7.5–10 μ; cellulae mediae coloratae subglobosae, concolores, olivaceae vel umbrinae, translucentes, 12.5–16 μ longae, ad septa paulo constrictae, tunicis obscurioribus, guttulis oblongis olivaceis; cellula apicalis hyalina, conico-cylindrica, setulis 2, interdum 4, rare 2 vel 5, 19–37 μ longis praedita; cellula basalis hyalina, longe conica vel cylindrica; pedicellus crassus.

Pustules globose-lenticular to oblong, numerous, punctiform, 75–375 × 75–150 μ, erumpent at maturity, tearing the epidermis in a linear manner, exposing the black contents. Conidia 4-celled, 19–25 × 7.5–10 μ; intermediate colored cells subglobose olivaceous or umber and clear, concolorous, 12.5–16 μ, rather constricted at septa, the walls dark, oblong guttules olivaceous; apical hyaline cell conic-cylindric, crowned with 3, sometimes 4, rarely 2 or 5 setulae, 19–37 μ long; basal hyaline cells long conic or cylindric; pedicels coarse and rather long.

On twigs of *Berberis*, Arlington, Mass., June 3, 1893, (Burt) sub *P. truncata* Lév. in herb. Farlow [Fig. 14]. Handwriting accompanying the specimen states that the conidia measure 14–16 × 8.7 μ. This species is related to *P. stevensonii* Peck but the dimensions of the conidia and attachments are much larger.

71. **Pestalotia siliquastri** Thuem. var. **italica** Cif., Ann. Mycol. 20:50–51,1922, tab. 1, fig. 12.

Conidia 4-celled, oblong-elliptic, 26 × 3–5 μ, the 2 intermediate cells dark, exterior cells obtuse-conic, hyaline; setulae 2, terminal, 9 μ long; pedicels 3 μ long.

On living leaves of *Cercis siliquastrum* L., near Alba, Italy.

72. **Pestalotia eupyrena** Fl. Tassi, Boll. Lab. Ort. Bot. R. Univ. Siena 2:105, 1899; Sacc. Syll. Fung. 16:1014,1902.

Acervuli scattered, 666 μ in diam, prominent, black, perithecia-like. Conidia fusoid, 4-celled, somewhat constricted at septa, the intermediate cells fuliginous, exterior cells hyaline, 20–30 × 7 μ; setulae 5, 30–40 μ long.

On pods of *Bossiaea ensata* Hook. [= *B. riparia* A. Cunn.], New Holland, Sydney, Australia.

73. **Pestalotia moorei** Harkn., Bull. Cal. Acad. Sci. 1:34,1884; Sacc. Syll. Fung. 3:795,1884.

Acervuli numerous, suborbicular or elongate lenticular, 350–700 × 140–280 μ, erumpent in a longitudinal manner, sooty, contents oozing out and

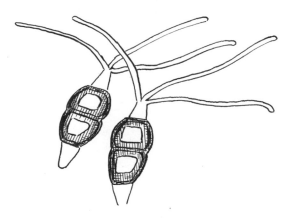

Fig. 14 [70]. *Pestalotia berberidis* Guba.

staining the matrix.   Conidia 22–26.6 μ, fusiform or cylindric-fusoid, erect or slightly curved, 4-celled, only slightly constricted at septa; 2 intermediate colored cells 14–18 × 7.5–9 μ, olivaceous, equally colored, oblong-guttulate; exterior cells hyaline, conical, sometimes acute, the apical cells often long cylindric bearing 3 or usually 4 long curved, divergent setulae, 30–52 μ or twice as long as the conidia, the basal cell long, conic, tapering; pedicels twice as long as the conidia, usually deciduous.

On dead stems of *Hosackia glabra* Torr. [=*Lotus scoparius* (Nutt.) Otley], Antioch, Cal., July, J. P. Moore, and named in his honor [Fig. 15].   The pustules are quite generally distributed on the stems rather than confined to pale orbicular spots as reported by the author.   The only measurements supplied by Harkness are, conidia 32 × 9 μ and setulae twice as long.   Voglino (Atti Soc. Ven.-Trent Sci. Padova 9:209–243,1885) found conidia 28 × 7 μ, setulae 40–62 × 1 μ, pedicels 18–28 × 2 μ.

74. Pestalotia helichrysii Severini, Ann. Bot. 11:1,205,1913; Syll. Fung. 25:
    600,1931.

Acervuli scattered, black, conic-hemispherical, erumpent, 300–450 μ in diam.   Conidia fusiform, usually with long pedicels, 4-celled, somewhat or slightly constricted at septa, 23–27 × 9–10 μ, the intermediate cells fuliginous, large; exterior cells small, hyaline; setulae 5, divergent, filiform, 18–35 μ; pedicels 20–40 × 2 μ.

On dry stems of *Helichrysum stoechas* (L.) DC., Monte Malbe, Province of Perugia, Italy.

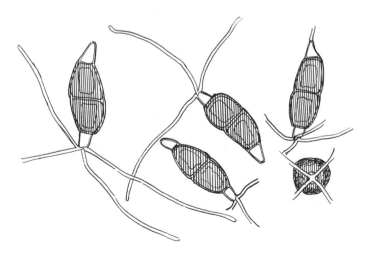

FIG. 15 [73].   *Pestalotia moorei* Harkn.

75. **Pestalotia torrendii** Alm. & Camara, Rev. Agron. Portugal 3:255,1905, tab. 5, figs. 4–5 ("torrendia"); Bol. Soc. Broteriana 24:208,1909; Sacc. Syll. Fung. 22,1221,1913.

Acervuli amphigenous, small, conical, numerous, dark, at first covered, then erumpent. Conidia fusiform, 4-celled, 27–30 × 10–11 μ; 2 intermediate cells brown, large, cuboid; exterior cells hyaline, acute at both ends; setulae usually 3, rarely 2, simple, 30–40 μ long; pedicels hyaline, 10–13 × 2–2.5 μ, deciduous.

On phyllodes of *Acacia* or *Mimosa*, near Castle Branco, Portugal (C. Torrend).

Section *Quinqueloculatae*

Species Nos. 76–258

Spathulatae

Species Nos. 76–90

76. **Pestalotia phoenicis** Vize, Cooke, Grevillea 5:14,1876, tab. 74, fig. 7; Syll. Fung. 3:796,1884.

Pustules scattered, punctiform, globose-lenticular, erumpent, rupturing the epidermis in irregular manner, 75–280 × 75–200 μ, usually hypophyllous; on sharply bordered, pale or brown spots running together into large discolored areas. Conidia 5-celled, 16–22 × 5–7 μ, erect or slightly curved, intermediate colored cells umber or olivaceous, 11–14 μ long, equally colored or upper two colored cells sometimes slightly darker; apical hyaline cells conic-cylindric, basal cells long conic; setulae 3, usually straight, sometimes 2, rarely branched, rarely 4, up to 22 μ long, often up to 15 μ, the extremities usually knobbed; pedicels short.

On brown or ashen gray spots on leaves of *Phoenix dactylifera* L. and other *Palmaceae*.

Specimens examined: *Cocos nucifera* L. (leaves); herb. Col. Agr. No. 23, Los Baños, Philippines, Feb. 1918, O. A. Reinking sub *P. palmarum* Cooke; C. F. Baker, F. Malayana, No. 65, Mt. Maquiling near Los Baños, Laguna, Philippines, July 1913, sub *P. palmarum*; Sydow, Fungi exot. Exs. 289, Taytay, Palawan, Philippines, March 5, 1913, E. D. Merrill sub *P. palmarum* [Fig. 16a]; herb. Dept. Agr., Fed. Malay States, May 1927, sub *P. palmarum*; herb. F. L. Stevens, Los Baños, Philippines, July 29, 1930, F. L. Stevens.

On dead leaves of *Connarus* sp., Los Baños, Luzon, Philippines, Oct. 1913, S. A. Reyes, No. 1782, sub *P. pauciseta* Sacc. [Fig. 16b]. Conidia

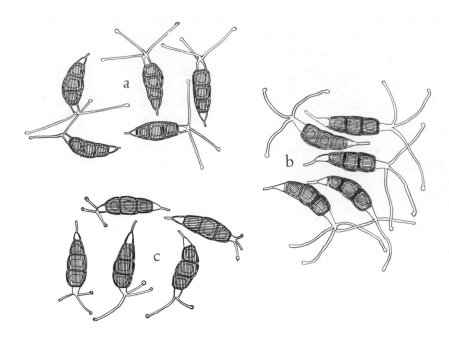

Fig. 16 [76]. *Pestalotia phoenicis* Vize.

15–19 and 19–25 × 5–7 μ, intermediate cells brown, concolorous, 11–16 μ, setulae 3, rarely 4, knobbed, 9–22 μ long. Both long and short conidia occur in the same matrix. The species with short conidia is *P. phoenicis* Vize and it also appears on leaves of *Uvaria*, the second in order of host plants in the original description of *P. pauciseta* listed by Saccardo. The other form with longer conidia is *Pestalotia fici* (Stey.) Guba.

On brown spots on living leaves of *Malachra capitata* L., Inarjan, Guam, No. 966, R. G. Oakley, July 29, 1938, Nat. Fungus Coll., U.S.D.A.

On leaves of *Phoenix dactylifera* L. in Vize, Microf. Exot. No. 7, East Indies, 1876, Col. Hobson, herb. Kew (type) [Fig. 16c].

On brown weathered leaves of *Uvaria* sp., Palawan, Taytan, Philippines, April 1913, E. D. Merrill, No. 8749, sub *P. pauciseta* Sacc.

The original description of *P. pauciseta* Sacc. also embraced forms on *Litsea glutinosa* C. B. Rob., Los Baños, C. F. Baker, No. 1779, on *Ptychosperma macarthurii* H. Wendl. [= *Actinophloeus macarthurii* (Wendl.) Becc.], Los Baños, S. A. Reyes, No. 1843, and on *Guioa* sp. [= *Cupania*], Palawan, Taytay, E. D. Merrill, No. 886. Saccardo stated that the fungus has 2-setulate conidia, setulae 8–15 μ long and conidia 20–24 × 4.5–5 μ. These three forms lack the spatulate conidia and differ otherwise from *P. phoenicis*

Vize, the species on *Connarus* and *Uvaria*.   The name *P. pauciseta* is retained
for the form on *Litsea*.   The species on *Ptychosperma* is *P. palmarum* Cooke.
The species on *Guioa* [= *Cupania*] is *P. virgatula Kleb.*

Cooke, in Grevillea 5:14,1876, pl. 74, fig. 7, showed nothing of value.
The colored portion of the conidia is $18 \times 7\mu$, according to Vize.   In Klebahn's
paper [Myc. Centralbl. 4:1–19,1914, fig. 35 (II)], the upper two of the three
dark cells are the darkest, but the setulae are shown without knobbed
extremities.   The conidia measure $21–24 \times 7–8 \mu$ and the setulae 15–26 μ.

De Bary (Gard. Chron. 21 (n.s.) 799, 1884) found a *Pestalotia* on brown
diseased areas in leaves of *Corypha australis* R. Br. [= *Livistona australis*
(R. Br.) Mart.] and *Phoenix* submitted to him from England.   Healthy leaves
of *C. australis* removed from the plant and placed in a moist chamber were
killed by the fungus.   Healthy seedlings of *Phoenix dactylifera* L. and
Chamaerops were not infected, even in moist bell jars.   Infection of *Corypha*
seedlings was destructive under adverse growing conditions.   Smith (Gard.
Chron. 22 (n.s.) 429,1884) claimed that the fungus is *Pestalotia phoenicis*
Vize (figs. 77 and 78).

77. **Pestalotia javanica** Guba nom. nov.

Pustules amphigenous, erumpent.   Conidia oblong-fusoid, 5-celled 16–
$18 \times 5–6.5 \mu$, apical hyaline cells conic or cylindric, basal hyaline cells
acuminate, 3 median cells dark colored, rather strongly constricted at septa;
setulae 2–3, knobbed at extremities, 30–32 μ, curved or flexuous; pedicels
filiform, continuous, fasciculate, 60–75 μ.

On leaves and twigs of *Myrica javanica* Blume, Mt. Sendoro, near Sigatok,
Prov. Kedu, Java, Aug. 1904, leg. Koorders.

The new name is proposed to replace *P. myricae* Koord. (Verh. K. Akad.
Wetenschappen Amsterdam 13:224–225,1907; Syll. Fung. 22:1225,1913) a
later homonym of *P. myricae* Ell. & G. Martin (Am. Naturalist 18:70,1884.)
Koorders considered the fungus parasitic on leaves and twigs of young seedlings, reporting a loss of more than 5,000 seedlings.   His illustration of the
conidia (see above, fig. 5:33, p. 217) shows knobbed setulae, but this character is not cited in the original description.   The illustration is exactly like
that of Koorders' drawing of the conidia of *P. elasticae* Koord., deposited
without specimen in herb. Berlin Bot. Mus.

78. **Pestalotia fici** (Stey.) Guba comb. nov.
> *Pestalotiopsis fici* Stey., Bull. Jard. Bot. État Bruxelles 19:324–325,1949,
> fig. 24C.
>
> *P. papposa* Stey., Bull. Jard. Bot. État Bruxelles 19:325,1949, pl. 14C–D.

Spots circular, straw colored, surrounded by reddish-purple colored zone.
Pustules elongate or polygonate, 100–200 μ diam, covered by epidermis, then

rupturing it longitudinally.   Conidia narrow, fusoid, erect, 5-celled, 19–26 ×
5–7 μ; intermediate colored cells pale brown, concolorous, guttulate, 14–19 μ
long; exterior cells long conoid, apical cell with 2–4 usually 3 setulae, 9–20 μ
long, knobbed at extremities; pedicels 2–6 μ long.

On leaves of *Ficus*, Uganda, Kiagwe, June 1938, C. G. Hansford, No.
33014, in herb. Myc., Dept. Agr. Uganda, No. 2452, type.

Pestalotiopsis papposa Stey. is the same fungus described on leaves of
Cocos nucifera L., Sierra Leone, Njala (Kori), Feb. 6, 1948, F. C. Deighton.

On dead leaves of *Connarus* sp., Los Baños, Luzon, Philippines, Oct. 1913,
S. A. Reyes, No. 1782, sub *P. pauciseta* Sacc. associated with *Pestalotia
phoenicis* Vize.

79. **Pestalotia elasticae** Koord.   Ver. K. Akad. Wetenschappen Amsterdam
13:223,1907; Syll. Fung. 22:1225,1913.

    P. theae Sawada var. *minor* Stey., Bull. Jard. Bot. État Bruxelles 19:184,
    1948, pl. 6, fig. A.

    Pestalotiopsis theae (Sawada) Stey. var. *minor* Stey. Bull. Jard. Bot. État
    Bruxelles 19:327–328,1949; pl. 14, fig. E, fig. 24A.

Pustules subepidermal, finally erumpent, black, cushion-shaped, circular,
scattered or gregarious, on insect injuries.   Conidia fusiform, erect, 5-celled,
27.5 × 6 μ; colored cells olivaceous-brown, somewhat constricted at septa,
25 μ long; setulae 3, filiform, 32 μ long, knobbed at extremities; apical
hyaline cells cylindric, basal hyaline cells tapering; pedicels 5 μ long.

On margins of insect wounds on living leaves of *Ficus elastica* Roxb.,
Penunggalan, Prov. Kedu, Central Java, Oct. 1905, Koorders.   The fungus
is reported as rare, existing as an inhabitant of wounds made by feedings of
a locust.

On leaves of *Martinezia caryotaefolia* H.B. & K., Buitenzorg, Java, 1907–
1908 in herb. Hoehnel No. 4159, sub *P. palmarum* Cooke in herb. Farlow.
Conidia 19–27 × 6–7 μ, 3 setulae 12–28 μ.

On pale brown spots in leaves of *Coffea arabica* L., Stanleyville, Belgian
Congo, Nos. 41a and 66c, R. L. Steyaert, 1930.   Conidia 24–33 × 6.5–8 μ,
setulae 3, 19–35 μ long.

On leaves of *Ecdysanthera utilis* Hay & Kawakami, Sinchu, Taiwan,
July 20, 1902.   T. Kawakami sub *P. ecdysantherae* Sawada.

On leaves of *Klainedoxa jabonensis* Pierre, Wombali, near Banningville-
Kwango, Kasai, Belgian Congo, Aug. 1915, H. Vanderyst, sub *Pestalotia
theae* Sawada var. *minor* Stey.; also sub *Pestalotiopsis theae* (Sawada) var.
minor Stey.   According to the type description, the conidia measure 21–28 ×
6–7 μ, intermediate cells olivaceous, concolorous, setulae spatulate, 18–29 μ
long, differing from *Pestalotia theae* Sawada by the smaller conidia.   Steyaert
included two additional specimens with his variety *minor* as follows: Sydow,
Fungi exot. Exs. 146 on leaves of *Camellia thea* (L.) Kuntze [= *C. sinensis*
(L.) Kuntze], and culture from leaves of the same host, Buitenzorg, Java,

C. M. Doyer. Both specimens, in my judgment, belong with *Pestalotia theae* Sawada. Steyaert found two other conidial forms on leaves of *Klainedoxa*, which he identified as *P. clavispora* Atk. (conidia 20–25 × 7–9 μ, setulae 11–32 μ, colored part versicolorous, upper 2 cells fuliginous) and *P. mangiferae* P. Henn. (conidia 18–22 × 5–7 μ, setulae 8–16 μ, colored cells olivaceous, concolorous). According to my studies, both forms occur in the same acervuli and the larger matured and most frequent form with versicolored cells is like *P. versicolor* Speg.

No conidia with spatulate setulae (var. *minor*) were found in my examination of type material on *Klainedoxa jabonensis* but Steyaert's type description of *P. theae* (Sawada) Stey. var. *minor* Stey. indicates that the species is the same as *Pestalotia elasticae* Koord. Steyaert (Trans. Brit. Mycol. Soc. 36: 240,1953) reported the same fungus on leaves of *Borassus aethiopum* Mart. [= *B. flabellifer* L.], and *Dioscorea* sp., Gold Coast, West Africa, June 1949, S. J. Hughes.

80. **Pestalotia theae** Sawada, Special Rep., Agr. Exp. Sta., Taiwan (Formosa) 11:113,1915, pl. 4, figs. 7–9, tab. 4; (Japanese), transl. by Tanaka in Mycologia 9:171,1917; Syll. Fung. 25:607,1931.
   Pestalotiopsis theae (Sawada) Stey., Bull. Jard. Bot. État Bruxelles 19: 327,1949; tab. II, fig. 24B.

Brownish spots coalescing and forming irregularly margined areas, especially common along leaf margins. Spots 1 cm or more in diam, marked by concentric rings of alternate lighter and deeper shades. Pustules punctate, chiefly epiphyllous, often arranged in concentric circles or scattered without order, 88–176 μ diam, subepidermal, erumpent forming black crusts. Conidia long fusiform, erect, 4-septate, slightly constricted at the septa, 23–30 × 7–8 μ; 3 intermediate colored cells 16.5–19 μ, dark olivaceous, equally colored; exterior cells hyaline, 4–6 μ long, basal cells conic, apical cells cylindric with 2–4, commonly 3 hyaline, filiform setulae, 25–48 μ, the ends usually knobbed; pedicels filiform, rigid or curved to one side, 5–9 μ, sometimes knobbed.

On living leaves of *Thea* [= Camellia] causing the disease known as gray blight. Large pustules appear in concentric zones but on the lower leaf surface the zones are not always distinct and the pustules are usually few. The fungus occurs generally in tea growing regions.

Specimens examined: On leaves of *Thea* sinensis L. [= Camellia]. Sydow, Fungi exot. Exs. 146, Peradeniya, Ceylon, sub *P. palmarum* Cooke [Fig. 17a]; on leaves of *Camellia thea* Link. [= Camellia sinensis (L.) Kuntze], Nov. 1912, Petch, sub *P. palmarum* Cooke; Ceylon, May 1927; Buitenzorg, Java, May 1927; Taihoku, Formosa, Aug. 8, 1924, K. Sawada.

On pale spots on living leaves of *Antidesma platyphyllum* H. Mann., F. L. Stevens, Hawaiian Fungi Nos. 453–462, in herb. University of Illinois [Fig. 17b].

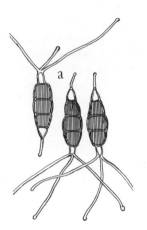
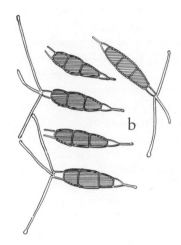

Fig. 17 [80].   *Pestalotia theae* Sawada.

On blighted leaves of *Illicium religiosum* Sieb. & Zucc. [= *I. anisatum* L.], Mt. Azachi, Kokura-shi, Fukuoka-Ken, Japan, May 15, 1952.   T. Hino.

On spots on leaves of *Latania borbonica* [= *Livistona chinensis* R. Br.] Bot. Gard., Bruxelles, Belgium, P. Staner No. 840, Eala, Oct. 1931, sub *Pestalotiopsis aeruginea* Stey.

Like *P. palmarum*, the identity of the tea fungus was not known until Butler (*Fungi and disease in plants*, Calcutta and Simla, 1918), Sawada (Special Rep., Agr. Expt. Sta., Taiwan, Formosa, no. 11, p. 113, 1915), and Bertus (Ceylon Dept. Agr. Year book, pp. 43–46, 1923; Ann. Roy. Bot. Gard. Peradeniya 10:197–241,1927) recognized it as a distinct species, *P. theae* Sawada.   Previously, the fungus was incorrectly designated *P. guepini* Desm. and regarded as of cosmopolitan host range.

LaRue and Bartlett (Am. Jour. Bot. 9:79–92,1922) could not recognize *P. theae* as valid because previous authors had associated *P. guepini* with the tea disease.   They felt that Sawada's description failed to make a clear case for the distinctiveness of the tea fungus.

P. theae attacks leaf blades, petioles, and stems of tea.   The fungus grows from the blades through the petioles into perennial parts of the bush and causes cankers.   Carruthers (Agr. Jour. Roy. Bot. Gard., Ceylon, Circ. 2:4–7,1902; Adm. Reps. Roy. Bot. Gard., Peradeniya, pt. 4, pp. 5–6, 1903), and Petch (Trop. Agr. and Mag. Ceylon Agr. Soc. 25:630–631,1905; Agr. Jour. Roy. Bot. Gard., Ceylon, Circ. 3:277–286,1906; *Diseases of the tea bush*, London, 1923) reported destruction of shoots following infection at the cut ends of stems left in gathering the tea, leaving a "crow's foot" structure of dead twigs.   Tunstall (Indian Tea Assn. Sci. Dept. Quart. Jour. 3:73–86,1927) and Tunstall and Bose (Indian Tea Assn. Sci. Dept. Quart. Jour. 4:152–154, 1920) successfully infected the cut shoots of tea with the gray blight fungus. They reported that it frequently attacks margins of young immature leaves after a period of hot, dry weather, causing rim blight, and that attacks of red spider also make leaves susceptible to infection.

Carruthers observed in Ceylon that gray blight appears after the tea bushes are allowed to go 18 months without pruning. According to Tunstall, attacks of gray blight are an indication of unsatisfactory soil conditions. The fungus does not attack vigorous, healthy leaves. Its attacks are confined to old damaged bushes or to those previously weakened by some other cause.

Bertus found that *P. theae* was able to infect tea and coconut leaves through wounds but not through healthy leaves, while Doyer (Med. Phyto-path. Lab., "Will. Comm. Scholt." 9:1–72,1925), failed to obtain infection of tea with a *Pestalotia* from *Cocos* incorrectly designated *P. theae*, or with a *Pestalotia* from *Cocos* incorrectly designated *P. guepini*. Doyer regarded forms from *Cocos nucifera* and *Altingia* as *P. theae* Sawada because of the knobbed setulae. She was apparently unaware of the fact that the setulae of *P. phoenicis* Vize, and others, have knobbed extremities. Since *P. theae* is restricted to tea, inoculating tea with forms from palm, as Doyer has done, might be expected to give negative results. Speshnev (Trudy Tiflisk Bot. Sad. 63:47–129,1904; German transl., *Die Pilzparasiten des Teestrauches*, Berlin, 1907) observed at Tschakwa, near Batum, that *Thea sinensis* L. was parti-cularly susceptible, and that the native species *Thea assamica* Mast. [= *Camellia sinensis* (L.) Kuntze] suffered much less damage. The fungus des-cribed by Speshnev is a 4-celled conidial form crowned with 4 setulae. It is designated *P. guepini* Desm. but it is neither *P. guepini* nor *P. theae*. These species are characterized by 5-celled conidia. Other accounts of gray blight are given by Delacroix (Jour. d'Agr. Trop. 2:67–72,1902), Delacroix and Maublanc (*Maladies des plantes cultivées dans les pays chauds*, Paris, 1911), and Bernard (Teysmannia 17:780–784,1906; Bull. Dept. Agr. Indes Neérland 6:1–55,1907). *P. theae* is a parasite of the leaves of *Diospyros kaki* L. in Japan and this association is the subject of commendable papers by Nojima (Bull. Kagoshima Imp. Col. Agr. For. 7, 1929; Byochugai Zasshi 15:2,1928; Japanese Jour. Bot. 5:1, pp. 16–17, 1930, Abstr.). The spots on leaves of *Diospyros* are similar to those on *Thea*. Nojima has given accurate repre-sentations of *P. theae* (1929, fig. 1, p. 6, and pl. I, fig. 3).

Steyaert (Bull. Jard. Bot. État Bruxelles 19:184,1949) created the new variety *P. theae* Sawada var. *minor* Stey. on leaves of *Klainedoxa gabonensis* Pierre, Belgian Congo, Africa. The name was changed to *Pestalotiopsis theae* (Sawada) Stey. var. *minor* Stey. (Bull. Jard. Bot. État Bruxelles 19:327, 1949) and given to a culture of the fungus from *Camellia thea* (L.) Kuntze [=*C. sinensis* (L.) Kuntze] made by C. M. Doyer. Agreement was also reported with specimens of *P. theae* Sawada in Sydow, Fungi exot. Exs. No. 146 on *Camellia thea* (L.) Kuntze [= *C. sinensis* (L.) Kuntze]. In my judgment, both of the specimens are *P. theae* Sawada. The type on *Klainedoxa* is the same as *Pestalotia elasticae* Koord.

81. **Pestalotia annulata** Berk. & Curt.   Grevillea 2:155,1874; Syll. Fung. 3: 787,1885.

　Pestalotiopsis annulata (Berk. & Curt.) Stey., Bull. Jard. Bot. État Bruxelles 19:316,1949.

Pustules punctiform, black, subglobose, mostly epiphyllous, annulate or concentrically disposed, surrounded by the torn epidermis, 125–250 μ in diam, sometimes springing from large marginal spots with definite dark borders or in other cases generally distributed over the matrix.   Conidia long, fusiform, tapering toward the base, 5-celled, 23–30 μ, erect, sometimes prominently constricted at septa, median cells dark, olivaceous, umber or brown, equally colored, 17–21 × 6–8.5 μ, guttulate; exterior hyaline cells elongate, the basal cells long conic, tapering, apical cells long, cylindric, bearing 2–4, usually 3, widely divergent setulae, 10–22 μ, frequently knobbed at the extremities; erect pedicel 6–12 μ long.

On leaves of *Ilex opaca* Ait., usually on spots.   Specimens examined: herb. Berkeley No. 4871, Alabama, Beaumont, in herb. Roy. Bot. Gard., Kew [Fig. 18]; Ellis, N. Am. Fungi No. 34 sub *P. stellata* Berk. & Curt.; herb. J. B. Ellis No. 2599, Newfield, N. J., sub *P. stellata* Berk. & Curt.

The original description is vague and meaningless.

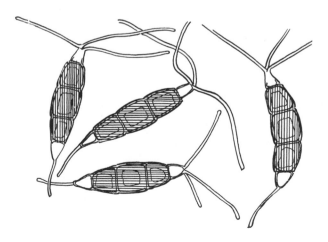

Fɪɢ. 18 [81].   *Pestalotia annulata* Berk. & Curt.

82. **Pestalotia clavata** Cooke & Ell., Grevillea 6:85,1878, pl. 99, fig. 7; Syll.
Fung. 3:796,1884; Voglino Atti Soc. Ven.-Trent. Sci. Nat. Padova 9:
209–243,1885, pl. 9, fig. 17.
Coryneum smilacis Schw. Trans. Amer. Philos. Soc. 4:307,1834; Syll.
Fung. 3:780,1884.
Pestalotia grandis Berk. & Curt., in Crié, Ann. Sci. Nat. Bot. VI, 7:59,
1879, pl. 8, fig. 21; 1878 (publ. 1879). Voglino, Atti Soc. Ven.-Trent.
Sci. Nat. Padova 9:209–243,1885 (reprint, p. 32); Syll. Fung. 10:491,
1892. Curtis, Geol. and Nat. Hist. Survey North Carolina Bot. III,
118,1867, nom. nud.

Acervuli numerous, punctiform, crowded, 100–175 μ in diam, amphigenous, sometimes entirely epiphyllous, lenticular, subepidermal then erumpent, seated on brown concentrically zoned spots with purple margins.
Conidia fusiform, elliptic-clavate, usually slightly curved, 5-celled, 25–31 μ,
slightly constricted at septa; intermediate colored cells umber, sometimes
olivaceous, equally colored, 16–21 × 7–8.5 μ; exterior cells hyaline, prominent, apical cells long cylindric, bearing 2–3 (usually 3) curved divergent
setulae; basal cells broad conic with straight pedicels, 2–7.5 μ; setulae 9–20 μ
with a conspicuous knot at the extremities.

On living leaves of *Smilax*. Specimens examined: herb. Curtis No. 4046,
from Peters, No. 437, Alabama, sub *P. grandis* Berk. & Curt.; herb. Schweinitz
in herb. Curtis, fol. 214 in herb. Farlow, on stems of *Smilax rotundifolia* L.,
Bethlehem, Pa., sub *Coryneum smilacis* Schw.; Ellis, N. Am. Fungi No. 350,
on living leaves of *Smilax*, Sept. 1879 [Fig. 19]; Bartholomew Fungi Col. No.
4247, on leaves of *Smilax rotundifolia* L., Shreveport, La., Oct. 16, 1913,
E. Bartholomew, associated with *Phyllosticta smilacis* Ell. & G. Martin;
Ellis, Fungi of New Jersey No. 2740, on leaves of *Smilax*, Newfield, N. J.,

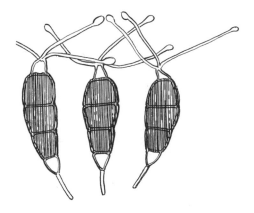

FIG. 19 [82]. *Pestalotia clavata* Cooke & Ellis.

J. B. Ellis; herb. S. M. Tracy No. 5242, on leaves of *Smilax laurifolia* L., Ocean Springs, Miss., S. M. Tracy, May 2, 1898, sub *P. funerea* Desm.; herb. N. Y. State Mus., on living leaves of *Smilax glauca* Walt., Babylon, Long Island, N. Y., Sept. 19, 1915, sub *P. guepini* Desm.

The original description of this fungus by Cooke and Ellis mentions 3-celled conidia although the accompanying illustration shows 5 cells and 3 setulae. Voglino found 4-septate conidia and setulae with knobbed extremities.

This species was originally named *P. grandis* Berk. & Curt. by Curtis, but Berkeley, who described many of Curtis' specimens, failed to publish a description for it. Crié cited this species and published an illustration of the conidia which, however, offers an incorrect interpretation of *P. grandis*. Voglino listed *P. grandis* without its host or the source of the specimen. He furnished a brief description based on Crié's figure of the conidia which, however, is untenable. Crié obtained type specimens from Berkeley, but since the description of *P. clavata* Cooke & Ell. antedates Crié's publication, *P. grandis* becomes a synonym. An example of this species was found and recorded by Schweinitz in 1832, seven years previous to the published description of the genus *Pestalotia* in Italy.

83. **Pestalotia capitata** Ell., Bull. Torrey Bot. Club 9:133,1882; Syll. Fung. 3:796,1884.

Pustules subepidermal, raised, erumpent in a linear manner, surrounded or partly covered by torn shreds of epidermis, oblong, lenticular to hysteriform, sometimes confluent, $150-600 \times 150-300 \mu$, somewhat sooty at maturity. Conidia 5-celled, long fusiform, clavate-oblong, tapering to the base, only slightly constricted at septa, $25-32 \times 7.8-9 \mu$; intermediate colored cells umber, equally colored, only slightly constricted at septa, $19-21 \mu$ long; apical hyaline cells long cylindric, crested with 3 setulae, divergent, $22-26 \mu$ long, knobbed at the extremities, basal hyaline cells long, acute or conoid; pedicels $6-10 \mu$ long.

On dead leaves of *Xerophyllum asphodeloides* (L.) Nutt., Willow Grove, N. J., May 1882. Differs, according to Ellis, from *P. clavata* Cooke & Ell. The pustules bear some resemblance to the sori of *Puccinia*. Ellis described 4-celled conidia, but the type specimen shows only 5-celled conidia. On brown weathered leaves of *Liriodendron tulipifera* L., Tuskegee, Ala., G. W. Carver, Aug. 26, 1901, sub *P. liriodendri* Ell. & Ev. (herbarium name), in herb. Farlow, folio 184, No. 6. A brief description of the fungus in Ellis's handwriting is deposited with the specimen.

Grove (British Stem and Leaf Fungi II, 1937, p. 345) erroneously asserted that the knobbing at the extremities of the setulae is an optical illusion caused by the curling of the extreme tips towards the lens which thus become slightly out of focus.

84. **Pestalotia aeruginea** Stey. Bull. Jard. Bot. État Bruxelles 19:186,1948, pl. VI, B 1–8.

P. theae Marchal & Stey., not Sawada, Bull. Soc. Roy. Belg. 41:166, 1929.

Pestalotiopsis aeruginea (Stey.) Stey., Bull. Jard. Bot. État Bruxelles, 19: 322,1949.

P. gigas Stey. Trans. Brit., Mycol. Soc. 36:86–87,1953, fig. 4.

Spots and dead areas ash colored, irregular, delimited. Pustules puncti-form, largely epiphyllous, erumpent, circular, conoid-truncate, surrounded by torn shreds of epidermis, 150–300 μ diam. Conidia long, narrow fusiform, equilateral, 5-celled, 28–38 × 6–8 μ, sometimes 6-celled, rarely 1–2–6 septate, abnormal forms extremely variable; three intermediate cells umber, con-colorous, often 4 colored cells, the lowest the longest, 19–22 μ long; basal cells long acute, hyaline, often colored; apical cells long, narrow cylindric or acute, crested with usually 3, sometimes 4, long filiform, widely divergent setulae, 18–39 μ long or with 2 to 4 abnormal, short, coarse, spatulate or horn-like, auriculariform or antennaeform setulae with visible lumen; pedicels 3–9 μ long, sometimes absent.

On leaves of *Camellia thea* Lk. [= *C. sinensis* (L.) Kuntze], Yangambi, Belgian Congo, Ghesquière 543 (type), in herb. Bot. Gard, Brussels, Belgium [Fig. 20].

Both normal and abnormal conidia exist together. Variability and poly-morphism of conidia are remarkable. In addition to normal 5-celled narrow

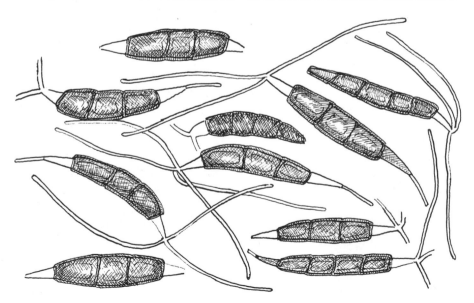

FIG. 20 [84]. *Pestalotia aeruginea* Stey.

conidia with 3 long setulae (Steyaert, Bull. Jard. Bot. État Bruxelles 19, 1948, pl. VI, B1) there is a range of abnormal forms, comprising muticate completely colored conidia (pl. VI, B6), conidia bearing 6 setulae and one colored cell (B3), conidia with antennaeform setulae (B8) and with visible lumen beginning at the base; others with short and thick auriculariform setulae, simple or swollen at the extremities. The basal cells may be colored and pedicels lacking (B2). My study of type material did not reveal knobbed or spatulate setulae featured by Steyaert except that in some instances there is a faint indication of swollen extremities.

The specimen on *Latania borbonica* Lam. [=*Livistona chinensis* R. Br.], included by Steyaert as a host with *Camellia thea*, is different, and according to my studies belongs with *Pestalotia theae* Sawada. The conidia are long, intermediate cells umber, concolorous, setulae long and knobbed at the extremities.

Pestalotiopsis gigas Stey. was named for a fungus in artificial nutrient culture isolated from a leaf of *Thea sinensis* L. [=*Camellia sinensis* (L.) Kuntze], Kericho, Kenya, Africa, R. M. Nattrass. The figures by Steyaert do not show the versicolorous conidia or spatulate setulae as indicated in the description.

85. **Pestalotia trichocladi** Laughton, Bothalia 4:829–830,1948.

Pestalotiopsis trichocladi (Laughton) Stey., Bothalia 6:381,1954, fig. 2.

Pustules epiphyllous, seated in large indeterminate, discolored areas, minute, scattered, circular to elliptic, borne under the epidermis, erumpent, the torn shreds surrounding and partially covering the black mass, 175–250 μ diam. × 75–85 μ high. Conidia 5-celled, fusiform, erect, or slightly curved, slightly constricted at septa, 32–38 × 7.5–9 μ; intermediate cells umber, concolorous, or lowest colored cells somewhat paler, 20–25 μ long; basal cells conical or turbinate, slightly colored; apical cells cylindric, 5–7.5 μ long, bearing 2–4, usually 3, rather stout setulae, 45–60 μ long, tapering toward the extremities, spatulate, with wide lumen extending nearly the whole length.

On living leaves of *Trichocladus crinitus* Pers., Storms River, South Africa, Doidge, No. 17169 and D. J. le Roux, No. 34307. Fungus is noted for its long conidia and long spatulate setulae with wide lumen.

86. **Pestalotia gossypii** Hori, Byochu-gai Zasshi (Jour. Plant Protection, Japan) 4: pt. 3, 27–28,1917, transl., Tanaka, Mycologia 11:154,1919; Syll. Fung. 25:603,1931.

Spots reddish or ochraceous-brown, about 16 mm in diam. with irregularly zoned fuliginous margins. Acervuli punctate, conspicuous, first covered by the epidermis, then erumpent, black, 212–225 μ wide. Conidia 5-celled, clavate, 18–27 × 4–8 μ, thickened at the apices, gradually narrowed toward the base; exterior cells hyaline, 3 intermediate cells dull yellowish brown, the middle one the darkest; setulae 2–3, slightly swollen at the apices, hyaline, 6–16 × 1.6 μ; pedicels hyaline, 2–4 × 0.6–0.9 μ.

On leaves of *Gossypium herbaceum* L., Shidzuoka-Ken (prefecture), Ogasa-gun Hikimura, S. Tsuruda, Dec. 10, 1916. Considered to be the cause of a leaf blotch responsible for damage to upland cotton in Shidzuoka prefecture, Japan, during wet harvest season of 1916.

87. **Pestalotia lapageriae** P. Henn., Hedwigia 36:243,1897; Syll. Fung. 14: 1030,1899.

   Cryptostictis lapagericola Speg., Fungi Chilenses, Libreria Nac. Buenos Aires, 1910, p. 164; Syll. Fung. 22:1074,1913.

Pustules subepidermal, globose-lenticular, erumpent and exposing the black elevated mass, amphigenous, 150–450 μ in diam, scattered, or crowded and confluent, sometimes in concentric order, distinct, somewhat crustaceous, sooty, spreading over the matrix. Conidia usually erect, 5-celled, subclavate, tapering, broad, or ovate-fusoid, 24–29 × 7–9.5 μ, only slightly constricted at the septa; intermediate colored cells 15–20 μ long, guttulate, the upper 2 umber, the lowest olivaceous, the walls darker, the middle cells the darkest; apical hyaline cells long cylindric bearing a crest of 3, sometimes 4, coarse, widely divergent and curved setulae, 12–22 μ long, the extremities conspicuously knobbed, the knobs 3–3.5 μ in diam, vaculate; basal hyaline cells broad conic; pedicels 3–7 μ long.

On irregular yellow areas on weathered leaves of *Lapageria rosea* Ruis. & Pav., Conception, Chile, F. Neger, in herb. Berlin Bot. Mus.; herb. Spegazzini, Cerro Caracol de Conception, Chile, Jan. 1909, C. Spegazzini, sub *P. lapagericola* Speg. [Fig. 21a]; Nat. Fungus Coll., U.S.D.A., Santiago, Chile, C. E. Porter, 1913 [Fig. 21b].

The specimen collected and studied by Spegazzini was described as a new species, *Cryptostictis lapagericola* Speg., but the herbarium specimen bears the name *Pestalotia lapagericola* Speg. The pustules are reported as 120–150 μ in diam, setulae 5–10 μ, pedicels 20–30 μ. Spegazzini regarded the fruiting structure as a pycnidium, but study reveals acervuloid pustules. All three specimens from Chile have 5-celled conidia and 3 setulae with knobbed extremities, which in spite of the specific importance of this character is not mentioned or illustrated by either Hennings or Spegazzini. Hennings reported the pustules to measure 0.5–1.5 mm in diam, conidia 3-septate, 17–21 × 7–8 μ, setulae 4–6 μ, pedicels 4–6 μ long. Hennings described 4-celled conidia, the two middle cells darkening with age and the basal cells sometimes weakly colored. The description was enough in error to cause Spegazzini to describe his specimen as a new species.

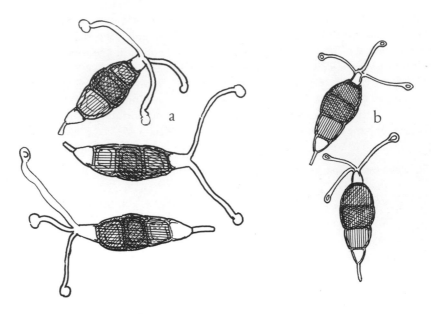

FIG. 21 [87].   *Pestalotia lapageriae* P. Henn.

88. **Pestalotia antennaeformis** B. J. Murray, Trans. and Proc. New Zealand
    Inst. 57:222–224,1947.

Pustules numerous, gregarious, scattered over large light brown areas, minute, globose-lenticular, erumpent, 132–165 μ in diam.   Conidia erect or curved, 5-celled, fusiform, constricted at the septa, 21–36 × 6.5–9 μ; upper two colored cells umber or dark, the lowest pale or olivaceous; basal hyaline cells the smallest, pale olivaceous to hyaline; apical hyaline cells conic; setulae 3, arising a little below the rounded apex, the extremities frequently knobbed, reflexed at right angles to the conidium, 13–50 μ long, sometimes 2 or 4 setulae, rarely forked; pedicels 3–7 μ long.

On living stems and dead leaves of *Rubus cissoides* A. Cunn., Nelson, July 19, 1925; Wakapuaka, New Zealand, Sept. 20, 1925.   On living leaves of *Rubus australis* Forst., Wakapuaka, New Zealand, Sept. 20, 1925, B. J. Murray (Mycol. herb. 355a, 355b).   The acervuli are densely distributed over large cankered areas partially girdling the living stem.   The fungus also occurs on dead spots in living leaves with other fungi.

89. **Pestalotia ilicis** West., Bull. Acad. Roy. Belg., 2nd ser., 7:90–91,1859,
    fig. 21; Syll. Fung. 3:788,1884; Steyaert, Bull. Jard. Bot. État Bruxelles
    19:67–68,1948.
    Pestalotiopsis ilicis (West.) Stey., Bull. Jard. Bot. État Bruxelles 19:340,
    1949.

Pustules dense, circular, at length erumpent, seated on poorly defined spots. Conidia large claviform, erect, 5-celled, 22–30 × 7–10 μ (average 26.2 × 8.7 μ); upper 2 colored cells dark chestnut brown, opaque, fuliginous, the lowest colored cells olivaceous or pale brown, 15–20 μ long (average 17.3 μ); apical hyaline cells conic cylindric, basal hyaline cells long conoid; pedicels sometimes spatulate, 6–15 μ; setulae 3, broad, continuous with walls of apical cells, 21–46 μ (average 34.4 μ), knobbed at extremities.

On living leaves of *Ilex aquifolium* L., Dumont, Belgium, 1895, R. P. Clem.

Westendorp described 4-celled conidia, 25 × 7.5 μ, with 2 or 3 setulae longer than the conidia and with contrasted colored cells. There are errors in the type description, but the drawing by Westendorp agrees. The setulae are coarse, long, divergent, knobbed at the extremities. The walls of the setulae according to Steyaert are continuous with the walls of the apical cell, thus they are part of the apical cell. The species according to Steyaert corresponds to the description of *P. gibbosa* Harkn.

90. **Pestalotia gibbosa** Harkn., Bull. Cal. Acad. Sci. 2:439–440,1887.

Pustules epiphyllous, sparse, rarely confluent, punctiform, subglobose, covered by the papery epidermis, 100–225 μ wide, erumpent, tearing the epidermis irregularly, exposing the black contents, seated in pale dead spots or irregular areas with definite borders. Conidia 5-celled, unequilateral, pyriform, constricted at septum dividing the two lower colored cells, 25–30 × 8–10.5 μ; intermediate colored cells 16–20 × 8–10 μ, the upper 2 fuliginous, subglobose and gibbous, the lowest olivaceous, sub-cylindric; exterior cells hyaline, the basal cells long conic or tapering into short, filiform pedicels up

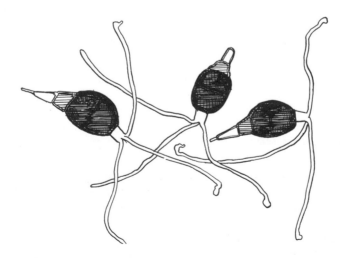

FIG. 22 [90].   *Pestalotia gibbosa* Harkn.

to 6.4 μ long, sometimes knobbed at the base; apical hyaline cells long cylindric, bearing 2–4, usually 3, long, coarse, widely divergent setulae, 30–60 μ long, often knobbed at the extremities.

On living leaves of *Gaultheria shallon* Pursh, Seattle, Wash., Dec. 1893, C. V. Piper [Fig. 22]; Mercer Island, near Seattle, A. M. Parker, herb. Young Naturalists Society No. 208, sub *P. guepini*.

According to Harkness, the fungus collected at Point Reyes, Cal., June 1886, and distributed in Pacific Coast Fungi No. 4130, frequently covers nearly the entire leaf, which is blackened with conidia. The fungus is common about the coastal area of Washington. Zeller (Mycologia 26:291, 1934) found the discomycete *Dermatea brunneo-pruinosa* Zeller in the same spots with *Pestalotia gibbosa* and believed that there was a connection between them. Bonar (Mycologia 34:180,1942) grew cultures from single ascospores and single conidia and obtained *Pestalotia gibbosa* in both series. No apothecia were obtained in laboratory cultures. Seaver (Mycologia 34:298, 1942) stated that the fungus has none of the characters of *Dermatea* and following the tendency of segregating genera on the basis of the conidial stage where it is known, he proposed the new genus *Pestalopezia* for these cup fungi having *Pestalotia* as their conidial stage. Then *Dermatea brunneo-pruinosa* Zeller is *Pestalopezia brunneo-pruinosa* (Zeller) Seaver.

Non-Spathulatae
Species Nos. 91–258

Concolorae, Olivae-Pallidae
Species Nos. 91–160

91. **Pestalotia toxica** Ell. & Ev., Proc. Acad. Nat. Sci. Phila., 1894, p. 374; Syll. Fung. 11:578,1895.

Spots 4–6 mm in diam, deciduous, grayish-white with narrow, black borders. Pustules epiphyllous, scattered, 100–110 μ in diam, convex, prominent above, visible below. Conidia clavate-oblong, 5-celled, 12–15 × 4–5 μ; intermediate colored cells pale brown, about 12 μ long; exterior cells short, conical, hyaline; setulae 3, spreading, 6–7 μ long; pedicels shorter than conidia.

On leaves of *Rhus toxicodendron* L., Nuttallburg, W. Va., Aug. 1894, L. W. Nuttall, No. 567. Oudemans (Enum. Syst. Fung. 3:1123,1921) erroneously listed *P. toxica* Ell. & Ev. as a synonym of *Marsonia toxicodendri* (Ell. & G. Martin) Sacc.

In dead areas on leaves of *Cocos nucifera* L., Sanibel Island, Fla., Dec. 28, 1899, sub *P. palmarum* Cooke var. *microspora* Hume (herb. name), Hume, Fungi of Florida No. 53 in herb. Ellis, folio 179, No. 24, in herb. Farlow.

92. **Pestalotia espaillatii** Cif. & Gonz.-Frag., Est. Agron. de Haina, Rep.
Dominicana, Ser. Bot. no. 1:13,1925.

Pustules numerous, sparse, epiphyllous, black, circular, flattened, up to
260 μ in diam. Conidia 5-celled, subfusoid, 12–17 × 5–6 μ; intermediate
colored cells olivaceous or dark, exterior cells hyaline; setulae 2–3, divergent,
up to 16 μ long; pedicels short.

In pale spots in leaves of *Garcinia mangostana* L., Santiago, Dominican
Republic, leg. R. Ciferri. In white papery areas on living leaves of *Musa
sapientum* L. [= *M. paradisiaca* var. *sapientum* (L.) Kuntze], Hawaii, July
1922, Stevens, Hawaiian Fungi No. 582 (533), in herb. University of Illinois
[Fig. 23], dedicated to Rafael A. Espaillat, former Secretary of Agriculture
of the Dominican Republic. Ciferri (Riv. Pat. Veg. 17:244–247,1927) found
the fungus *P. espaillatii* associated with dead areas in tips and margins of
mangostan leaves. Attempts to produce infection with conidia were not
successful.

93. **Pestalotia fibricola** Grove, Jour. Bot. 24:198,1886, tab. 266, fig. 7; Syll.
Fung. 10:487,1892; Grove, British Leaf and Stem Fungi II, 346–347,
1937.

Pustules oblong-elliptic, 125–450 × 125–225 μ, black, gregarious, raising
and tearing fibers of matrix, at length erumpent, exposing the sooty contents.
Conidia 5-celled, elliptic to narrow-fusiform, tapering toward the extremities,
15–18 × 4.5–5.5 μ; intermediate colored cells olivaceous, often guttulate, the
upper 2 colored cells often faintly darker, 9–12 μ long; apical hyaline cells
elongate, attenuate, 4–5 μ long; setulae 2 to 3, mostly 2, and joined at base,
often branched, 11–19 μ long, divergent and recurved, sometimes somewhat

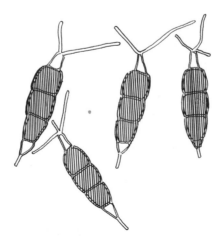

Fig. 23 [92]. *Pestalotia espaillatii* Cif. & Gonz.-Frag.

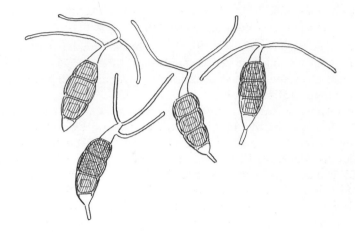

Fig. 24 [93].   *Pestalotia fibricola* Grove.

off the apices, one longer and oblique; basal hyaline cells short, broad conic or acute; pedicels 3–5 μ long.

On wood of *Tilia* sp., Sutton near Birmingham, England, Grove, Sept. 9, 1885 [Fig. 24].

94. Pestalotia senegalensis Speg., Anal. Mus. Nac. Buenos Aires 26:131–132, 1915; Syll. Fung. 25:599,1931.

Acervuli dense, gregarious, black, amphigenous, at first covered by the epidermis, then erumpent, conoid and small, 100–150 μ diam. Conidia 5-celled 14–18 × 5 μ, somewhat elliptic-cylindric, hardly inequilateral, unequal in size, colored cells olivaceous, concolorous, the lowest of the central colored cells often twice as large as the others, somewhat constricted at the septa; apical cells bearing 2 to 4 setulae, chlorine colored, 15–20 μ long, the lowest hyaline cells attenuated into short pedicels, 5 μ long.

On dry somewhat leathery leaves of *Anaphrenium concolor* E. Mey., Bel Air, near Dackarr, Senegal, Africa, June 1913.

95. Pestalotia citri Mundk. & Kheswalla, Mycologia 34:312,1942.

Acervuli minute, punctiform, black, seated in large bleached spots with raised edges. Conidia 5-celled, exterior cells hyaline, tapering, 10–20 × 5–5.5 μ; intermediate colored cells guttulate, umber to olivaceous, 6.5–14.5 μ long, not constricted at septa; setulae 3 to 4, divergent, 10–20 μ long.

On living leaves of *Citrus grandis* Osbeck, Kirkee, India, Nov. 8, 1914, H. M. Chibber, No. 2209, in herb. Crypt. Ind. Orient. and herb. Imp. Mycol. Inst., Kew.

96. **Pestalotia distincta** Guba sp. nov.

Pustulae maculicolae, amphigenae, punctiformes, dispersae vel gregariae, 75–150 μ in diam, globoso-lenticulares, stellatim vel in lineis erumpentes; conidia 5-cellularia, late clavata vel elliptico-fusoidea, 14–18 × 6.8–8.2 μ, leniter inaequilateralia vel interdum recta, subconstricta; cellulae apicales hyalinae, crassae, hemisphaericales, setulis 3–9 brevibus, curvatis, usque 10 μ longis cristatae; cellulae mediae coloratae brunneae vel umbrinae, concolores, 9.5–13 μ longis, septis tunicisque obscurioribus; cellulae basales hyalinae, obtusae, latae, subhemisphaericales; pedicelli curvati, 3–7 μ longi.

Spots or dead areas, irregular with definite dark brown borders, prominent above, obscure below. Pustules amphigenous, punctiform, scattered or gregarious, 75–150 μ diam, globose-lenticular, subepidermal, erumpent in stellate or linear manner, surrounded by torn shreds of the epidermis. Conidia 5-celled, broad clavate or elliptic-fusoid, 14–18 × 6.7–8.2 μ, slightly unequilateral, sometimes straight, more or less constricted at septa; hyaline apical cells thick, sheath-like, hemispherical, obscure, crested with 3–9 short curved setulae up to 10 μ long, extending above the conidia; three intermediate colored cells brown or umber, concolorous, 9.5–13 μ long, the septa and walls darker or fuliginous; basal hyaline cells obtuse, somewhat broad, hemispherical: pedicels curved, 3–7 μ long.

On leaves of *Pasania cuspidata* Oerst. [=*Lithocarpus cuspidata* (Oerst.) Nakai] Matsukawa, Pref. Fukuoka, Japan, Nov. 12, 1922, leg. Asano, in herb. Agr. Inst. Yokohama Nat. Univ. No. 2702 [Fig. 25]. Fungus is unusual in the absence of conspicuous hyaline apical cells, and the mass of short setulae adorning the apex of the conidia.

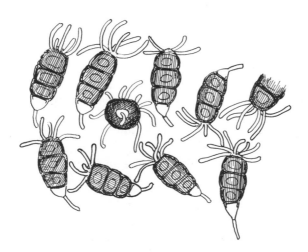

FIG. 25 [96]. *Pestalotia distincta* Guba.

97. **Pestalotia fuchsiae** Thuem., Inst. Rev. Sci. Litt. Coimbra, Ser. 2, 27:326–327,1880; Syll. 3:790,1884.

Spots brown, limited by purple margin, circular, indistinctly zoned. Pustules globose, black, epiphyllous, scattered, subepidermal, erumpent, surrounded by torn shreds of the epidermis, up to 80 μ in diam. Conidia 5-celled, elliptic-fusoid, erect, 14–18 × 5–6.5 μ; intermediate cells guttulate, olivaceous, equally colored, 10–13 μ long; basal hyaline cells short, conic or obtuse, apical hyaline cells narrow-conic or acute; setulae usually 2, sometimes branched near the extremities, or 3 and simple, sometimes 1 and branched, 6–16 μ long, unequal: pedicels short, deciduous, less than 3 μ long.

On living leaves of *Fuchsia coccinea* Soland., Bot. Gard., Coimbra, Portugal, Nov. 1878, leg. A. Moller, No. 187, in herb. Jard. Bot. Univ. Coimbra, No. 344 and herb. Berlin Bot. Mus.

Thuemen reported conidia 20–21 μ and 3 setulae 6 μ long. Klebahn (Myc. Centralbl. 4:7, fig. 34, 1914) reported conidia 15–17 × 5.5–6 μ and 1, mostly 2, rarely 3 setulae, 9–17 μ long. The fungus is very close to and probably identical with *P. guepini* Desm.

98. **Pestalotia guepini** Desm.   Ann. Sci. Nat. Bot. II, 13,182–184,1840, pl. 4, fig. 1–3; Mem. Soc. Roy. Sci. Agr. Arts, Lille, 1840: 35–37,1841; Syll. Fung. 3:794,1884.

   Coryneum camelliae Mass. Grevillea 20:8,1891. Kew Bull. Misc. Inform. 138:106–109,1898; Syll. Fung. 10:482,1892.

   Pestalotia karstenii Sacc. & Syd., Syll. Fung. 14:1030,1899.

   P. inquinans Karst. Hedwigia 30:301,1891; Syll. Fung. 10:487,1892; not Cooke & Harkn., Grevillea 12:94,1884.

   P. puttemansii P. Henn.   Hedwigia 41:115,1902; Syll. Fung. 18:479,1906.

   P. funerea Desm. var. *camelliae* Brun., Actes Soc. Linn. Bordeaux 42:102, 1888; Syll. Fung. 14:1024,1899.

   Pestalotiopsis gallica Stey., Bull. Jard. Bot. État Bruxelles 19:308,1949, pl. 9, fig. F, G.

   Pestalotia gallica (Stey.) Galluci, Ann. Sper. Agraria Roma (n.s.) 8:1440, 1954.

   Pestalotiopsis guepini (Desm.) Stey., Bull. Jard. Bot. État Bruxelles 19: 308,1949, pl. 10, fig. C.

   P. karstenii (Sacc. & Syd.) Stey. Bull. Jard. Bot. État Bruxelles 19:305, 1949, pl. 9, fig. A, F.

Spots and dead areas papery, about 1.5 cm in diam. or variable in area and shape, ash gray on upper surface, sometimes with dark or reddish brown border, often confined to margins of leaves, or leaves entirely brown and covered with the fungus. Pustules punctiform, black, 90–170 μ diam, amphigenous, globose-lenticular, rupturing the epidermis, the black contents darkening the matrix. Conidia erect, 14–21 μ, elliptic-fusoid, 5-celled, hardly constricted at septa; exterior cells hyaline, short and broad conic, sometimes rather inconspicuous; intermediate cells olivaceous, guttulate, 10–14 × 5.5–6.6 μ; setulae 1–3, rarely 4, sometimes minutely knobbed at apices, 10–24 μ long, divergent, commonly branched; pedicels short, straight, often deciduous.

On stems and leaves of *Camellia japonica* L., usually associated with gray colored spots.

Specimens examined: on leaves. Desmazières, Plantes Crypt. Fr. 22: 1084,1840, Angers, France [Fig. 26a]; Roumeguère Fungi Galliae Exs. 315, in Hort. Lotharingiae and Alsatiae; Thuem., Fungi Austriaci Exs. 1070, Bohemia, 1873; herb. Berlin Bot. Mus. No. 1167 sub *Sporocadus maculans* Cda. [= *Hendersonia maculans* Lév.]; Comm. Geog. Geol., São Paulo, Brazil, No. 147 sub *P. puttemansii* P. Henn., in Berlin Bot. Mus.; Ellis, N. Am. Fungi No. 526, Westchester, Pa., in greenhouse, G. Martin, Sept. 1880 [Fig. 26b]; Briosi and Cavara, Funghi Par. VI, 150, Pavia, 1890; Rabenhorst Fungi europ. Exs. 2352, in Hort. Bot. Neapolitano, Cesati; Tuskegee Inst., Ala., March 7, 1925, G. W. Carver; Alabama, Feb. 17, 1912, F. A. Wolf in Nat. Fungus Coll., U.S.D.A., sub *P. inquinans* Cooke & Harkn. [Fig. 26c]; Washington, D.C., in greenhouse, May 20, 1907, W. A. Orton, in Nat. Fungus Coll., U.S.D.A., sub *P. camelliae* Pass. [Fig. 26d]; Pass Christian, Miss., Jan. 29, 1916, E. Martin, Nat. Fungus Coll., U.S.D.A.; Waltham, Mass. (greenhouse) March 30, 1938, E. F. Guba; herb. J. A. Stevenson No. 1304, Oneco, Fla., Feb. 10, 1921; Washington D.C., Plant Quar. Intercept. No. 5099, U.S.D.A., from Nantes, France; Cooke, Fungi Brit. Exs. 625, 2nd ed.; on twigs, ex. herb. Phyt. Sta. Pflanzschutz Tetsch-Lieb No. 23, in greenhouse, Neschwitz, Bohemia, April 1923, F. Zimmermann, sub *P. funerea* Desm. var. *camelliae* Brun.; culture on wheat kernels, K. Roder, No. 5998, Mar. 6, 1937, in Biol. Reichs. Anst. Land. u. Forstw., Berlin.

Desmazières (Ann. Sci. Nat. Bot. II, 13, 1840) described *P. guepini* on *Camellia* and *Magnolia* leaves. His colored illustration of the fungus embraces a leaf of *Camellia* bearing the fungus (fig. 1), a portion of the upper surface of the leaf showing acervuli much enlarged (fig. 2), and conidia (fig. 3). Did Desmazières select the fungus on *Magnolia* leaves in preparing the type description of *P. guepini* and for his figure of the conidia rather than the fungus on *Camellia* leaves? This would appear unlikely since the illustration of *P. guepini* includes a figure of the fungus on *Camellia* and also only *Camellia* leaves are distributed in the exsiccati. While the fungus on *Magnolia* leaves would be welcomed for study, it has not been found. The *Camellia* leaves might even have been mistaken for *Magnolia*. The fungus on *Camellia* should be considered the type. Exsiccati published after the one in question and usage support this view (Guba, Mycologia 24:415–418, 1932).

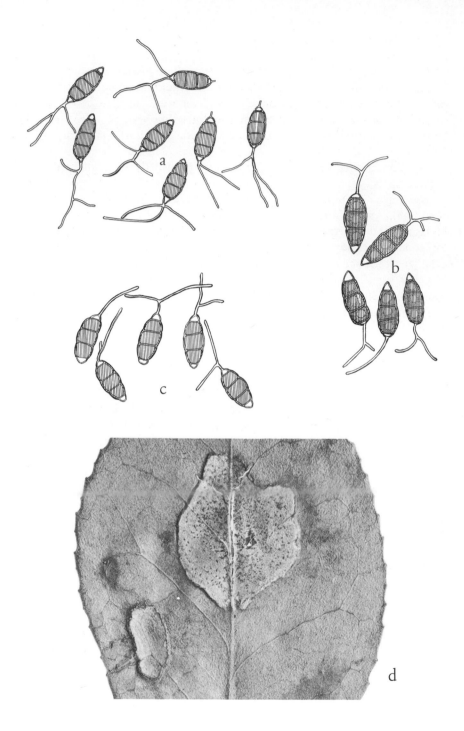

FIG. 26 [98].   *Pestalotia guepini* Desm.   Gray leaf spots on *Camellia japonica* L., dotted with fruiting pustules.

Steyaert (Bull. Jard. Bot. État Bruxelles 19:305–308,312–316,1949) reported that the fungus on *Camellia* in Desmazières' collection No. 14 (Mus. d'Hist. Nat., Paris) corresponds to Desmazières' description and drawings of *P. guepini*. Another specimen on the same host and same herbarium sheet (Desmazières, Plantes Crypt. Fr. No. 1084) is according to Steyaert, *Pestalotiopsis gallica* Stey. The same material is duplicated in the herbarium of Westendorp (Jard. Bot. État Bruxelles, Belgium) and here, according to Steyaert, the matrix bears both *P. guepini* and *P. gallica*. Steyaert's drawings of the conidia of *P. guepini*, Exs. Coll. Desmazières, 1863, No. 8 (pl. 10, fig. C), are not representative and his drawings of *Pestalotiopsis karstenii* and *P. gallica* (pl. 9) are identical.

Thus, according to Steyaert, type and cotype material collected by Guepin at Angers, France, is *Pestalotiopsis karstenii* (Sacc. & Syd.) Stey., *P. gallica* Stey., and *P. guepini* (Desm.) Stey. The writer has examined the Desmazières specimens in the Paris Museum and considers them all *Pestalotia guepini* Desm.

Steyaert (Bull. Jard. Bot. État Bruxelles 19:312–316,1949) has made *Pestalotia sydowiana* Bres., *P. macrotricha* Kleb., and *P. rhododendri* (D. Sacc.) Guba synonyms of *Pestalotiopsis guepini* (Desm.) Stey. According to this writer's studies, they are totally different. Steyaert (Trans. Brit. Mycol. Soc. 36:82,1953, fig. 1; 237, fig. 1) described two macroscopic forms of *P. guepini* Desm., one as *Pestalotiopsis nattrassi* based on a culture of the fungus from leaves of *Thea sinensis* L. [= *Camellia sinensis* (L.) Kuntze], the other *P. guepini* (Desm.) Stey. var. *major* Stey. on dead leaves of *Encephalartos barteri* Carruth. The two are identical.

Pestalotia guepini Desm. has been cited incorrectly on a wide range of host plants. Speshnev (Die Pilzparasiten des Teestrauches, Berlin, 1907, tab. I, figs. 1–5; Trudy Tiflisk Bot. Sad. 63:47–129,1904) reported the fungus in the tea plantations of Tschakwa, near Batum, and also its occurrence on *Camellia*, *Magnolia* and *Citrus* about Tschakwa and the coast of the Black Sea, an observation confirmed by Jaczewsky (Pilze d. Teeblätter, Appendix in Simonson, Prakt. Leit. Theekultur u. Theebereit., 1901, Petrograd) and that it had also been observed in the southern Caucasus on *Rhododendron* and *Vitis*. Speshnev reported that the *Rhododendron* fungus differed from the form on *Camellia* and that the latter agreed with the form on tea. The typical fungus on tea leaves was described with 4-celled conidia, $20 \times 5 \mu$ and 4 setulae which therefore could not be *P. guepini* Desm. Artificial infection of *Thea* and *Camellia* leaves was successful only through the lower leaf surfaces.

Saccardo (Syll. Fung. 3:794,1884) erroneously reported *P. guepini* on *Rhododendron*, *Citrus*, *Lagerstroemia*, *Magnolia*, *Smilax* and *Amygdalus* [= *Prunus*]. La Rue (Genetics 7:142–201,1922) and La Rue and Bartlett (Am. Jour. Bot. 9:79–92,1922) believed that *P. guepini* is a polymorphic fungus containing many strains causing the gray blight of tea, leaf spot of coconut, betel-nut palm, African oil palm, para rubber, and other plants, but this view is not acceptable in the light of studies by Butler (Fungi and Disease in Plants. Calcutta and Simla, 1918), Bertus (Ceylon Dept. Agr. Yearbook, pp. 43–46, 1923; Ann. Roy. Bot. Gard. Peradeniya 10:197–241, 1927), and Archer (Ann. Mycol. 24:66–67,1926), which showed that the forms on tea, palm, and *Camellia* are distinct species. According to my studies, *P. guepini* is restricted to *Camellia*.

Massee and Cooke (Nuovo Gior. Bot. Ital. 10:27,1878) regarded *Hendersonia theicola* Cooke (Grevillea 1:90,1872) synonymous with *P. guepini* Desm., and Speshnev found both together frequently in the same gray blighted leaves. Speshnev reported that cultures made from *Hendersonia* conidia never produced appendaged *Pestalotia* conidia. Massee (Kew Bull. Misc. Inform. 138:106–109,1898), like Speshnev, illustrated and described 4-celled conidia. Massee failed to offer proof that *Pestalozzina camelliae* Pass. (Rev. Mycol. Fr. 9:146,1887) is identical with *P. guepini* Desm. The original description of the former is distinctly that of a *Pestalozzina*.

The type specimen of *P. guepini* Desm. in Desmazières' Plantes Crypt. Fr. 22:1084,1840, was inaccurately described and illustrated, but the characters of the original specimen agree with the description of *P. inquinans* Karst. (Hedwigia 30:301,1891) [=*P. karstenii* Sacc. & Syd. (Syll. Fung. 14:1030, 1899)] on living leaves of *Camellia*. The name *P. karstenii* was substituted for *P. inquinans* Karst, not for *P. inquinans* Cooke & Harkn. (Grevillea 12:94,1884) on dead leaves of *Eucalyptus*.

According to Klebahn (Myc. Centralbl. 4:1–19,1914) the conidia of *P. guepini* in Roumeguère Fungi Galliae Exs. 315, do not agree with the type illustrated by Desmazières. This specimen has short elliptic-fusoid conidia, with occasionally forked setulae, in contrast to long, narrow-fusoid conidia with simple setulae illustrated by Desmazières. Massee (Kew Bull. Misc. Inform. 138:106–109,1898) illustrated conidia with 3 to 4 simple setulae but with only 3 septa. Voglino (Atti. Soc. Ven.-Trent. Sci. Nat. Padova 9:209–243,1885) figured conidia of *P. guepini* similar to Desmazières' illustrations. His description of the fungus is accompanied by reference to the following exsiccati: Rabenhorst, Fungi europ. Exs. 2352, Cooke, Fungi Brit. Exs. 625, 2nd ed., Thuemen, Fungi Austriaci Ex. 1070, on leaves of *Camellia japonica* L. and Ravenel, Fungi Am. Ex. 553, on leaves of persimmon. The latter, labeled *P. guepini*, is *P. flavidula* Fl. Tassi.

Karsten's description of the setulae of *P. inquinans* Karst. is as follows, "Setulae 2, rarely 1 or 3, divided, divergent, somewhat equal, hyaline, 15–35 μ long. Further, it differs from *Pestalozzia guepini* Desm. on *Camellia* in the acervuli being formed on pale spots and soon becoming superficial: also in the fewer setulae." Allescher (Rabh. Krypt. Flora 1, Abt. 7:685,1902) and Klebahn (Myc. Centralbl. 4:1–19,1914) regarded *P. karstenii* as a synonym.

Hoehnel (Fragm. z. Myk. 1030,1917) observed from his study of *P. guepini* Desm. (Plantes Crypt. Fr. 22:1084,1840) that the setulae are often branched and that *P. inquinans* Karst. is identical. My study confirms this view. Desmazières figured conidia of the type with pointed setulae, but Lacroix (Ann. Soc. Linn., Dept. Maine et Loire, Angers 2:10–16,1856) never observed pointed setulae in his studies on conidial development, and the author has never encountered them. Since the fungus was carelessly described, Karsten was unable to reconcile his fungus with the description of *P. guepini,* whereupon he created a new species.

Massee showed that *P. guepini* is a parasite and the cause of a common leaf spot of *Camellia.* White (New Jersey Agr. Exp. Sta., Ann. Rep. 1930: 266,1931) noted that the white leaf spots come from sunscald and that sporulation of the fungus is abundant on the upper leaf surfaces. Infection was produced in twigs by inoculation through wounds and in leaves injured by scalpel abrasions. The fungus causes cankers in twigs, blasts the buds, and increases the size of sunscalded areas on the leaves. Servazzi (Boll. Lab. Sper. Reg. Osserv. Fitopat. Torino 18, 19–21, 1939) furnished a good description and historical review of *P. guepini.* The fungus is the subject of an excellent contribution by Ito, Chiba, Ono, and Hosaka (Bull. Govt. For. Exp. Sta. 70, 103–124, June 1954, Tokyo) entitled "Pestalotia Disease of *Camellia japonica.*" *Camellia* is cultivated in the southern districts of Japan for the oil in its seed. The disease affects both fruit and leaves but infection occurs only through wounds. Identical symptoms were induced in leaves of *Thea sinensis* L. [= *Camellia sinensis* (L.) Kuntze] by artificial inoculations at wounds. Gallucci-Rangone (Ann. Sper Agraria Roma (n.s.) 8:5,1437–1457, 1954) described the morphological and cultural characters of *P. gallica* (Steyaert) Gallucci. The author considered the genus Pestalotiopsis superfluous.

99. **Pestalotia quercicola** Kuhnholtz-Lordat & Barry, Bull. Soc. Mycol. Fr. 65:128,1949.

Spots amphigenous, orbicular, up to 5 mm diam, brown then gray, purple-bordered. Pustules black, amphigenous. Conidia fusoid, 5-celled, 16–20 × 4–6.5 μ, setulae 2, divergent, of equal length, 4–6 μ long.

On living leaves of *Quercus coccifera* L. Herault, Bords de la Mosson, near Grabels (N. Montpellier), France, G.K.L. Oct. 19, 1948.

100. **Pestalotia bromeliicola** Speg., Bol. Acad. Nac. Ci. Cordoba, Argent. 23:526–527,1918; Syll. Fung. 25:600,1931.

Spots amphigenous, elliptic-elongate, the central part clear, first yellow, then white, finally ash-colored, the border thick, sometimes grayish. Pustules amphigenous, subepidermal then erumpent, lenticular-conoid, 75–120 μ

in diam, black. Conidia elliptic-fusoid, 5-celled, slightly constricted at septa, $15–18 \times 5–6 \mu$, straight or somewhat curved; exterior cells small, hyaline, intermediate cells olivaceous, equally colored, the central cell the largest; apical hyaline cells bearing 2 setulae, $5–8 \mu$ long, straight, the basal cells supported by pedicels up to 5μ long.

On living leaves of *Bromelia* sp., near Trinidad, Paraguay, 1891, leg. J. D. Anisitz. No. 50.

101. **Pestalotia aletridis** (Pat.) Guba, Mycologia 24:361,1932.

> *Pestalozzina aletridis* Pat. in Duss, Enum. Meth. Champ. Guadel. et Mart. 90,1903; Syll. Fung. 18:475,1906.

Fruiting pustules $75–150 \mu$ in diam, subglobose, punctiform, largely epiphyllous, subepidermal, later erumpent, seated in pale dead spots with definite borders. Conidia 5-celled, oblong or elliptic-clavate, tapering to the base, erect, $16–17 \mu$, intermediate cells pale olivaceous, equally colored, slightly constricted at septa, guttulate, $10–13 \times 5–7 \mu$; apical hyaline cells short, cylindric, bearing 2 divergent setulae, $6–10 \mu$ long; basal hyaline cells broad conic, usually acute, tapering; pedicels $1–2 \mu$ long.

On dried leaves of *Aletris fragrans* L. [= *Cordyline fragrans* (L.) Planch.], Basse-Terre, Guadelupe, R. P. Duss, herb. Patouillard, in herb. Farlow [Fig. 27]. According to Patouillard, the conidia are colorless, 4–5-septate and $20 \times 6 \mu$. Hoehnel (Mitt. Bot. Lab. Techn. Hochsch., Wien 2:26–29, 1925) regarded the species as a pale-colored *Pestalotia*.

102. **Pestalotia sorbi** Pat., Rev. Mycol., Fr. 8:182,1886; Syll. Fung. 10:486, 1892.

> *P. fuscescens* Sorauer var. *sacchari* Wakker, in Wakker and Went, De Ziekten Suikerriet o Java 1898, pp. 162–166, pl. 18, figs. 1–8; Krüger,

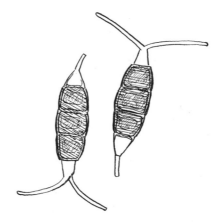

FIG. 27 [101]. *Pestalotia aletridis* (Pat.) Guba.

"Krankh., Feinde Zuckerrohrs," Med. Proefsta. Zuckerrohr West Java 16, 1896.

P. swieteniae Gonz-Frag. & Cif., Estac. Agron. Moca, Rep. Dominicana, Ser. Bot. 8:57,1927.

P. lucumae Tehon, Bot. Gaz. 67:509,1919; Syll. Fung. 25:606,1931.

Pustules black, epiphyllous, sparse, punctiform, circular, on small brown spots, less than 1 cm in diam. Conidia elliptic-fusoid, 5-celled, straight, $16–18 \times 5–6.6 \mu$, constricted at the septa; intermediate colored cells olivaceous or umber, concolorous, $10–13 \mu$; setulae 2, or rarely 3, divergent, $6–11 \mu$ or slightly longer; basal hyaline cells tapering, apical hyaline cells short cylindric; pedicels up to 4μ long.

On leaves of *Sorbus* sp., Yunnan, China, 1887, Delavy, herb. Patouillard, in herb. Farlow.

On fruits of *Erythroxylon coca* Lam., Santiago de Las Vegas, Cuba, Plant Quar. Insp. Sta., U.S.D.A., Washington, D. C., May 19, 1916. Plant Disease Survey, U.S.D.A., No. 1890.

On leaves of *Lucuma multiflora* DC., Monte Alegrillo, Puerto Rico, July 20, 1913. F. L. Stevens, No. 2301, sub *P. lucumae* Tehon. The fungus was described on spots 2–5 mm in diam, pustules grouped, 0.5–2 mm in diam, conidia $14–18 \times 4–5 \mu$, setulae 2, filiform, $7–10 \mu$ long.

On leaves of *Mangifera indica* L., Rio Piedras, Puerto Rico, Oct. 5, 1913, J. A. Stevenson, No. 174 [Fig. 28a]; St. Thomas, West Indies, June 7, 1917, H. Morrison, No. 3544 [Fig. 28b].

On living leaves of *Saccharum officinarum* L., Java, Dutch East Indies, sub *P. fuscescens* Sor. var. *sacchari* Wakker. The author was unable to affirm the parasitism of the fungus. Similarly, *P. fuscescens* Sorauer would not infect *Corypha australis* R. Br. [=*Livistona australis* (R. Br.) Mart.]. These circumstances suggested the affinity of the two forms. The conidia

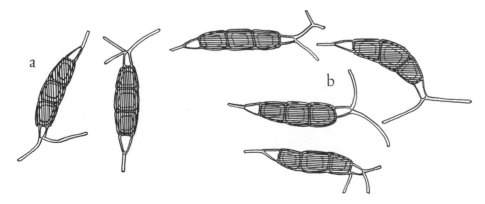

FIG. 28 [102]. *Pestalotia sorbi* Pat.

of the variety are smaller.   On dead areas on leaves of *S. officinarum* L. Zamboanga, Mindanao, Philippines, June 1921, E. W. Brandes.   Acervuli are linear, elongate, or globose lenticular, 75–170 × 75–110 μ; setulae 3, short.

On spots on leaves of *Swietenia mahogani* Jacq.   Haina, Dominican Republic, R. Ciferri, sub *P. swieteniae* Gonz-Frag. & Cif.; South Miami, Fla., Jan. 1943, C. A. Bass, sub *P. dichaeta* Speg. in herb. Florida Agr. Exp. Sta.; Miami, Fla., Feb. 26, 1944, A. S. Rhoades.   Pustules small; conidia 5-celled, 16–22 × 5–7 μ; setulae 2–3, up to 16 μ long; intermediate-colored cells pale yellow brown.   Common in the West Indies and southern Florida.

103. **Pestalotia calabae** West., Bull. Acad. Roy. Belg., Ser. II; 2:556,1857; Syll. Fung. 3:788,1884.   Steyaert, Bull. Jard. Bot. État Bruxelles 19: 65,1948, pl. I, fig. A.

P. piperis Petch, Ann. Roy. Bot. Gard. Peradeniya 9:326,1925.

Pestalotiopsis calabae (West.) Stey., Bull. Jard. Bot. État Bruxelles 19:308, 1949.

Spots epiphyllous, marginate, diffuse.   Pustules sparse, circular, hypophyllous, black, immersed then erumpent, 200–500 μ in diam.   Conidia fusoid, straight, curved, 5-celled, the cells often irregularly superimposed, 15–20 × 3–5 μ; intermediate cells umber, brown, equally colored, 9–13 μ; apical hyaline cell conoid, setulae 2 or 3, 4–11 μ long; basal hyaline cells tapering, pedicels 2–6 μ long.

On living leaves of *Calophyllum calaba* L., greenhouse, Bot. Gard., Brussels, Belgium.   The species was originally described with 3 brown cells, measuring 30 × 10 μ.

On leaves of *Saraca indica* L., Australia No. 545 in herb. Guba [Fig. 29].

On leaves of *Piper nigrum* L., Peradeniya, Ceylon, Feb. 3, 1917, No. 5051 sub *P. piperis* Petch.   A description of this fungus was also published by

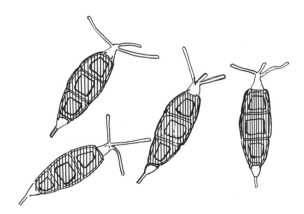

FIG. 29 [103].   *Pestalotia calabae* West.

Roger, "Phytopathogie des pays chauds," Encyc. Mycol. XVIII, p. 1876, 1953. The conidia are reported to measure $17-22 \times 4-5\,\mu$; setulae 3, $8-10\,\mu$ long; 3 central colored cells $10-15\,\mu$ long. The identity of the fungus in the absence of study is not clear.

104. **Pestalotia cryptomeriae** Cooke, Grevillea 12:24,1883; Syll. Fung. 3: 792,1884.

    P. funerea Desm. var. *pini-massonianae* Maire, Ann Mycol. 11:356,1913; Syll. Fung. 26:601,1931.

Pustules sparse, convex, subglobose, punctiform, $75-150\,\mu$ in diam. Conidia 5-celled, elliptic-fusoid or broad lanceolate, erect, $14-18\,\mu$; intermediate cells umber or olivaceous, equally colored; guttulate, hardly constricted at septa, $10-13 \times 5-7\,\mu$; apical hyaline cells short, conic-cylindric, rather broad, bearing usually 3, sometimes 2 setulae, $5-14\,\mu$ long; basal cells short, usually obtuse or somewhat hemispherical; pedicels $2-6\,\mu$ long.

On needles of *Cryptomeria japonica* D. Don., Aiken, S. C., in Ravenel, Fungi Am. Ex. 554. Cooke's description mentions small pustules, lanceolate conidia, $12 \times 3.5\,\mu$, with 3 intermediate dark-colored cells, hyaline exterior cells and 3 setulae.

    P. funerea Desm. var. *pini-massonianae* Maire is similar; conidia $13-21 \times 5-6\,\mu$, pale olivaceous-colored cells, $2-4$ setulae up to $13\,\mu$ and pedicels up to $5\,\mu$ long; on withering needles of *Pinus massoniana* Lamb., Tonkin, French Indo-China, Roulet, 1906.

105. **Pestalotia siliquastri** Thuem., Inst. Rev. Sci. Litt. Coimbra 28:42,1880; Syll. Fung. 3:786,1884.

Spots on leaves dry and torn, brown, irregularly shaped. Acervuli epiphyllous, gregarious, rather large, black, pustulose, elevated. Conidia 5-celled, cylindric-elliptic, usually slightly curved, acute at extremities, $15-18 \times 6.5\,\mu$, attenuated into hyaline pedicels; setulae 3, curved; intermediate colored cells gray or dilute brown, exterior cells hyaline.

On living leaves of *Cercis siliquastrum* L., Choupal, near Coimbra, Portugal, Oct. 1888, A. Moller. The original material at the University of Coimbra and Berlin Bot. Mus. was collected in Oct. 1879 (Contr. Myc. Lusit. No. 577, Moller, No. 818), but both specimen packets are empty. *P. siliquastri* Thuemen may be the same as *P. adusta* Ell. & Ev. and being the earlier of the two species would have priority.

106. **Pestalotia adusta** Ell. & Ev., Jour. Mycol. 4:51,1888; Syll. Fung. 10: 486,1892.

    P. foliorum Ell. & Ev. var. *rosae* Ell. & Ev. nom. nud., Ellis & Everhart, Fungi Col. No. 1552, Dec. 1901.

P. homalomenae Roldan, Philippine Jour. Sci. 60:2:122,1936, pl. I, fig. 6, pl. II, fig. 7.

P. kalmicola Ell. & Ev., Jour. Mycol. 4:51,1888; Syll. Fung. 10:488,1892.

P. mume S. Hori, Shokubutsu byogai Kowa (Lectures on Plant Diseases), Tokyo 2:167,1916; K. Hara, List of Japanese Fungi, 2nd ed., 1917.

P. pallidicolor Speg., Ann. Mus. Nac. Buenos Aires III; 13:412,1911; Syll. Fung. 22:1227,1913.

P. vaccinicola Guba, Mycologia 24:384–385,1932, fig. 3.

P. vermiformis Mass., Kew Bull. Misc. Inform. 1901:156,1901; Syll. Fung. 18:479,1906.

P. bischofiae Sawada Rep. Govt. Research Inst. Formosa 85:84,1943.

Pestalotiopsis adusta (Ell. & Ev.) Stey., Trans. Brit. Mycol. Soc. 36:82, 1953.

Pustules amphigenous, usually epiphyllous, black, minute, 70–120 μ diam, free, spherical or subconic, punctiform, subepidermal, erumpent on maturity, seated on brown, circular, margined spots and dead areas, not exceeding 0.5 cm diam. Conidia 5-celled, oblong or elliptic-fusoid, erect, usually 16–20 × 5–7 μ; intermediate colored cells olivaceous, concolorous, 11–14 μ long, only slightly constricted at septa; exterior cells hyaline, apical cells short conic bearing a crest of 3, rarely 2 setulae, erect or divergent at right angles, usually 5–12 μ, sometimes up to 15 μ long; basal cells short, obtuse; pedicels 2–7 μ long.

On leaves of cultivated plum, *Prunus cerasus* L. Newfield, N. J., July 1887 (type). On dead leaves of *Acer platanoides* L., Point Pleasant, N. J., Oct. 9, 1928, R. P. White. On leaves of *Amelanchier*, Tallulah Falls, Ga., Sept. 12, 1920, A. H. Graves; northeastern Massachusetts, June 18, 1931, in herb. Chester No. 768. On stems of *Barringtonia speciosa* L. [= *B. asiatica* (L.) Kurz], Agr. Exp. Sta., Bermuda, H. S. Cunningham, June 7, 1929. On circular spots in leaves of *Bischofia javanica* Bl., Taipeh, Taiwan, in herb. Univ. Imp. Taihokuensis sub *P. bischofiae* Sawada. On leaves of *Carpinus betulus* L., Selva, Italy, Sept. 9, 1876, P. A. Saccardo sub *P. breviseta* Sacc. Specimen on leaves of *Pyrus communis* L. has larger conidia and this being the first of the two hosts mentioned in the original description is considered the type of *P. breviseta* Sacc. The specimen on *Carpinus* is more like *P. adusta* Ell. & Ev. On leaves of *Cercis canadensis* L., Mohamet, Ill., W. G. Solheim. On leaves of *Chrysobalanus*, Puerto Rico, June 22, 1913. F. L. Stevens, Puerto Rican Fungi No. 258. In dead areas on leaves of *Coccoloba uvifera* L., Palm Beach, Fla., F. Robert, Nat. Fungus Coll., U.S.D.A., sub *P. coccolobae* Ell. & Ev. The specimen is distinct from *P. coccolobae* Ell. & Ev. Specimens collected by Hume in southern Florida and reported by Ellis (Bull. Torrey Bot. Club 27:576,1900) as having conidia 3.5–5 μ wide were not studied. On dead leaves of *Encephalartos laurentianus* de Wild., Pasadena, Cal., Apr. 3, 1933, O. H. Plunkett. On leaves of *Eriobotrya japonica* Lindl.,

Devonshire, Bermuda, Oct. 1927, Ogilvie No. 441; Bot. Gard., Bermuda, Oct. 15, 1913, V. K. Charles in Nat. Fungus Coll., U.S.D.A., sub *P. erio-botryae* McAlp. [Fig. 30a]. *P. adusta* Ell. & Ev. appears to fit one of the two forms of *Pestalotia* associated with the fruit rot and gray leaf spot of loquats in Japan as reported by Konishi (Inst. Pflanzenkr. K., Univ. Kyoto 3:137–146,1937, figs. 1–4). The characters of the second form agree with *P. sapotae* P. Henn.

On leaves of *Eugenia* sp., Mt. Cook, Endeavour River, Queensland, Bailey, in herb. Kew No. 1132, sub *P. vermiformis* Massee [Fig. 30b]. Type description by Massee is in error. On leaves of *Hamamelis virginiana* L., Albany, N. Y., D. B. Young [Fig. 30c].

On leaves of *Homalomena philippinensis* Engl. Luzon, Laguna Prov., Philippine Islands, Sept. 10, 1934, E. F. Roldan, sub *P. homalomenae* Roldan. On stems of *Hydrangea paniculata* Sieb. in herb. Dearness No. 7893, Long Island, N. Y., Roy Latham. In dead spots on living leaves of *Kalmia latifolia* L., Wilmington, Del., Apr. 1887, A. Commons, No. 481, sub *P. kalmicola* Ell. & Ev. Type description mentions setulae with thickened tips, which the author did not observe. On leaves of *Pandanus luzonensis* Merrill, Mt. Maquiling, Los Baños, Philippines, Nov. 1913, in C. F. Baker, Fungi Malayana No. 65, suppl. 1, sub *P. palmarum* Cooke. In spots and dead areas on leaves of *Pavonia multiflora* A. St. Hil., Rio de Janeiro, Brazil, in herb. Inst. Biol. Veg., Rio de Janeiro No. 38, E. Rangel, Dec. 8, 1910. In dead areas on leaves of *Persea gratissima* Gaertn. [= *P. americana* Mill.], Bayamon, Puerto Rico, June 1923, W. D. Griffiths; Southland, Warwick, Bermuda, March 20, 1924, L. Ogilvie, No. 236. On leaves of *Pithecolobium*, Toba, Sumatra, Sept. 27, 1916, reported by Lund (Bot. Tidsskr. 43:308,1935).

On leaves of *Prunus mume* Sieb. & Succ., Hasuda, Pref. Saitama, Japan, June 2, 1950, Y. Urasawa sub *P. mume* S. Hori. The type specimen in herb. Imp. Central Exp. Sta., Nishigahara, Tokyo, was not studied. The fungus is often associated with *Colletotrichum mume* S. Hori.

On leaves of *Prunus cerasus* L., Orient Point, Long Island, N. Y., Aug. 7, 1911, Roy Latham in herb. N. Y. State Mus.

On leaves of *Prunus serotina* Ehrh. Orient Point, Long Island, N. Y., July 31, 1911, Roy Latham in herb. N. Y. State Mus. [Fig. 30d]; Arlington, Va., Nov. 10, 1929, R. W. Davidson in Nat. Fungus Coll., U.S.D.A.; Nantucket Island, Mass., Sept. 1935, E. F. Guba.

On leaves of *Pyrus arbutifolia* L. [= *Aronia arbutifolia* (L.) Ell.], Orient Point, Long Island, N. Y., Roy Latham, Aug. 28, 1911, in herb. N. Y. State Mus.

On weathered leaves of cultivated *Rosa* sp. in Ellis & Everhart Fungi Col. No. 1552, Dec. 1901; Tuskegee, Ala., Sept. 14, 1900, G. W. Carver, sub *P. foliorum* Ell. & Ev. var. *rosae* Ell. & Ev., nom. nud.: on rose cuttings, Indiana, Dec. 1924, Dietz.

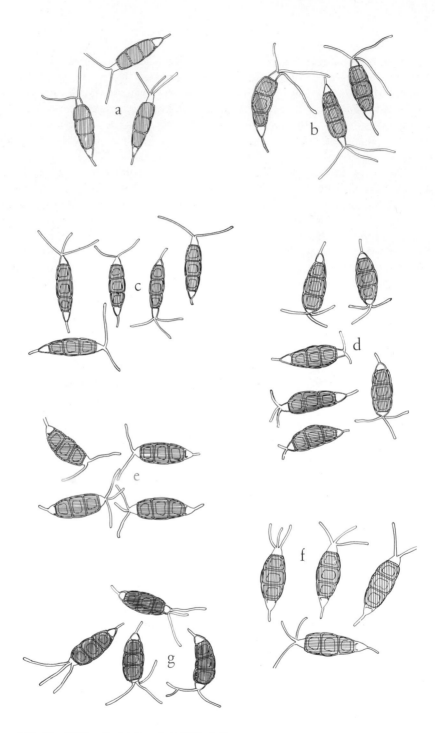

FIG. 30 [106]. *Pestalotia adusta* Ellis & Ev.

On leaves of *Rubus* (purple raspberry), Orient Point, Long Island, N. Y. Aug. 7, 1911, Roy Latham [Fig. 30e]; on leaves of *Rubus* (blackberry), same location, Aug. 28, 1911, Roy Latham. On leaves of *Sarcocephalus esculentus* Afzel. in herb. Inst. Biol. Veg., Rio de Janeiro, Brazil, No. 1938, Rio de Janeiro, May 5, 1934, N. Azevedo.

In spots on leaves of *Smilax* sp. associated with *Phyllosticta*, Orient Point, Long Island, N. Y., Oct. 2, 1912, Roy Latham, sub *P. funerea* Desm. in Nat. Fungus Coll., U.S.D.A.; St. John's River, Sanford, Fla., Jan. 24, 1923, A. C. Foster sub *P. funerea* Desm.; Society Hill, S. C., September, M. A. Curtis in herb. Curtis No. 2720, in herb. Farlow. The fungus in the Curtis specimen is generally distributed over the dead leaves.

On brown leaves of *Sterculia acuminata* Beauv. [= *Cola acuminata* (Beauv.) Schott & Endl.], Plant Introduction Garden, Miami, Fla., G. R. Lyman, Feb. 4, 1917.

On dry or decaying scapes of *Synandrospadix vermitoxicus* Engl., Bot. Gard., La Plata, Argentina, Oct. 1910, Spegazzini, sub *Pestalotia pallidicolor* Speg. [Fig. 30f].

On spots on living leaves of *Vaccinium arboreum* Marsh, Green Cove Springs, Fla., G. Martin, Ellis & Everhart Fung. Col. No. 1352, sub *P. stellata* Berk. & Curt. [Fig. 30g]. This fungus was renamed *P. vaccinicola* Guba (Mycologia 24:384–385,1932). In reality it is *P. adusta* Ell. & Ev. The fungus on leaves of *Quercus tinctoria* Bartr. [*Q. velutina* Lam.] in Ellis & Everhart Fungi Col. No. 1352 designated *P. stellata* Berk. & Curt. was given the new name *P. quercina* Guba (Mycologia 24:380,1932), which is the same as *P. breviseta* Sacc.

107. **P. virginiana** Oud., Rev. Mycol. Fr. 24:107,1902.

    P. polygoni Ell. & Ev., Proc. Acad. Nat. Sci., Phila., 1894, p. 374; Syll. Fung. 11:578,1895.

    Sporidesmium hypodermium Niessl, nom. nud., Rabenhorst Fungi europ. Exs. 2545, 1880; Hedwigia 20:146,1881.

    Ceratophorum hypodermium (Niessl) Sacc., Syll. Fung. 4:397,1886.

    Pestalotiopsis hypodermia (Niessl) Stey., Bull. Jard. Bot. État Bruxelles 19:328,1949, pl. 13, fig. B.

Spots dull, reddish brown, irregularly shaped, definitely bordered. Pustules amphigenous, punctiform, globose-hemispherical, scattered, erumpent and surrounded by torn shreds of epidermis, 75–150 μ diam. Conidia 5-celled, clavate or elliptic-fusoid, straight, hardly constricted at septa, 17–20 $\times$ 6–8 μ; intermediate colored cells olivaceous or yellow brown throughout, 11–14.5 μ long, guttulate; apical hyaline cells short, conic-cylindric, bearing 3, sometimes 2 setulae, 8–16 μ long, widely divergent; basal cells obtuse or rounded; pedicels about 3 μ long.

On living leaves of *Polygonum virginianum* L. Stanton, Delaware, Aug.

1894, A. Commons, No. 2560. The new name was made necessary since *P. polygoni* Ell. & Ev. is a later homonym of *P. polygoni* Wint. (Hedwigia 10: 162,1871) on *Polygonum aviculare* L. The fungus *Pestalotia unicolor* Berk. & Curt. [= *Pestalozzina unicolor* (Berk. & Curt.) Sacc.] is present on the same matrix with *P. virginiana* Oud.

Pestalotiopsis hypodermia (Niessl) Stey. on leaves of a conifer, Bot. Gard., Calcutta, India (S. Kurz) in Rabenhorst, Fungi europ. Exs. 2545, sub *Sporidesmium hypodermium* Niessl also belongs here. *Ceratophorum hypodermium* (Niessl) Sacc. and two other species of *Ceratophorum* were placed in the subgenus *Pleiochaetia* by Puselli (Boll. R. Staz. Pat. Veg. Rome 8:50–84,1928). Hughes (Comm. Mycolog. Inst. Mycolog. Papers 36, p. 26, 1951) compiled a repetition of Steyaert's treatment of the species.

108. **Pestalotia torulosa** Berk. & Curt., Geol. Nat. Hist. Surv. North Carolina, Pt. 3 (Bot.) 118,1867, nom. nud.; Grevillea 2:155,1874; Syll. Fung. 3:795,1884.

Acervuli punctiform, scattered, frequently confluent, subepidermal, erumpent and exposed, usually convex, 72–190 μ diam, usually seated on black spots. Conidia 5-celled, clavate, torulose and strongly constricted at septa, usually curved, 17–20 × 5.5–7 μ; intermediate colored cells olivaceous, guttulate, 13–16 μ long; apical hyaline cells cylindric, the basal hyaline cells long conic, tapering into short pedicels, 2–5 μ long; setulae 2–3, divergent, 6–11 μ long.

On seeds of watermelon, *Citrullus vulgaris* Schrad., South Carolina, herb. Curtis No. 5035, in herb. Farlow and similar specimens in herb. Berkeley, Kew [Fig. 31]. This species was originally reported to have 2-septate conidia, but Voglino (Atti. Soc. Ven.-Trent. Sci. Padova 9:209–243,1885) corrected the error.

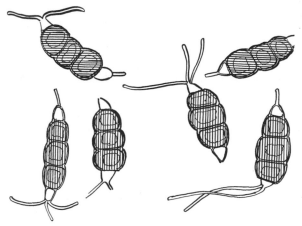

FIG. 31 [108].   *Pestalotia torulosa* Berk. & Curt.

109. **Pestalotia flavidula** Fl. Tassi, Boll. Lab. Ort. Bot. Univ. Siena 3:130, 1900; Syll. Fung. 16:1015,1902.

Acervuli scattered, subcuticular, then erumpent, more or less globose, 100–180 μ diam, black. Conidia 5-celled, elliptic or oblong-fusoid, 18–20 μ; intermediate colored cells yellowish or pale brown, narrow; basal hyaline cells small, obtuse or tapering into short pedicels; apical cells short, turbinate, bearing 3 divergent setulae, 10–20 μ long.

On dead stems of *Helichrysum citrinum* Hym. [= *H. stoechas* (L.) DC.], near Viareggio, Italy, Oct. 1900. On brown dead leaves of *Diospyros virginiana* L., Aiken, S. C. in Ravenel, Fungi Am. Exs. 553, sub *P. guepini* Desm. [Fig. 32]. Cultures from decomposed cellulose, U. S. Military Supplies, Pacific Area, World War II, Nos. 51B4J, 54B4I, C1A4F, PQMD 68a, listed without identification in Res. Rep. QMG Lab. Microbiol. Ser. 15, Aug. 3, 1949, p. 68, QMC Project No. 60.

110. **Pestalotia kawakamii** Sawada. Descriptive Catalogue of Formosan Fungi, Taihoku, pp. 588–589, 1919, and Special Bull. 19, Agr. Exp. Sta., Formosa. K. Hara in Shirai, "A List of Japanese Fungi," 3rd ed., 1927, p. 253.

Spots large, irregular in shape, central part straw or gray colored, margin dark brown, scattered with minute pustules. Conidia fusiform, 5-celled, 20–24 × 4–5 μ, intermediate cells sooty colored, 10–17 μ long; setulae 3, rarely 4, acuminate, 5–10 μ long; pedicels slender 2–3.5 μ long.

On leaves of *Oryza sativa* L., Formosa. Occurring rarely and considered to be parasitic, this fungus is unusual for its narrow conidia and study is needed for confirmation.

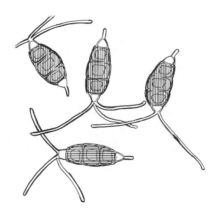

FIG. 32 [109]. *Pestalotia flavidula* Tassi.

111. **Pestalotia algeriensis** (Sacc. & Berl.) Guba, comb. nov.

   P. funerea Desm. var. *algeriensis* Sacc. & Berl., Rev. Mycol. Fr. 8:36,
   1886; Syll. Fung. 10:485,1892.

Pustules black, dense, punctiform, minute, globose-lenticular, coalescing, erumpent in linear or stellate manner, surrounded by torn shreds of the epidermis, 75–150 μ diam, black and sooty.

Conidia slender-fusiform, tapering to the base, 5-celled, hardly constricted at septa, 17–23 × 5–7 μ; intermediate colored cells olivaceous, concolorous, the upper 2 colored cells sometimes darker, 12.5–16 μ long; appendages 1 to 3, usually 2 or 3, up to 16 μ long, often monochaetioid, longest when 1 appendage, when 3 usually up to 10 μ, of unequal length, curved, and separated at base and sometimes arising below the apex; basal hyaline cells acute, conoid, apical cells cylindric to broad conic; pedicels short.

On canes of *Rosa sempervirens* L., Algeria, Feb. 1883, in herb. P. A. Saccardo, sub *P. funerea* Desm. var. *algeriensis* Sacc. & Berl. [Fig. 33a]; on *Rosa* sp., New Jersey, R. H. White; rambler rose, Waltham, Mass., Aug. 2,

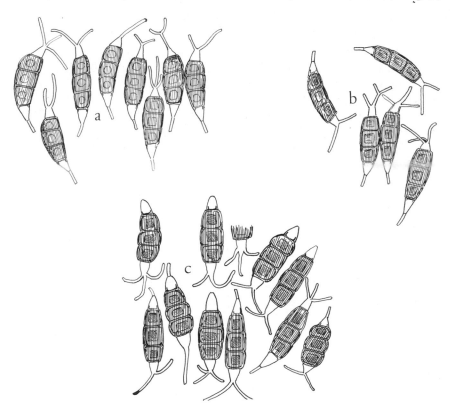

FIG. 33 [111].   *Pestalotia algeriensis* (Sacc. & Berl.) Guba.

1928, Guba; on capsules of *Rosa* sp., Newfield, N. J., Aug. 1886, herb. Ellis, in herb. Farlow.

Cultures from decomposed cellulose, U. S. Military Supplies, Pacific Area, World War II, Nos. C1C2C, 4NHB5D sub *P. royenae* (D. Sacc.) Guba in Research Rep. QMG Lab. Microbiol. Ser. 15, Aug. 3, 1949, p. 68, QMC Project No. 60.

On fruit shells of *Achradelpha viridis* O. F. Cooke [= *Calocarpum viride* Pittier], Plant Quar. Insp., Washington D. C., J. T. Rogers, from Guatemala, Oct. 20, 1916, in Nat. Fungus Coll., U.S.D.A. On spots on leaves of *Cassine maurocenia* L., Bot. Gard., Padua, Italy, June 1902, in D. Saccardo, Myc. Ital. No. 1174, sub *P. breviseta* Sacc. [Fig. 33b]. Klebahn (Mycol Centralbl. 4:11,1914, fig. 34, 1D) placed this fungus and specimen in D. Saccardo, Myc. Ital. No. 181 (on *Ilex aquifolium* L. sub *P. funerea* Desm.) and in D. Saccardo, Myc. Ital. No. 183 (on *Cocculus laurifolius* DC., sub *P. guepini* Desm.), Botanic Garden, Padua, under *P. gracilis* Klebahn.

On leaves of *Euonymus radicans* Sieb. [= *E. fortunei* (Turcz.) Hand.-Mazz.], South Natick, Mass., Aug. 20, 1946, E. F. Guba, associated with *Phyllosticta* and *Diplodia*; on twigs, South Sudbury, Mass., July 6, 1950, Paul Rhoads [Fig. 33c].

On fruits of *Mimusops* sp. Elizabethville, Union of South Africa, J. B. Davy, Plant Quar. Insp., Washington, D. C., Oct. 1919, sub *P. guepini* Desm.

On ripe fruits of *Nephelium litchii* Cambess [= Litchi chinensis Sonn.] Honolulu, Hawaii, Plant Quar. Insp., Washington, D. C., June 7, 1918, sub *P. funerea* Desm. The fungus is associated with a ripe rot of Lychee fruits in South Africa and may be recovered in all stages of fruit growth, indicating that some infection occurs during or just after flowering. Ventilation, dry, cool conditions, and dusting the fruit with fungicide after harvest reduce wastage. References: I. B. Pole Evans, Ann. Rep., Div. Plant Industry, Union South Africa IX, 105, 539–548, 1934; XIII, 153, 519–538, 1938; XIV, 165, 520–540, 1939. R. H. Marloth, *Ibid.* Hort. Ser. 13; Bull. No. 286, 1942.

On fruits of *Sapindus saponaria* L., El Sombrero, Venezuela, W. A. Archer, Feb. 4, 1935, Nat. Fungus Coll., U.S.D.A.

On leaves of *Stanhopea wardii* Lodd., from Guatemala, San Francisco Plant Quar. Sta., Apr. 25, 1938, W. H. Wheeler, Nat. Fungus Coll., U.S.D.A.

On blighted leaves of *Vaccinium* sp., Nantucket Island, Mass., May 29, 1936, E. F. Guba.

112. Pestalotia heterocornis Guba sp. nov.

Pustulae maculicolae, plerumque hypophyllae, globoso-lenticulares, punctiformes, 70–150 μ in diam, subepidermicales, erumpentes, fuliginae; conidia 5-cellularia, fusiformia, recta, vix constricta, 18–26 × 5–8 μ; cellulae mediae pallide brunneae vel olivaceae, concolores, 12–16 μ longae; cellulae apicales hyalinae, cylindricae usque conicae, setulis 2–3, rare 1 vel 4 praeditae;

setulae late divergentes, longitudine inaequales, 9–22 μ, vel aequales, 9–16 μ et ad apicem cellularum apicalium unitae; cellulae basales hyalinae, mediocriter longae, acutae, attenuatae vel interdum obtusae; pedicelli usque 7 μ longi.

Spots or dead areas large, brown beneath, reddish brown above. Pustules largely hypophyllous, scattered or gregarious, globose-lenticular, punctiform, 70–150 μ diam, subepidermal, erumpent, circinate, and surrounded by torn epidermis, sooty on maturity, the contents staining the matrix. Conidia 5-celled, fusiform, tapering toward the extremities, straight, hardly constricted at septa, 18–26 × 5–8 μ; intermediate cells pale brown, olivaceous, concolorous, 12–16 μ long, apical hyaline cells cylindric to conic, bearing 2 to 3, rarely 1 or 4 widely divergent setulae, one a prolongation of apical cell and attenuated, the other one or two setulae filiform, laterally divergent, arising from slope and peak of apical cells, unequal in length, 9–22 μ long, when 3 or 4, filiform, 9–16 μ long, of same length and joined at apex of apical cells; basal hyaline cells rather long, acute, tapering, sometimes obtuse; pedicels up to 7 μ long.

On leaves of *Anacardium occidentale* L., Cantanduva, São Paulo, Brazil, leg. H.P.K. and A.S.C., Jan. 19, 1935, in herb. Inst. Agron., Est. Campinas, Brazil, No. 575 [Fig. 34a]. On twigs of *Prunus persica* (L.) Stokes, Chefoo, China, intercepted at Plant Quar. House, Washington, D. C., May 12, 1916, J. T. Rogers [Fig. 34b]; in sediment in pool of water, Lytle Creek, Clinton County, Ohio, March 5, 1952, W. B. Cooke; Sunday Creek, above Chauncey, Perry County, Ohio, April 10, 1954, W. B. Cooke.

113. **Pestalotia bicilia** Dearn. & Bisby, Fungi of Manitoba, 1929, p. 134.

Pustules somewhat pycnoid, subepidermal, erumpent, thickly scattered and punctiform, globose-lenticular, rupturing the epidermis in longitudinal fissures, 70–200 × 70–100 μ, dotting the bark. Conidia straight, narrow-fusiform, 5-celled, 21–25 × 5–6.5 μ, hardly constricted at the septa; inter-

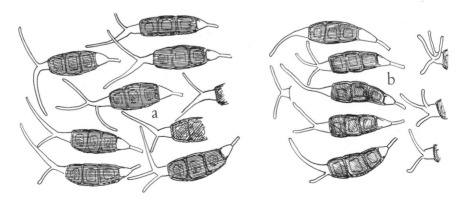

Fig. 34 [112]. *Pestalotia heterocornis* Guba.

mediate colored cells pale brown, concolorous, 13–16 μ long; exterior cells dilute yellow, paler than the intermediate colored cells, apical cells cylindric, bearing 2 divergent setulae, 9–15 μ long; basal cells long conic; pedicels up to 3 μ long.

On dead stems of *Viburnum opulus* L., Winnipeg, Canada, May, 1926, April, 1927, Nos. 2557, 3335, D6301. The fungus is also listed in Bisby *et al.*, "Fungi of Manitoba and Saskatchewan," 1938, p. 131. The conidia are narrow fusiform, 20–27 × 4.5–5.5 μ; intermediate colored cells 15–18 μ long, pale brown, darker than the exterior colored cells, setulae 2, equal and divergent, 10–20 μ long.

114. Pestalotia lawsoniae Mundk. & Kheswalla, Mycologia 34:315,1942.

Spots numerous, circular, some coalescing into whitish to light brown patches. Acervuli black, subepidermal, amphigenous, erumpent, minute, 54–96 μ diam. Conidia 5-celled, fusiform to elliptic-fusoid, usually erect, constricted at septa, 14.5–26 × 4–7.5 μ; intermediate cells olivaceous, equally colored, 11–15 μ long; setulae 2, widely divergent, 8–21 μ long.

On leaves of *Lawsonia alba* Lamk. [=*L. inermis* L.], Pusa, India, Oct. 19, 1906. Inayat Khan, in herb. Crypt. Ind. Orient., New Delhi.

115. Pestalotia vismiae Petr., Sydowia 4:561–562,1950.

Spots irregular, sometimes abundantly distributed over surface, amphigenous, mostly solitary, orbicular or elliptic, 2–8 mm diam, sharply bordered, surrounded by purple brown zones. Pustules usually epiphyllous, loosely distributed, circular, 150–250 μ diam, subepidermal, at maturity bursting epidermis irregularly. Conidia oblong-fusiform, tapered at ends, weakly curved, 5-celled, 18–22 × 5–6.5 μ; colored part 13–15 μ long, olive brown, concolorous, transparent; exterior hyaline cells obtuse, conoid, mostly hyaline or pale yellow brown; setulae 2, 10–23 μ long, slightly attenuated toward extremities; pedicels 2.5–5 μ long.

On living leaves of *Vismia obtusa* Spruce, Prov. Tungurahua, Hacienda San Antonio, near Banos, Ecuador, Dec. 10, 1937, No. 493a. The fungus is present in association with *Phomopsis vismiae* Petr., *Colletotrichum* sp. and *Glomerella* sp. and is asserted to be parasitic.

116. Pestalotia carveri Guba sp. nov.

Pustulae plerumque hypophyllae, late distributae vel interdum dense aggregatae, atrae, punctiformes, 75–175 μ in diam, sub-globosae vel globoso-lenticulares, coalescentes, erumpentes; conidia 5-cellularia, aequilateralia vel subcurvata, fusiformia, 20–26 × 6–7 μ, subconstricta; cellulae mediae coloratae pallide olivaceae, concolores, 14–17.5 μ longae, guttulatae; cellulae extimae hyalinae, longe, conoideae, apicales setulis 2, rare 3, curvatus, divergentibus, filiformibus, 12–26 μ longis coronatae; cellulae basales saepe setula brevi obliqua ad basim praeditae; pedicelli filiformes, usque 10 μ longi.

Matrix brown, dead, weathered, free of spots or discolored areas. Pustules largely hypophyllous, generally distributed, densely aggregated in places, black, punctiform, 75–175 μ in diam, subglobose or globose-lenticular, coalescing freely, erumpent, tearing epidermis in a stellate manner, contents sooty, staining the matrix.   Conidia 5-celled, equilateral or slightly curved, fusiform, 20–26 × 6–7 μ, only slightly constricted at septa; intermediate colored cells pale olivaceous, concolorous, 14–17.5 μ long, guttulate; exterior cells hyaline, long conoid, the apical cells crowned with usually 2, rarely 3, curved divergent, filiform setulae, 12–26 μ long; basal cells with contents often with a short oblique setula projecting from the base adjoining the point of attachment of the pedicel; pedicels filiform, up to 10 μ long.

On dead weathered leaves of *Quercus rubra* L., Tuskegee, Ala., Aug. 27, 1935, G. W. Carver [Fig. 35].   Named after the collector, the late Dr. George Washington Carver, naturalist, scientist, and correspondent, and a notable example of scholarship among the colored race.

117. **Pestalotia eugeniae** Thuem., Inst. Rev. Sci. Litt. Coimbra II, 27:326, 1880; Syll. Fung. 3:785,1884.

   P. cuboniana Brizi, Boll. Soc. Bot. Ital. no. 5, 81–83,1895; Syll. Fung. 14: 1025,1899.

   P. eriobotryae-japonicae Sawada, Trans. Nat. Hist. Soc. Taiwan 33:9, 1943; Rep. Dept. Agr., Research Inst. Formosa 85:84,1943.

Pustules epiphyllous, scattered, globose-lenticular, black, 75–120 μ diam, sometimes concentrically arranged, borne under the papery epidermis, erumpent and surrounded by the torn shreds, seated in white or brown spots of indefinite shape with narrow purple margins, the papery centers desiccated with age, breaking and falling away.   Conidia 5-celled, elliptic or cylindric-fusiform, equilateral, 19–23 × 6–7 μ long; intermediate colored cells olivaceous, or pale brown, concolorous, only slightly constricted at septa, 14–16 μ

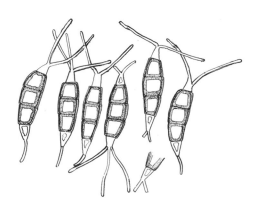

Fig. 35 [116].   *Pestalotia carveri* Guba.

long; exterior hyaline cells short, conic; setulae 3, divergent, 3–11 μ long; pedicels short.

On living leaves of *Eugenia uniflora* L., Bot. Gard., Coimbra, Portugal, Nov. 1878, A. Moller. Contr. Myc. Lusit. 342, Ser. II, herb. Jard. Bot., University of Coimbra, No. 204. According to Thuemen (see above), the conidia are cylindric-elliptic, 22–24 × 6–8 μ; intermediate colored cells ash gray, the setulae 3, 8 μ long.

Pestalotia cuboniana Brizi was described on dead leaves of *Myrtus communis* L., Porto d'Anzio, Italy, Cuboni.

Pestalotia eriobotryae-japonicae Sawada. On dead spots in leaves of *Persea americana* Mill., Taihoju, Formosa, April 12, 1920, F. Kurosawa. The leaf spots are circular, brown and gray, indistinctly zoned; the acervuli are up to 250 μ in diam. The specific name of the fungus implies the loquat. However, its host is the avocado.

Specimens examined: On leaves of *Eriobotrya japonica* Lindl., Gontazaka, Yokohama, Japan, Aug. 16, 1949, Y. Urasawa; on leaves of *Fatsia japonica* Decn. & Plan., Hokozaki, Fukuoka, Japan, Oct. 10, 1941, S. Katsuki; on leaves of *Lauraceae*, Costa Rica, Feb. 3, 1931, H. Schmidt; on leaves of *Lepironia mucronata* Rich., Taipeh, Taiwan, Nov. 22, 1913, Y. Fujihuroi, herb. Univ. Imp. Taikohuensis, sub *P. lepironiae* Sawada (herbarium name); on twigs of *Platanus orientalis* L., Tachiarai, Fukuoka, Japan, Feb. 10, 1941, S. Katsuki.

On leaves of *Pistacia vera* L., in herb. Inst. Pat. Veg. Bologna, Italy, G. Goidanich.

118. **Pestalotia ilicicola** T. Fukui, Mie-kônô Dôsôkai Gakujutsu Iho (Japan) 5:55,1936.

Acervuli scattered, punctiform, blackish brown, subepidermal, erumpent, 150–300 μ in diam. Conidia 5–6 celled, fusiform, 18–24 × 5–6 μ, somewhat constricted at the septa: exterior cells hyaline, the intermediate cells fuscous; setulae 3, 8–16 × 1.2 μ; pedicels 5–10 × 1.2 μ.

On leaves of *Ilex latifolia* Thunb., Japan. The specific name was published as *iicicola*, a misspelling.

119. **Pestalotia microspora** Speg., Anal. Soc. Ci. Argent. 10:31–32,1880; Syll. Fung. 3:789,1884.

    P. brideliae Shen, Contr. Biol. Lab. Sci. Soc. China (Bot.) Ser. 7, 5:138–139,1932.

    P. copernica Speg., Anal. Mus. Nac. Buenos Aires III; 13:411,1911; Syll. Fung. 22:1227,1913.

    P. funerea Desm. var. *hedychii* Mariani, Atti Soc. Ital. Sci. Nat., Milan 50:171,1911; Syll. Fung. 22:1226,1913.

    P. dichaeta Speg., Anal. Mus. Nac. Buenos Aires III: 13:411–412,1911; Syll. Fung. 22:1220,1913.

P. harongae P. Henn. Bot. Jahrb. 34:55,1904; Syll. Fung. 18:481,1906.

P. lycopodina Ell. & Ev., Proc. Acad. Nat. Sci. Phila. 1893, p. 461; Syll. Fung. 11:579,1895.

P. micheneri Guba, Mycologia 24:371–372,1932.

P. nandinae Gutner, Trudy Bot. Inst. Akad. Nauk. U.S.S.R., Ser. II; Spor. Rasteniia (Acta Inst. Bot. Acad. Sci., Russia, Ser. II, Plant. Crypt.) 1:305–306, tab. 2, 53,1933.

P. nucicola Ell. & Ev., Proc. Acad. Nat. Sci. Phila., 1893, p. 461; Syll. Fung. 11:578,1895.

P. royenae (D. Sacc.) Guba, Mycologia 24:380–381,1932.

P. funerea Desm. var. *royenae* D. Sacc., Myc. Ital. 2:182,1898; nom. nud.

Pestalotiopsis acrocomiarum Batista, Ann. Soc. Biol. Pernambuco, 12: 44–45, 1954.

P. royenae (D. Sacc.) Stey., Bull. Jard. Bot. État Bruxelles 19:320–322, 1949, pl. 12B.

P. dichaeta (Speg.) Stey., Bull. Jard. Bot. État Bruxelles 19:308–309,1949, pl. XI, fig. A.

Pustules conic, hemispherical or globose-lenticular, amphigenous, loosely gregarious, dense in places, rarely confluent, erumpent, 75–250 μ often 75–150 μ in diam. Conidia 5-celled, narrow fusoid, tapering to the base, straight or sometimes slightly curved, hardly constricted at septa, 19–24 × 5–7 μ, median cells olivaceous, concolorous, upper two colored cells rarely darker, guttulate, 13–16 μ long, apical hyaline cells short, conic or cylindric, bearing a crest of usually 3 straight setulae, 3–15 μ long; basal hyaline cells long, tapering; pedicels 4–5 μ.

On pale or brown weathered leaves of *Hedera helix* L., Bot. Gard., College of Argentina, Buenos Aires, April 1880, Spegazzini [Fig. 36a].

Ellis and Everhart gave to their new species on *Quercus coccinea* leaves the epithet *P. microspora* Ell. & Ev. (Jour. Mycol. 4:46,1888) but the name was recognized by the authors later to be a homonym. Thereupon they gave the new name *P. minor* Ell. & Ev. to the fungus as issued as N. Am. Fungi No. 2178 (1889). Saccardo and Sydow (Syll. Fung. 14:1030,1899:15,242,1901) named the fungus *P. ellisii* Sacc. & Syd. The fungus is a *Monochaetia* with 4-celled conidia, *M. saccardiana* (Vogl.) Sacc.

P. brideliae Shen was described on leaves of *Bridelia monoica* (Lour.) Merrill, Fung Wong Chin, Canton, China, L. T. Lam, Jan. 23, 1929 (Teng. No. 774).

P. copernica Speg. On decaying immature fruits of *Copernica cerifera* Mart., Puerto Leon, Misiones, Argentina, June 1909, Spegazzini [Fig. 36b], Author reported conidia 20–25 × 5–7 μ, 2–3 setulae 6–12 μ long.

P. dichaeta Speg. On weathered leaves of *Lithraea molleoides* (Vell.) Engler, Bella Vista, Corrientes, Argentina, Feb. 1905, C. Spegazzini [Fig. 36c]. Conidia 20–25 × 5–7 μ; setulae 3, sometimes 2, 6–14 μ long. The

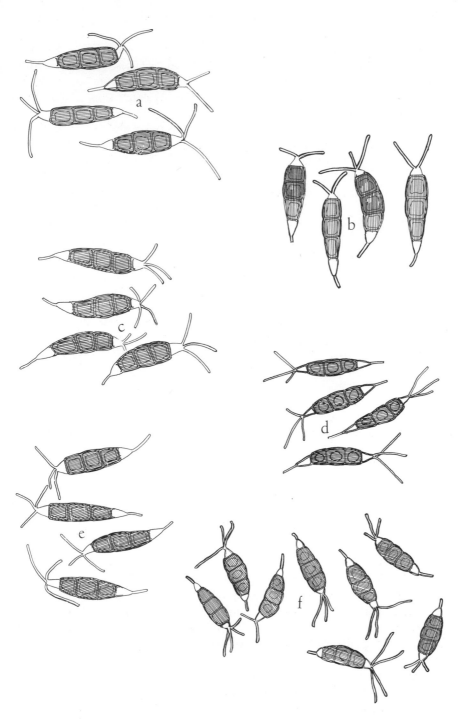

FIG. 36 [119].   *Pestalotia microspora* Speg.

usual number of setulae is 3; thus the specific name is misleading.   Steyaert (Trans. Brit. Mycol. Soc. 36:235,1953) placed this species in his subsection *Bisetulatae*.   The present author does not recognize the grouping of species based on the number of setulae except the monosetulate forms of the genus *Monochaetia*.

P. funerea Desm. var. *hedychii* Mariani.   On stems and leaves of *Hedychium coronarium* Koenig, Bot. Gard., Coimbra, Portugal, 1903 (Maggio). The conidia have 3 setulae up to 10 μ long.   Mariani reported conidia with 2, rarely 3 or 4 setulae.

P. harongae P. Henn.   On leaves of *Haronga paniculata* Lodd. [= *H. madagascariensis* Chois.], East-Usambara, Derema, Tanganyika, Africa, July 1902, Zimmermann.   Conidia 19–23 × 5–6.5 μ; setulae 3, 6–16 μ long. Hennings described conidia as 13–15 × 3.5–5 μ, setulae 15–25 μ long.

P. lycopodina Ell. & Ev.   On *Lycopodium complanatum* L. Naaman's Creek, Del., 1893, A. Commons, No. 2049.

P. micheneri Guba.   On leaves of *Araucaria imbricata* Pav. [= *A. araucana* Koch], New Garden, Chester Country, Pa., 1885, herb. Michener No. 2517, Nat. Fungus Coll., U.S.D.A. and herb. Curtis in herb. Farlow, sub *P. guepini* Desm. and *P. araucariae* Berk. & Curtis [Fig. 36d].   Michener sent specimen No. 2517 to Curtis, who named the fungus *P. araucariae*.   He also sent specimen No. 5564 to Berkeley, who identified it as *P. guepini*.

P. nandinae Gutner.   On leaves of *Nandina domestica* Thunb., Leningrad, Russia.

P. nucicola Ell. & Ev.   On hickory nuts (*Carya* sp.), Newfield, N. J. (1) May 20, 1893 and (2) May 15, 1894, J. B. Ellis in herb. N. Y. Bot. Gard. Ellis and Everhart reported that the colored part of the conidia measures 12 × 4 μ, setulae 3, 7–10 μ long.   Fairman (Proc. Rochester Acad. Sci. 6:88,1921) found the conidia in the Ellis collection to measure 13.5–17.6 × 4.5 μ, the colored portions 12–13 × 4.5 μ.

Pestalotiopsis acrocomiarum Batista.   On living leaves of *Acrocomia intumescens* Drude, Afogados-Recife, May 20, 1953, No. 4507, Inst. Pesquisas Agr., Pernambuco, Brazil.

P. funerea Desm. var. *royenae* D. Sacc. was described on leaves of *Royena lucida* L., Bot. Gard., Padua, Italy, Nov. 1897 [Fig. 36e].   The fungus was renamed *P. royenae* (D. Sacc.) Guba and *Pestalotiopsis royenae* (D. Sacc.) Stey. Steyaert's plate 12B, drawn from a culture named *P. canangae* Koord., is *P. palmarum* Cooke.   D. Saccardo, Myc. Ital. No. 182 refers to Syll. Fung. 3:791,1884 for a description of *P. funerea* Desm. var. *royenae* D. Sacc., but this is an error.

On dead leaves of *Ananas comosus* (L.) Merr., Tucker's Town, Bermuda, Mar. 1, 1929 (Cunningham).   On *Araucaria* sp., (cone scales) Bermuda, Nov. 24, 1940, Seaver and Waterston, in herb. N. Y. Bot. Gard.   On *Carya* sp., Myc. Fairmanii No. 5263, Orient Point, Long Island, N. Y., 1919, R. Latham.

On leaves of *Cola nitida* A. Chevalier, in lath house, Miami, Fla., Feb. 22, 1923, W. B. Wood, SPI, U.S.D.A., 54307, sub *P. guepini* Desm.

On *Juniperus bermudiana* L. (needles), Gibb's Hill Lighthouse, Dec. 3, 1938, Seaver and Waterston, Bermuda Fungi 107B; cultures No. 66 and No. 73, J. M. Waterston, April and Sept. 1942. The fungus occurs as a secondary invader and was reported on blighted needles of *Juniperus bermudiana* L. as *P. unicolor* and *P. funerea* by Waterston [Rep. Bd. Agr., Bermuda, 1937, pp. 24–37 (publ. 1938); 1938, pp. 22–34 (publ. 1939).

On *Platanus occidentalis* L. (leaves). Santee, S. C., herb. Berkeley 1879, at Kew and Mus d'Hist. Nat. Paris; South Carolina, August, Ravenel, with *P. stictica* Berk. & Curt., herb. Curtis No. 1638 in herb. Farlow; Society Hill, N. C., August and September, herb. Curtis in herb. Farlow [Fig. 36f]. All of these specimens are named *P. stictica* Berk. & Curt. *P. stictica* (herb. Curtis No. 1638) has conidia with two fuliginous swollen cells and one olivaceous-colored cell and long setulae. This is the form implied by the original description. A second form on *Platanus* leaves has conidia 16–22 × 5–7 μ, pale olivaceous intermediate cells, setulae 3, rarely branched, 6–16 μ long which agrees with *P. microspora* Speg. A collection of this fungus on leaves of *Platanus occidentalis* L. was made by G. W. Carver, Tuskegee, Ala., Nov. 2, 1926.

P. stictica was originally described with 2-septate conidia. The error was corrected by Voglino. The name was reported originally without description by Curtis (Geol. & Nat. Hist. Surv. North Carolina, Pt. III (Bot.) p. 118, 1867). The specimen on *Tilia* leaves from Alabama (Beaumont, No. 266, Curtis, No. 4608 in herb. Farlow and Kew), and the second host plant cited in the original description of *P. stictica* Berk. & Curt. is different and was renamed *P. tiliae* Guba (Mycologia 24:383–384,1932).

On *Stanhopea bucephalus* Lindl. (leaves), Mexico, Intercepted U.S.D.A. Plant Quar. Insp., San Francisco, Cal., No. 16236, Mar. 7, 1939.

On *Taxus baccata* L. (leaves), Washington, D. C. April 22, 1925, G. G. Hedgcock, Forest Path, U.S.D.A. No. 41977; Italy, in herb. P. A. Saccardo, sub *P. funerea* Desm.; Wellesley, Mass. Oct. 4, 1934, I. H. Crowell.

Taxodium distichum Rich., Victoria, Texas, Sept. 2, 1909, F. D. Heald and F. A. Wolf, No. 2535 in Nat. Fungus Coll., U.S.D.A., sub *P. funerea* Desm.

120. **Pestalotia podocarpi** Dennis, Phytopathology 24:1026–1028,1934, fig. 1.
  P. funerea Desm. var. *podocarpi* Sacc. nom. nud., in herb. O. Pazschke
   VII, 1912, in Berlin Bot. Mus.

Pustules seated in rows parallel with mid-rib, epiphyllous, innate, 200–240 × 130–170 μ, black, in sharply defined spots, purplish brown below. Conidia 5-celled, narrow fusiform, tapering toward the extremities, straight or slightly curved, hardly constricted at septa, 17.5–24.5 × 4.5–7 μ, intermediate cells olivaceous, usually concolorous, 12–17.5 μ long, exterior hyaline cells, conic: setulae 3, sometimes 2, rarely 1, 5–16 μ, usually up to 10 μ long: pedicels short.

On leaves: *Podocarpus elongata* L'Her., Bot. Gard., Glasgow, Scotland, 1932, R. W. G. Dennis. *Podocarpus* sp., Bot. Gard. Padua, Italy, 1880, P. A. Saccardo in herb. O. Pazschke VII, 1912, Berlin Bot. Mus.; *Podocarpus neriifolia* D. Don, Missouri Bot. Gard., St. Louis, April, 1915, H. W. Anderson, No. 2760; *Podocarpus chilinus* Rich. [=*P. saligna* Lamb.], Kew Gardens, England, G. D. Darker, No. 3660, Nov. 1931 in herb. Farlow. Fungus was reported by Dennis in association with a severe leaf spotting on *Podocarpus* in a greenhouse, Glasgow, Scotland, but efforts to reproduce the disease artificially were unsuccessful.

On fruits of *Psidium pomiferum* L. [=*P. guajava* L.], Los Angeles, Cal., May 1902, C. Harrison sub *P. psidii* Pat., Nat. Fungus Coll. U.S.D.A.

121. **Pestalotia breviseta** Sacc., Michelia 1:92,1877; Syll. Fung. 3:787,1884.
> *P. banksiana* Cav., Atti Ist. Bot. Univ. Pavia, Ser. II, 1:425–435,1888, tab. 6, figs. 15–16; Syll. Fung. 10:489,1892.
> *P. funerea* Desm. var. *punctiformis* Sacc., Michelia 2:284,1881.
> *P. leucodisca* Penz. & Sacc., Malphigia 15:239 (1901), 1902; Syll. Fung. 18:483,1906.
> *P. quercina* Guba, Mycologia 24:380,1932.
> *Pestalotiopsis breviseta* (Sacc.) Stey., Bull. Jard. Bot. État Bruxelles 19: 316–318,1949, pl. 12c.

Spots definite, circular, gray. Pustules small, punctiform, gregarious, subglobose, largely hypophyllous. Conidia 5-celled, elliptic fusiform, 18–24 × 6–8 μ, hardly constricted at septa, intermediate colored cells olivaceous, concolorous, sometimes slightly contrasted, 12–16 μ long; setulae 3, sometimes 2, 3–12 μ long; exterior hyaline cells short, apical cells conic-cylindric, the basal cells broad conic; pedicels short.

On leaves of *Pyrus communis* L., Selva, Italy, Sept. 1876, P. A. Saccardo. Type description specifies conidia 25–26 × 7 μ and 3 setulae 8–10 μ long. The fungus is widespread among many host plants.

On leaves of *Cercis chinensis* Bunge, Gontazaka, Yokohama, Japan, Aug. 16, 1949, Y. Urasawa.

On *Chamaecyparis pisifera* (Sieb. & Zucc.) Endl., Greensboro, N. C., Jan. 2, 1924, H. F. Hedgcock. On leaves of *Diospyros kaki* L. f., Toyotsumura, Miyako-gun, Fukuoka-ken, Japan, Oct. 12, 1951, T. Hino; on leaves of *Euonymus japonicus* L., Louisiana, Nov. 17, 1886, in herb. A. B. Langlois sub *P. euonymi* Vize. On dead leaves of *Fagus sylvatica* L., Bot. Gard., Padua, Italy, April 1878, P. A. Saccardo, in herb. Berlin Bot. Mus. designated *P. funerea* Desm. var. *punctiformis* Sacc. On dead samarae of *Fraxinus americana* L., Bethany, Conn., Oct. 1935, J. R. Hansbrough, in herb. John Dearness. On stems of *Hydrastis canadensis* L., Bot. Lab., Cornell University, Ithaca, N. Y., Jan. 1905, H. H. Whetzel No. 1992.   On gray spots in leaves of *Nerium oleander* L., Ocean Springs, Miss., Feb. 19, 1898, herb. S. M. Tracy, sub *P. versicolor* Speg.   On brown dejected leaves of *Persea carolinensis* Nees [=*P. borbonia* (L.) Spreng.], St. Martinsville, La., Nov. 1, 1888, A. B. Langlois, No. 1552 sub *P. laurina* Mont. in Nat. Fungus Coll., U.S.D.A. Similar material in Nat. Fungus Coll., U.S.D.A. and herb. Ellis in herb. Farlow, designated *P. maura* Ell. & Ev. (Jour. Mycol. 4:123,1888), bears, in addition, a fuliginous colored conidial form which is *P. glandicola* (Cast.) Guba.   Further specimens of the olivaceous concolorous conidial form by Langlois, supplementing No. 1552, were collected April 4, 1896 and also designated *P. maura* Ell. & Ev.

On leaves of *Photinia* sp., Italy, Saccardo, in herb. P. A. Saccardo.

In spots on leaves of *Prunus tomentosa* Thunb., Gontazaka, Yokohama, Japan, Aug. 15, 1949.   Y. Urasawa in herb. Agr. Inst., Yokohama Nat. Univ.

On decayed fruits of *Pyrus malus* L. [=*Malus sylvestris* Mill.], Ithaca, N. Y., Sept. 27, 1906, herb. Dept. Pl. Path. Cornell University, H. H. Whetzel, No. 869.

On leaves of *Quercus* sp., Italy, P. A. Saccardo, sub *P. funerea* Desm. var. *breviseta* Sacc. (herb. name), in herb. P. A. Saccardo; St. Martinsville, La. Nov. 1, 1888, A. B. Langlois, Flora Ludoviciana No. 1553 sub *P. maura* Ell. & Ev., herb. Ellis 7:61 in herb. Farlow and Jour. Mycol. 4:123,1888; Arlington, Va., C. L. Shear, No. 5785, Mar. 31, 1929.   On dead leaves of *Quercus tinctoria* Bartr. [=*Q. velutina* Lam.] with *Discosia* sp., in Ellis, N. Am. Fungi No. 34 and Ellis, Fungi of New Jersey No. 2640 sub *P. stellata* Berk. & Curt. and cited by Guba (Mycologia 24:380,1932) as the type of *P. quercina* Guba [Fig. 37].   The fungus is different from *P. stellata* Berk. & Curt., on leaves of *Ilex opaca* Ait.   The fungus was reported as *P. stellata* Berk. & Curt. by Cooke & Ellis (Grevillea 6:85,1878) and Saccardo (Syll. Fung. 3:787,1884); thus, both *Ilex* and *Quercus* have been cited as hosts.

On living leaves of *Rheum rhaponticum* L., Sept. 16, 1925, Matsudo, Japan, C. Kurado, in herb. Chiba College of Horticulture, Matsudo, Chiba-Ken, Japan.

In dead areas on leaves of *Sambucus canadensis* L., Tuskegee, Ala., Apr. 12, 1926, G. W. Carver.

P. banksiana Cav.   On leaves of *Banksia robur* Cav. [=*B. latifolia* R. Br.], Pavia, Italy, 1888.

P. leucodisca Penz. & Sacc.   On living leaves of an undetermined tree, Depok, Java, 1896.   Conidia 4-celled, 2 colored cells and 2 setulae.   The type specimen shows 5-celled conidia, $18–22 \times 6–7 \mu$ and 3 setulae, $6–15 \mu$ long.

P. breviseta Sacc. was reported on *Malus pumila* Mill. in Japan as *P. traevrseta* and *P. traverseta* by K. Hara (Shizuoka-ken Nokai Hô 359:43, 1926, and List of Japanese Fungi, pp. 244–245,1954), both misspellings.

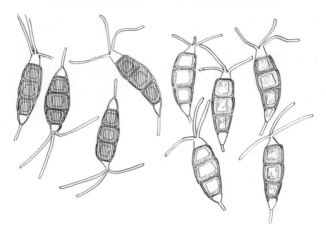

FIG. 37 [121].   *Pestalotia breviseta* Sacc.

122. **Pestalotia sinensis** Shen, Contr. Biol. Lab. Sci. Soc. China, Bot. Ser. 7:134–135,1932, fig. 1d.

Spots amphigenous, at first small, more or less circular, reddish brown, with darker margins, later elongate in the direction of the vein, often confluent finally involving most of the leaf. Acervuli largely epiphyllous, 75–150 μ diam, globose-hemispherical, or lenticular, punctate, gregarious and confluent, at first subepidermal then erumpent, distinct. Conidia elliptic-fusoid, generally curved, 5-celled, not, or only slightly constricted at septa, 18–24 × 6–8 μ; intermediate cells olivaceous, concolorous, 12–16 μ; exterior cells hyaline, apical cells short conic, bearing 2–3, mostly 3 setulae, 6–16 μ long; basal cells broad, short conic, sometimes acute; pedicels filiform, sometimes deciduous, 2–3 μ long.

On living leaves of *Ginkgo biloba* L., Central Univ. Agr. Coll., Nanking, S. C. Teng, No. 900, Aug. 25, 1931; S. C. Teng, No. 899, Sept. 1930.

The name *Pestalotia ginkgo* Hori appears in Shirai & Hara's List of Japanese Fungi (3rd ed. 1927, p. 252) and other Japanese literature. There is no published description of this species. Under the circumstances, Shen considered his fungus a new species.

123. **Pestalotia uvicola** Speg., in Thuem., Die Pilze des Weinstockes, 1878, pp. 13–14; Spegazzini, Ampelomiceti italici, in Riv. Viticoltura Enologia Ital. 2:340–341,1878, pl. 5; Syll. Fung. 3:789,1884.

Spots round, blackish, 0.5–0.8 cm in diam. Acervuli globose-lenticular, sometimes coniform, black, subepidermal, erumpent, surrounded by torn margins of the epidermis, 150–300 μ in diam. Conidia 5-celled, slender fusiform to elliptic, 18–25 × 5.5–7.5 μ, erect or slightly curved, hardly constricted at septa; intermediate colored cells guttulate, 12.5–16 μ long, olivaceous or pale brown, equally colored; apical cells long conic to cylindric, bearing a crest of 3, rarely 2, filiform setulae usually up to 13 μ, sometimes up to 22 μ long, often distinct at base, divergent or projecting forward; basal hyaline cells acute, conic; pedicels up to 7 μ long.

On ripe berries of *Vitis vinifera* L. varieties Verdisa and Dall'Occhio, near Conegliano, Venetia, Italy, C. Spegazzini, Sept. 1877. On berries of *Vitis vinifera* L., Amherst, Mass., Aug. 1930, W. H. Davis; Lincoln, Mass., Sept. 16, 1937, E. F. Guba; on stems, Bennett, No. 73, Rhode Island, herb. Curtis in herb. Farlow; Lincoln, Mass, Sept. 12, 1933, W. D. Whitcomb.

On leaves of *Vitis indivisa* Willd. Bohemia, La., Nov. 13, 1886. A. B. Langlois, No. 807, in Nat. Fungus Coll., U.S.D.A., sub *Pestalotia vitis* Ell. & Ev. (herb. name). The pycnidial fungus *Discosia* is abundant in the substratum.

Spegazzini found the fungus in spots on leaves with *Gloeosporium ampelophagum.* He described acervuli 300–400 μ in diam, conidia 5-celled, fusiform, 35×8–10 μ, pedicels 25–30 μ and 3 setulae, 8–10 μ long: intermediate colored cells olivaceous, concolorous. Prillieux and Delacroix (Bull. Soc. Mycol. Fr. 5:124,1889) reported this species in spots on leaves of *Vitis vinifera* near Bordeaux, France. Thuemen (Die Pilze des Weinreben., Klosterneuburg 15, 1891) designated this fungus *P. uvicola* Pass. var. *foliicola* Prill. Thuemen (Pilze des Weinstockes, 1878, tab. III, fig. 26), illustrated a species with 5-celled fusiform conidia, 3 olivaceous colored cells, 3 setulae, 2 of them projecting from the apex of the apical hyaline cells, which he designated *P. uvicola* Pass. No description of this species has been found in the literature.

Averna-Sacca (Bol. Agr. São Paulo, Ser. 22a : 1 & 2, 14–15, 1931) reported this fungus on leaves and berries of grape in São Paulo, Brazil. The foliage spots are of irregular shape and dotted with pustules. The spots in the berries are slightly whitish with a definite margin and dotted with prominent pustules of the fungus. The middle cells of the conidia are characterized by thick walls and the 3 setulae arise from the apex of the superior cell.

According to Spegazzini and Thuemen the fungus is believed to be a parasite of ripe grapes. Wolf (Nebraska Agr. Exp. Sta. Ann. Rep. 21:69–72, 1908) successfully infected needle-punctured grapes with *P. uvicola* Speg. In a few weeks the characteristic circular depressions and dark pustules appeared. Sections of the pustules revealed pycnidial structures protruding through the ruptured epidermis and expanding above it into a mass of pseudo-parenchyma through which a narrow ostiole is formed.

124. **Pestalotia neglecta** Thuem. Inst. Rev. Sci. Litt. Coimbra II, 27:326, 1880; Syll. Fung. 3:788,1885.

P. *funerea* Desm. var. *euonymi-japonici* Thuem., Myc. Univ. 884,1887, nom. nud.

Pestalotiopsis neglecta (Thuem.) Stey., Trans. Brit. Mycol. Soc. 36:83, 1953.

Pustules usually epiphyllous, densely gregarious in places, coalescing but usually free, globose-conic, subepidermal, raising the epidermis, then surrounded by its torn shreds, exposing the sooty contents, usually 100–150 μ in diam, at maturity blackening the matrix.

Conidia 5-celled, narrow fusiform, straight or often curved, tapering to the base, usually 20–26 μ, slightly constricted at the septa; intermediate colored cells pale olivaceous, guttulate, 13–16 × 5–7 μ, the two upper colored cells often slightly darker than the lowest; apical hyaline cells long cylindric or conic, bearing a crest of 3 setulae, 9–23 μ long, usually up to 18 μ; basal hyaline cells long, attenuated into erect pedicels, 3–7 μ long.

On dead brown leaves of *Euonymus japonicus* L., associated with other fungi.

Specimens examined: On *Euonymus japonicus* L. (leaves), Venetia, Conegliano, Italy, Oct. 1876, Spegazzini, sub *P. funerea* Desm. var. *euonymijaponici* Thuem. in Thuemen Myc. Univ. 884 [Fig. 38]; Zombaria, Portugal, Jan. 1879, A Moller in Thuemen, Contr. Myc. Lusit. 343 (Ser. II), in herb. Jard. Bot. Univ., Coimbra, Portugal, No. 275; Polperro, Cornwall, England, F. Rilstone, June 1929, in herb. Grove; France, leg. Guepin, sub *P. guepini* Desm., herb. Tulasne, in herb. Mus. d'Hist. Nat. Paris.

On leaves of *Ceratonia siliqua* L., Malta, Spain, C. H. Kauffman, Plant Quar. Insp. House, Washington, D. C., No. 23608; On dead leaves and stems of *Dianthus caryophyllus* L., Hawaii, July 1922, No. 27–1040, F. L. Stevens.

On fruits of *Eriobotrya japonica* Lindl. Culture, Bermuda, Mar. 9, 1942, No. 486, J. M. Waterston.

On leaves of *Ilex aquifolium* L., Bot. Gard., Padua, Italy, Nov. 1897, in D. Saccardo, Myc. Ital. No. 181, sub *P. funerea* (*P. gracilis*), Kleb., Myc. Centralbl. 4:10–11,1914. On *Lauraceae* (leaves), Costa Rica, Jan. 3, 1931, H. Schmidt, comm. F. Petrak. On leaves of *Mangifera indica* L., Rio de

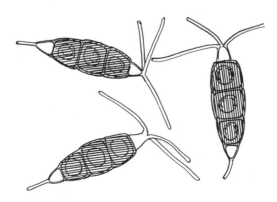

FIG. 38 [124]. *Pestalotia neglecta* Thuem.

Janeiro, Brazil, May 28, 1931, Luis A. Gomes in herb. Inst. Biol. Veg. No. 2023.

On dead stems of *Scirpus fluviatilis* (Torr.) Gray, La., Sept. 18, 1886, sub *P. scirpina* Ell. & G. Martin, herb. A. B. Langlois No. 733 in Nat. Fungus Coll., U.S.D.A.

This species is characterized by narrow, pointed conidia crested with 3 setulae. The fruiting pustules are densely arranged on either surface of the browned leaves. The specimen collected by Spegazzini at Conegliano, Italy, and named *P. funerea* Desm. var. *euonymi-japonici* Thuem., but not described, is distinct from *P. funerea* Desm. A later collection by Moller at Zombaria, Portugal, also submitted to Thuemen for identification, was described with the name *P. neglecta* Thuemen. The two specimens are identical.

Klebahn (Myc. Centralbl. 4:10–11,1914) wrongly included Thuem., Myc. Univ. No. 884 sub *P. funerea* Desm. var. *euonymi-japonici* Thuem. in his concept of *P. gracilis* Kleb. The latter name was also applied to several different species of *Pestalotia* of which the first listed occurs on *Laurus sassafras* L. [= *Sassafras albidum* (Nutt.) Nees] in Ellis & Everhart Fungi Col. No. 370b, sub *P. guepini* Desm. and which is the type of *P. gracilis* Kleb.

125. **Pestalotia disseminata** Thuem. Inst. Rev. Sci. Litt. Coimbra 28:501, 1880; Syll. Fung. 3:784,1884.

   P. eucalypti Thuem. Inst. Rev. Sci. Litt. Coimbra 28:501–502,1880; Syll. Fung. 3:785,1884.

   P. molleriana Thuem., Myc. Univ. 1988, July 1881; Guba, Phytopathology 19:223,1929.

   P. psidii Pat. Bull. Soc. Mycol. Fr. 8:136,1892, nom. nud.; Bull. Soc. Mycol. Fr. 11:232,1895; Syll. Fung. 14:1025,1899.

   P. andropogonis Rostr. Bot. Tidsskr. 24:363,1902; Syll. Fung. 18:484, 1906.

   P. feijoae Savelli, Boll. Soc. Bot. Ital. No. 6–7, 62–68, 1917, fig. 8; Syll. Fung. 25:604,1931.

   Pestalotiopsis disseminata (Thuem.) Stey., Bull. Jard. Bot. État Bruxelles 19:319,1949, pl. 13, fig. A.

Pustules amphigenous, sometimes almost entirely hypophyllous, disseminated, distinct, sometimes gregarious, globose-lenticular, conic and pyramidal, punctiform and seated without order, at first covered then erumpent, rupturing the epidermis or displacing it completely, exposing the black conidial mass, 75–150 μ, sometimes up to 250 μ in diam.

Conidia 5-celled, elliptic or clavate fusiform, tapering to the base, straight, only slightly constricted at the septa, 19–25 × 6–8 μ, usually 19–23 μ long; 3 intermediate colored cells olivaceous, equally colored or the 2 upper sometimes slightly darker, 13–17 μ long: exterior hyaline cells prominent, the apical cells conic to cylindric, the basal cells broad; setulae 3, sometimes 2, rarely 4, 8–20 μ long; pedicels 3–7 μ long.

On dead leaves of *Eucalyptus globulus* Labill., Choupal, near Coimbra, Portugal.

Specimens examined: On *Eucalyptus globulus* (leaves), Contr. Myc. Lusit. 578 (Ser. III), herb. Jard. Bot. Univ. Coimbra No. 578, June 1879 [Fig. 39a]; Rabenhorst, Fungi europ. Exs. 3094, 1883; Roumeguère Fungi Galliae Exs. 4069, Jan. 1887; Contr. Myc. Lusit. No. 579 (Ser. III), herb. Jard. Bot. Univ. Coimbra Nos. 523 and 589, May and June 1879, A. Moller, sub *P. eucalypti* Thuem.; Thuemen, Myc. Univ. No. 1988 and Roumeguère Fungi Galliae Exs. 5167 and herb. Jard. Bot. Univ. Coimbra, Choupal near Coimbra, Portugal, Oct. 1879, sub *P. molleriana* Thuem. [Fig. 39b]; McAllen, Texas, Dec. 10, 1914, R. K. Beattie, Forest Path. U.S.D.A. No. 2875; herb. P. A. Saccardo. Padua, Italy, sub *P. funerea* Desm.; Hawaiian Fungi No. 229, Wainai, Dec. 1, 1912, in herb. Lyon. On leaves of *Eucalyptus globulus* Lab. and *E. robusta* Smith, Peru, P. T. Llosa (Circ. Est. Exp. Agr., La Molina (Peru), 41:1–5, Oct. 1937). All of the collections on *Eucalyptus* from Portugal were made by A. Moller in Choupal in the period 1879 to 1887.

On spotted leaves of *Eugenia jambos* L. greenhouse, U.S.D.A., Yarrow, Md., June 1916, J. T. Rogers. On blighted leaves of *Lagerstroemia indica* L., Caracas, Venezuela. A. S. Müller, Dec. 28, 1938, No. 2321; North Carolina, M. A. Curtis, sub *P. guepini* Desm. in herb. N. Y. State Mus.

On dead areas on leaves of *Leptospermum* sp., Bot. Gard., Coimbra, Portugal, A. Moller, March 1891; in herb. P. A. Saccardo.

On *Podocarpus macrophylla* Lamb., Izumi-mura, Miyako-gun, Fukuoka-Ken, Japan, Dec. 13, 1951, T. Hino. On leaves of *Rhizophora mangle* L., Little River, Fla., Aug. 22, 1918, Fed. Hort. Bd. No. 25086, U.S.D.A. On leaves of *Terminalia arjuna* Wight & Arn., Coconut Grove, Fla., Feb. 16, 1939. H. F. Loomis in Nat. Fungus Coll., U.S.D.A., No. 73055.

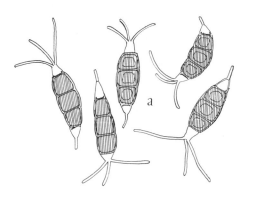
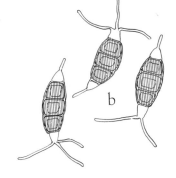

FIG. 39 [125]. *Pestalotia disseminata* Thuem.

P. andropogonis Rostr. was described on leaves of *Andropogon sorghum* Brot. [=*Sorghum vulgare* Pers.] collected in Siam. The significant characters of fungus are: conidia 5-celled, 20–22 × 7–8 μ, setulae 2–3, 16–18 μ long.

P. feijoae Savelli, on fruits of *Feijoa sellowiana* Berg., Bot. Gard., Florence, Italy, is a synonym.

P. disseminata and *P. eucalypti* were published in that order in Feb. 1881 and *P. molleriana* in July 1881. Thuemen stated that the conidia of *P. molleriana* and *P. disseminata* are 5-septate and that the latter species is distinct from *P. eucalypti* in the disposition of the fruiting pustules and the dimensions of the conidia. Voglino (Atti. Soc. Ven.-Trent. Sci. Padova 9:209–243,1885) noted the similarity of *P. molleriana* and *P. disseminata*.

The fungus was reported by Jenkins (Phytopathology 23:404–405,1943) in spots in leaves of *Terminalia arjuna* Wight & Arn., Coconut Grove, Fla. (Feb. 1937), and with *Phyllosticta* and *Phomopsis* (Fig. 1, A–C). Steyaert (Bull. Jard. Bot. État Bruxelles 19:174–176,1948) stated that Guba's measurements of conidia of *P. disseminata* and *P. molleriana* differ. The differences seem slight and of no significance.

Wollenweber and Hochapfel (Z. Pflanzenkr. 46:409,1936) produced a slow rot in apple with *P. disseminata* isolated from *Eucalyptus* leaves, Tanganyika, East Africa. Steyaert (Bull. Jard. Bot. État Bruxelles 19:338–340,1949, pl. 16, fig. D) questioned the name of the fungus and has given it the new name *Pestalotiopsis crassiuscula* Stey. with reference to the broad coarse setulae.

P. psidii Pat. was described on fruits of *Psidium pomiferum* L. [=*P. guajava* L.], Ecuador, Sept. 1891, G. de Lagerheim in herb. Patouillard in herb. Farlow. Narasimhan (Adm. Rep. Agr. Dept. Mysore, India (Mycology) 1936–37, 169–173, 1938) reported failure to infect wounded and unwounded unripe fruits of guava with spores from cultures made from diseased fruits. Gallucci-Rangone (Ann. Sper. Agraria Roma (n. s.) 8,5,1437–1457, 1954) reported a full description of *P. disseminata* on *Cattleya* sp. in Italy.

126. Pestalotia carissae Guba sp. nov.

Pustulae amphigenae, plerumque epiphyllae, dispersae vel dense aggregatae, coalescentes, globoso-lenticulares, 90–350 μ, vulgo minores quam 175 μ in diam; conidia 5-cellularia, anguste fusiformia, recta vel subcurvata, 21–26 × 5–6 μ, vix constricta; cellulae mediae coloratae 14.5–20 μ longae, olivaceae, concolores, cellulis individuis longioribus quam latioribus; cellulae extimae hyalinae, prominentes; cellulae apicales longe cylindricae, basales longe attenuatae; setulae 3, late divergentes, 14–28 μ longae, curvatae; pedicelli recti, 4–7 μ longi.

Pustules amphigenous, largely epiphyllous, numerous and scattered, dense in places, coalescing freely, globose-lenticular, 90–350 μ, usually less than 175 μ in diam. Conidia 5-celled, long, narrow fusiform, straight or slightly curved, 21–26 × 5–6 μ, hardly constricted at the septa; intermediate colored cells 14.5–20 μ long, olivaceous, concolorous, the component cells longer than wide; exterior hyaline cells prominent, apical cells long cylindric, the basal cells long tapering; setulae 3, widely divergent, 14–28 μ, curved; pedicels erect, 4–7 μ long.

On dead areas in leaves of *Carissa arduina* Lam., Mt. Maquiling, near Los Baños, Philippine Islands, Dec. 1915, sub *P. funerea* Desm. in Baker, Fungi Malayana No. 64, suppl. 1 [Fig. 40].

127. **Pestalotia olivacea** Guba sp. nov.

Pustulae sparsae, globoso-lenticulares, elevatae et erumpentes, 100–250 × 100–200 μ; conidia 5-cellularia, recta, elliptico-fusiformia, saepe subcurvata, ad basim attenuata, 22–25 × 6–8 μ; cellulae mediae 14–17 μ longae, totum olivaceae, vix constrictae; cellulae extimae hyalinae, prominentes, apicales conico-cylindricae, basales long conicae ad pedicellum rectum 3–7 μ longum attenuatae; setulae 2–3, apiculatae, 16–32 μ longae, divergentes.

Pustules sparse, globose-lenticular, raised and erumpent, surrounded by torn shreds of the epidermis, 100–250 × 100–200 μ. Conidia 5-celled, straight, elliptic-fusiform, frequently slightly curved, tapering toward the base, 22–25 × 6–8 μ; intermediate colored cells 14–17 μ long, olivaceous throughout, hardly constricted at the septa; exterior hyaline cells prominent, apical cells conic-cylindric, the basal cells long conic, tapering into a straight pedicel, 3–7 μ long; setulae apiculate, 2 or 3, long, divergent, 16–32 μ.

On dead twigs of *Diospyros discolor* Willd. (seedless Mabolo), Manila, Philippine Islands, March 29, 1917, W. H. Weston, Jr. [Fig. 41], intercepted at Plant Quar. Sta., U.S.D.A., Washington, D.C., No. 21213, associated with other fungi, notably *Phoma* and *Cytospora*. On leaves of *Quercus rubra* L. Vosges, France Sept. 1910, in herb. Mus. d'Hist. Nat. Paris.

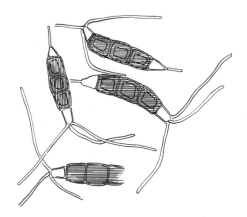

Fɪɢ. 40 [126]. *Pestalotia carissae* Guba.

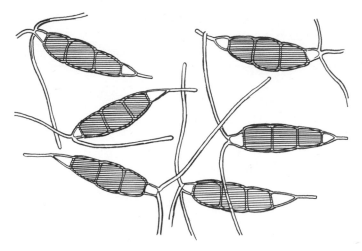

Fig. 41 [127]. *Pestalotia olivacea* Guba.

128. **Pestalotia bicolor** Ell. & Ev., Bull. Torrey Bot. Club 27:575,1900; Syll. Fung. 16:1016,1902.

Pustules amphigenous, punctate, subglobose, generally distributed, gregarious and coalescing freely, 15–125 μ diam, erumpent at maturity, the sooty contents spreading over the surface. Conidia clavate-fusiform, tapering, 5-celled, 19–25 × 6–8 μ, equilateral; intermediate colored cells 13–16 μ, guttulate, olivaceous throughout or upper two-colored cells slightly darker; basal hyaline cells long, conic, apical hyaline cells conic-cylindric; setulae usually 3, often 4, sometimes forked, 10–20 μ long; pedicels erect, 4–8 μ.

On dead leaves of *Salix* sp., Tuskegee, Ala., Dec. 12, 1897, G. W. Carver, No. 387, herb. Ellis, Folio 179, No. 19 in herb. Farlow; *Salix nigra* Marsh., Tuskegee, Ala., Nov. 3, 1926, G. W. Carver.

Ellis' description accompanying the specimen states that the conidia measure 20–22 μ, colored part 13–15 × 5–7 μ, setulae 3–5 and 14–16 μ long. The original description refers to yellowish-white pustules which darken with age, whence the name *bicolor*. The light colored markings are not related to the fungus. The pustules are small, punctate, and black.

129. **Pestalotia gravesii** Trav., Syll. Fung. 25:600–601,1931.

Conidia for the most part 5-celled, 25 × 5 μ, the 3 intermediate cells dark, exterior cells hyaline, sometimes 4-celled and 2 intermediate cells dark; setulae 3 to 4, filiform, hyaline, spreading, 11 μ long, 1 of them apical, the other 2 or 3 arising from bases of the apical cells; pedicels short, 5 μ long.

On cones of *Picea abies* (L.) Karst. and *P. rubens* Sarg., Biltmore Forest, N. C. The fungus was reported to be related to *P. funerea* Desm. but to differ principally in the insertion of the appendages. The fungus was originally reported by Graves (Phytopathology 4:67–68,1914, fig. 5) as an undetermined species occurring sparingly on withered leaves on diseased young shoots of Norway spruce.

130. **Pestalotia montellica** Sacc. & Vogl., Atti Soc. Ven.-Trent. Sci. Nat. Padova 9:215–216,1885; Syll. Fung. 10:489,1892.

    P. lucae Savelli Boll. Soc. Bot. Ital. no. 6–7,62–68,1917; Syll. Fung, 25:602,1931.

    P. querci-dentatae K. Sawada, Bull. Govt. For. Exp. Sta. (Japan) no. 105. 78–79,1958.

Pustules subglobose, punctiform, amphigenous, distinct or dense, circular, 120–175 μ in diam, distributed generally over the matrix or limited to definitely margined spots.   Conidia 5-celled, straight, fusiform and attenuated toward the ends, 21–26 μ; intermediate cells narrow, tapering, the basal cells acute, the apical cells conic-cylindric; 1 vertical setula at apices, 3 or sometimes 2 setulae arising from bases (acropleurogenous) of apical cells, 12–26 μ long; pedicels erect, 4–9 μ.

On leaves of *Quercus* in forest, Montello, Italy, P. A. Saccardo.

Specimens examined: on leaves of *Lithocarpus densiflorus* Rehd., Marin County, Cal., Jan. 13, 1923, Lee Bonar, sub *P. castagnei* Desm.; on leaves of *Quercus ilex* L., Ivy Hotel, Kew Green, England, July 1917, Grove; on leaves of *Quercus tinctoria* Bartr. [= *Q. velutina* Lam.] in Ellis & Everhart Fungi Col. No. 1352, West Chester, Pa., B. M. Everhart, sub *P. stellata* Berk. & Curt. [Fig. 42]; on dead leaves of *Quercus rubra* L., London, Ontario, Canada, March 9, 1947, W. D. Sutton.

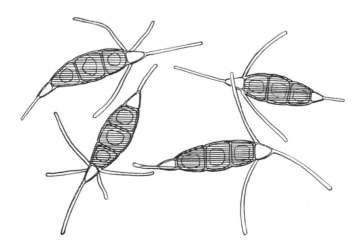

FIG. 42 [130].   *Pestalotia montellica* Sacc. & Vogl.

The deflection of 3 setulae around the base of the apical cells and one from the apex is characteristic of this species. Savelli (Boll. Soc. Bot. Ital. no. 6–7,62–68,1917) created the species *P. lucae* Sav. on leaves of *Quercus ilex* L. not var. *agrifolia* DC. and reported the conidia as 28–29 × 10–11 μ with 1 terminal setula and 2 deflected from the bases of the apical cells. *P. lucae* Savelli is regarded as a synonym. *P. castagnei* Desm. reported on *Lithocarpus densiflorus* Rehd., California (Bonar, Mycologia 20:292–300,1928), is *P. montellica*. *P. querci-dentatae* Sawada was reported on leaves of *Quercus dentata* Thunb. from the Tohoku district of Japan by K. Sawada. For a full description of the fungus see Bertini (Atti Ist. Bot. Univ. Pavia, Ser. 5:14 (1–3) 326–328,1957).

131. Pestalotia gaurae Guba sp. nov.

Pustulae depressae, globoso-lenticulares, atrae, dense punctiformes, singulae, interdum confluentes, erumpentes, plerumque 120–225 μ in diam; conidia 5-cellularia, elliptico-fusiformia, recta, valde constricta, 19–33 × 6.3–8 μ; cellulae mediae coloratae torulosae, pallide olivaceae, concolores, 12.5–15 μ longae; cellulae apicales hyalinae, breve turbinatae vel hemisphaericales; setulae 3 vel vulgo 4, interdum 2, 6–19 μ longae; cellulae basales hyalinae, latae, hemisphaericales; pedicelli 3–7 μ longi.

Pustules depressed, globose-lenticular, black, dense punctiform, solitary, sometimes confluent, borne under the epidermis, erumpent, surrounded by the torn epidermis, usually 120–225 μ diam. Conidia 5-celled, elliptic fusiform, straight, prominently constricted at septa, 19–23 × 6.3–8 μ; intermediate colored cells strongly torulose, pale olivaceous and equally colored, 12.5–15 μ long, with granular contents; apical hyaline cells short, turbinate or hemispherical; setulae 3 or usually 4, sometimes 2, 6–19 μ long, often up to 10 μ long, arising from the apices or often from different points about the periphery of the apical cells; basal hyaline cells broad, hemispherical; pedicel 3–7 μ long.

On ash-colored areas on stems of *Gaura parviflora* Dougl., Hays, Kan., July 10, 1930, in herb. E. Bartholomew, sub *P. oenotherae* Ell. & Barthol. [Fig. 43].

132. Pestalotia elaeagni Alm. & Cam., Bol. Soc. Broteriana 24:206–207,1919; Syll. Fung. 22:1223,1913.

Pustules epiphyllous, in dark colored or ashen spots, hemispherical-lenticular, small, black, at first covered by epidermis, later exposed. Conidia 5-celled, 20–22 × 7–8 μ, sub-fusiform, straight, somewhat constricted at septa, acute at both ends, exterior cells hyaline, the intermediate cells brown; setulae 4, up to 15 μ long.

On leaves of *Elaeagnus* sp., Bot. Gard., Coimbra, Portugal.

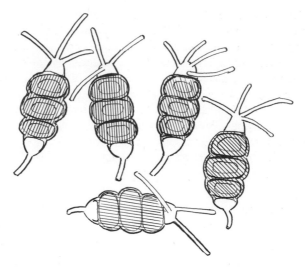

FIG. 43 [131]. *Pestalotia gaurae* Guba.

133. **Pestalotia weinmanniae** Petr. Sydowia 4:563–564,1950.

Pustules hypophyllous, sparse or densely distributed, mostly solitary, circular or elliptic, somewhat angular, 180–350 μ diam, subepidermal, covered by the torn epidermis, then erumpent. Conidia 5-celled, oblong-fusiform, strongly narrowed at base, straight or somewhat curved, only slightly constricted at septa, 18–26 × 5–7 μ, intermediate colored cells transparent, olive brown, exterior cells hyaline or subhyaline; setulae 3–5, 10–22 μ long; pedicels 4–7 μ long.

On wilting and dead leaves of *Weinmannia spruceana* Engl. associated with *Mycosphaerella* sp., Prov. Tungurahua, Hacienda San Antonio, near Banos, Ecuador, Jan. 4, 1938, No. 666.

134. **Pestalotia lespedezae** Syd., Mem. Bull. Herb. Boiss. 4:6,1900; Syll. Fung. 16:1015,1902.

P. cephalotaxi Sawada, Rep. Govt. For. Exp. Sta. 46:118,1950, Tokyo, Japan.

Pustules largely epiphyllous, punctiform, erumpent, circinate, surrounded by torn shreds of the epidermis, scattered, 100–150 μ in diam, seated on brown spots, 2–5 mm in diam, and dead marginal areas of irregular shape. Conidia 5-celled, oblong-elliptic, 20–25 μ; intermediate colored cells umber or olivaceous, equally colored or slightly contrasted, guttulate, 14–17 × 7–9 μ; basal hyaline cells obtuse, apical hyaline cells conic; setulae 2 or 3, usually 3, divergent, 15–24 μ long; pedicels short, erect, about 5 μ long.

On living or wilting leaves of *Lespedeza bicolor* Turcz., Bot. Gard., Tokyo, Japan, 1898, Kusano, herb. Sydow, Mus. Bot., Stockholm.

On leaves and stems of *Cephalotaxus nana* Nakai [=*C. harringtonia* (Forbes) K. Koch var. *nana* (Nakei) Rehd.], Japan, sub *P. cephalotaxi* Saw. Plate 1, fig. 25 by Sawada, shows setulae and conidia of the same length. Sawada reported that the fungus caused swellings in twigs and that it killed the leaves and twigs.

135. **Pestalotia quadriciliata** Bub. & Dearn., Hedwigia 58:31,1916; Syll. Fung. 25:607–608,1931.

Pustules subglobose to lenticular, epiphyllous, immersed and covered by the epidermis, 90–175 μ wide, sparse, seated on circular brown spots not exceeding 8 mm diam. Conidia elliptic-fusoid or broad-clavate, 5-celled, 21–26 μ, straight; intermediate colored cells olivaceous or umber, concolorous, 15–18 × 8–9.5 μ, slightly constricted at the septa; apical cells conic, crowned with 4 slender setulae, 9–17 μ; basal cells obtuse or rounded; pedicels short, 2–5 μ long.

On partly green leaves of *Vitis vulpina* L., London, Canada, Oct. 9, 1910, J. Dearness. The fungus is secondary and the spots are due to a *Phyllosticta* which is present in greater abundance.

136. **Pestalotia rhamni** Celotti, Miceti parco Dintorni, Scuola Naz. Agr., Montpellier, Conegliano, 1887, p. 11, fig. 6; Syll. Fung. 10:487,1892.
   P. asphodeli Boy. & Jacz. Bull. Soc. Bot. Fr. 40:296, fig. 9, 1893 (publ. 1894); Syll. Fung. 11:579,1895.

Acervuli scattered, small, brown-black, at first covered by the epidermis, then erumpent. Conidia narrow, elongate-fusiform, 25–30 × 5–8 μ; intermediate colored cells brown, apical hyaline cells long cylindric, setulae 2–3, 10–13 μ long, widely separated, arising at different points about the crown of the apical cells; basal hyaline cells attenuated into the pedicels.

On dry twigs of *Rhamnus alaternus* L., Montpellier, France. On wilted stems of *Asphodelus cerasiferus* J. Gay, Montarnaud, Montpellier, France, Jaczewski.

The original descriptions of *P. rhamni* and *P. asphodeli* are identical except that the former is reported to have 2 setulate conidia, the latter 3 setulate conidia.

137. **Pestalotia osyridis** Thuem., Boll. Soc. Adriatica Sci. Nat. Trieste 6:133, 1881; Syll. Fung. 3:790,1884.
   P. funerea Desm. var. *crassipes* Speg., Michelia 1:479,1879; Syll. Fung. 3:791,1884.
   P. opuntiicola Cif. & Gonz.-Frag. Est. Agron. de Haina, Rep. Dominicana, Ser. Bot. 4:7,1926.

Pustules gregarious, small, at first covered by the epidermis, at last protruded, hemispherical, black. Conidia acute at both ends, elongate-fusoid, 5-celled, straight or often somewhat curved, 22–28 × 5–7 μ, intermediate cells dark, exterior cells hyaline, acute; setulae 2 or usually 3, curved short, up to 14 μ long; pedicels short.

On *Osyris alba* L. (dead twigs), Pola, Austria.

On *Castanea crenata* Sieb. & Zucc. (fallen acorns), Firenze, Italy, Oct. 12, 1948, Vincento Grasso: *Castanea sativa* Mill. (living leaves), Fungi Minas Geraes, Brazil, Feb. 6, 1930, A. S. Müller, No. 121; *Eucalyptus rostrata* Schlecht. (leaves) [= *E. camaldulensis* Dehnh.], Minas Geraes, Brazil No. 333, A. S. Müller; *Feijoia sellowiana* Berg. (fruits), California, Dec. 1928, W. J. Horne in herb. University of California No. 469674; *Lonicera caprifolium* L. (dead twigs), Conegliano, Italy, 1876, Spegazzini sub *P. funerea* Desm. var. *crassipes* Speg. (conidia oblong-fusoid, 5-celled, 20–30 × 7 μ; 3 setulae, 10–12 μ; pedicels 5–10 μ long). *Mangifera indica* L. (dead twigs), Honolulu, Hawaii, H. F. Bain, Jan. 3, 1921, Plant Quar., Washington, D. C., No. 38932; on leaves, El Valle-Cali, Columbia, April 1938, C. Garcés, No. 47; Minas Geraes, Brazil, Dec. 29, 1910, E. Rangel, in herb. Inst. Biol. Veg. Brazil, No. 210; *Opuntia tunae* Mill. (branches), San Francisco de Macoris, Dominican Republic, R. Ciferri, sub *P. opuntiicola* Cif. & Gonz.-Frag. Pustules globose-applanate, conidia 20–30 × 5–7.5 μ; setulae 3, pedicels 10–15 μ. The fungus was reported to be associated with *Macrophoma opuntiicola* (Speg.) Sacc. f. *tunae* Cif. & Gonz.-Frag. and *Macrosporium opuntiicola* Cif. & Gonz.-Frag.

138. **Pestalotia mayumbensis** Stey., Bull. Jard. Bot. État Bruxelles 19:176–178,1948, pl. III, fig. D.

Pestalotiopsis mayumbensis (Stey.) Stey., Bull. Jard. Bot. État Bruxelles 19:320,1949.

Spots elliptic, straw-colored, surrounded by reddish-purple zone, 3–4 cm long. Pustules circular or elliptic, 150–300 μ diam. Conidia 5-celled, narrow-fusiform, straight or awkwardly curved, 22–28 × 6.5–8.5 μ, tapering to the base, hardly constricted at septa; intermediate cells olivaceous or umber and concolorous, or upper two sometimes darker or umber, 16–21 μ long, guttulate; exterior hyaline cells long, the basal cells acute, apical cells conic-cylindric; setulae 3 spreading, 8–15 μ long; pedicels 2–8 μ long.

On leaves of *Elaeis guineensis* Jacq. Luki, Boma District du Bas-Fleuve, Belgian Congo, Sept. 1942, herb. Steyaert Nos. 42,347; 42,349.

139. **Pestalotia cocculi** Guba sp. nov.

Pustulae hypophyllae, globoso-lenticulares, gregariae vel sparsae, subepidermicales dein in lineis erumpentes, 125–300 μ in diam; conidia 5-cellularia, anguste fusiformia, vix constricta, subcurvata, 22–29 × 5.5–7 μ; cellulae mediae coloratae guttulatae, 15–18 μ longae, olivaceae, concolores; cellulae apicales hyalinae, longe conicae cylindricae, basales longe conicae vel attenuatae, aliquando subhemisphaericales; setulae 3 vel interdum 2, tenues, late divergentes, 11–12 μ longae; pedicelli 4–9 μ longi.

Pustules hypophyllous, globose-lenticular, gregarious or sparse, solitary, subepidermal, then erumpent, raised, rupturing epidermis in a linear manner, 125–300 μ diam, exposing the black sooty contents. Conidia 5-celled, erect, slender fusiform, hardly constricted at septa, slightly curved, 22–29 × 5.5–7 μ; intermediate colored cells guttulate, 15–18 μ long, olivaceous, equally colored; apical hyaline cells long conic, cylindric, the basal long conic or tapering, occasionally sub–hemispherical; setulae 3, sometimes 2, slender, widely divergent, 11–12 μ long; pedicels 4–9 μ.

On dead leaves of *Cocculus laurifolius* DC., Bot. Gard., Padua, Italy, Nov. 1897, in D. Saccardo, Myc. Ital. No. 183, sub *P. guepini* Desm. The fungus is present generally over both surfaces of brown dead leaves and associated with other fungi.

In cultures from decomposed cellulose, U. S. Military Supplies, Pacific Area, World War II, Harvard University, No. 52B5H and 57 other cultures, all listed as *Pestalotia* sp. [Fig. 44]. Fungus is featured by long, narrow fusiform conidia, pale brown colored cells, 3 setulae, 15–25 μ long. (Weston and Linder, Resear Repdi. QMG Lab. Microbiol., Ser. 15, QMC Project 60, Aug. 3, 1949).

140. **Pestalotia mangifolia** Guba sp. nov.

Pustulae immersae, circulares, plerumque hypophyllae, punctiformes, subgregariae, saepe coalescentes, erumpentes, 100–250 × 100–200 μ, epidermidem papyraceum fissentes; conidia 5-cellularia, longe cylindrica, fusiformia, recta, 22–28 × 6–8.5 μ, paene constricta; cellulae mediae olivaceae vel

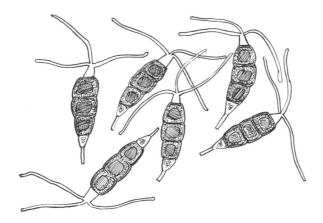

FIG. 44 [139]. *Pestalotia cocculi* Guba.

obscuriores, concolores, guttulatae, 14–19 μ longae; cellulae apicales hyalinae, longe cylindricae; setulae 3, 8–26 μ longae, divergentes; cellulae basales hyalinae, longe coniciae, attenuatae; pedicelli usque ad 5 μ longi.

Pustules embedded, circular, largely hypophyllous, punctiform, rather gregarious, often coalescing to form carbonaceous cushions, erumpent, 100–250 × 100–200 μ, tearing away the papery epidermis, on pale dead areas extending around the margin of leaf matrix. Conidia 5-celled, long-cylindric, fusiform, straight, 22–28 × 6–8.5 μ, only slightly constricted at septa; intermediate colored cells olivaceous or darker, concolorous, guttulate, 14–19 μ long; apical hyaline cells long cylindric, bearing 3 setulae, 8–26 μ long, divergent; basal hyaline cells long-conic, tapering; pedicels up to 5 μ long.

On dead brown areas in leaves of *Mangifera indica* L., Mt. Maquiling, near Los Baños, Philippine Islands, July, 1913, in C. F. Baker, Fungi Malayana No. 64, sub *P. funerea* Desm.; Kisantu, Belgian Congo, July 1906, Vanderyst No. 1386 in Berlin Bot. Mus. and Jard. Bot. État Bruxelles associated with *P. mangiferae* P. Henn. (type) and designated *P. annulata* Berk. & Curt. by Steyaert (Bull. Jard. Bot. État Bruxelles 19: 320,1949, pl. 14, fig. B).

141. **Pestalotia suffocata** Ell. & Ev., Jour. Mycol. 2:38,1886; Syll. Fung. 10: 485,1892.

Conidia 5-celled, long and narrow-fusiform, 22–27 × 5–7 μ or wider; intermediate cells olivaceous throughout, the upper two sometimes slightly darker, 15–18 μ long; rather acute at the extremities, the apical cells long cylindric; basal cells long acute; setulae 3, sometimes 4, spreading, 22–38 μ long.

On living leaves of *Rosa* sp., kept under a bell jar and associated with *Pilobolus*, F. L. Scribner. Specimens examined: culture from rose stem, Texas, G. H. Rogers, No. 287, July 20, 1935; living leaves of *Cydonia vulgaris* Pers. [= *C. oblonga* Mill.] in herb. Inst. Biol. Veg., Rio de Janeiro, No. 168.

142. **Pestalotia galactis** P. Henn. Notizbl. Kgl. Bot. Gard. Mus., Berlin 3: 39–40,1900; Syll. Fung. 18:482,1906.

Pustules amphigenous, scattered or gregarious, subglobose, innate-erumpent, surrounded by torn margins of the epidermis, 75–150 μ in diam. Conidia long-fusiform, 5-celled, tapering and pointed at the base, straight, 22–28 × 6.5–8 μ, not, or only slightly constricted at septa; intermediate cells olivaceous, acute; apical hyaline cells long conic; setulae 3, sometimes 4, slender, curved and divergent, 22–32 μ long; pedicels 6–13 μ long, often curved to one side.

On dead withered leaves of *Galax aphylla* L., Bot. Gard., Berlin, Germany, July, 1899, leg. Moorbeet, in herb. Berlin Bot. Mus. The author reported conidia 20–25 × 7–9 μ, setulae 3 to 5 and 30–45 μ long; pedicels 20–30 μ long.

143. **Pestalotia caroliniana** Guba sp. nov.

Pustulae amphigenae, plerumque hypophyllae, globoso-conoideae, generaliter 150 μ in diam, subepidermicales, punctiformes, gregariae, erumpentes; conidia 5-cellularia, longe fusiformia, non vel leniter constricta, 22–32 × 6–8 μ; cellulae mediae coloratae aequaliter olivaceae vel pallide brunneae vel interdum duae superiores paulo obscuriores, 15–23 μ longae; cellulae apicales hyalinae longe conicae, cylindricae, setulis 3, 15–38 μ longis ornatae, basales hyalinae, attenuatae, longe acutae; pedicelli usque ad 6 μ longi.

Pustules amphigenous, largely hypophyllous, globose-conoid, usually 150 μ diam, subepidermal, punctiform, gregarious, erumpent, surrounded by torn epidermis, the contents issuing in sooty black carbonaceous masses. Conidia 5-celled, long-fusiform, not or only slightly constricted at septa, 22–32 × 6–8 μ; intermediate colored cells olivaceous or pale brown throughout or upper 2 cells sometimes slightly darker, 15–23 μ long; apical hyaline cells long, conic-cylindric, bearing 3 setulae, 15–38 μ long or in slightly narrower range of length; basal hyaline cells tapering, long, acute; pedicels up to 6 μ long.

On leaves of *Euonymus japonicus* L., Norfolk, Va., Sept. 12, 1908, R. A. Pope; Society Hill, S. C., Sept. 30, 1916, J. T. Rogers. On leaves of *Euonymus europaeus* L., Seattle, Wash. (from Japan), intercepted Oct. 19, 1932, M. J. Forsell; Tuskegee, Ala., March 1906, G. W. Carver, in herb. Bartholomew; on leaves of *Calamus margaritae* Hance, Taipeh, Formosa, Dec. 16, 1908, K. Sawada sub *P. calami* Sawada in herb. Univ. Taihokuensis.

On leaves of *Podocarpus sinensis* Teijsm. & Binn. [=*P. macrophylla* Lamb. var. *makei* Sieb.], New Orleans, La., Feb. 6, 1945, I. Hein, No. C410.

144. **Pestalotia conglomerata** Bres., Rev. Mycol. Fr. 13:68–69,1891; Syll. Fung. 10:487,1892.

Acervuli superficial, densely gregarious, punctiform, applanate, black, covered by hairy white membrane. Conidia oblong-fusoid, 5-celled, 25–30 × 7–8 μ, somewhat constricted at septa, the intermediate cells dark, exterior cells hyaline, conoid; setulae 2–5, recurved, 10–15 μ; pedicels filiform, 12–20 μ, at length deciduous.

On pericarp of fruit of *Ononis* sp., Island of St. Thomé, West Africa, A. Moller. The surface of the fruit is covered by a white membrane on which are seated the black pustules of the fungus. The pedicels of the conidia are greatly prolonged.

145. **Pestalotia baarnensis** (Stey.) Guba comb. nov.

Pestalotiopsis baarnensis Stey., Bull. Jard. Bot. État Bruxelles 19:342–343, 1949, pl. 17, fig. A.

Conidia 5-celled, straight, fusiform, or somewhat curved, 20–27 × 6–7 μ; intermediate colored cells umber, concolorous, guttulate, 14–17 μ long;

superior hyaline cells long conoid; setulae 3 or 4, sometimes 4, often branched, stout, 10–33 μ, usually 13–25 μ long, with visible lumen, divergent at right angles to axis of conidia; basal hyaline cells narrow, tapering, often with 1 or 2 oblique setulae projecting from the bases adjoining the point of attachment of the pedicels; pedicels straight or curved, 6–14 μ long.

Culture obtained from *Rhododendron* sp. by Van Hall and determined by Van Luyck as *P. sydowiana* Bres.

146. **Pestalotia rosae** West., Bull. Acad. Roy. Belg., 2nd Ser., VII, 90,1859; Syll. Fung. 3:786,1884; Steyaert, Bull. Jard. Bot. État Bruxelles 19: 66,1948, pl. I, B.

Spots diffuse on branches. Pustules black, sparse, dispersed, covered by torn epidermis, elongate, erumpent, 350–670 × 125–250 μ. Conidia 5-celled, fusoid, straight or sometimes slightly curved, 24–30 × 5–8 μ (average 26.1 × 6.3 μ), 3 intermediate cells uniformly olivaceous, 14–20 μ (average 17.3 μ); exterior cells hyaline, conoid; setulae mostly 3–5, occasionally 6, 6–20 μ, basal cells tapering into pedicels, 4–12 μ long.

On cane of *Rosa* sp. near Gand, Belgium (Desnoy). The species was originally described with 3-septate conidia, 20–25 × 10 μ, apical cells hyaline surmounted by 2–3 setulae, as long as the conidia, the 3 others pale brown. Westendorp did not mention the basal cells or the pedicels. The species is close to *P. funerea* Desm. but distinguished from it by narrow-fusiform conidia.

147. **Pestalotia monochaetioides** Doyer, Med. Phytopath. Lab. "Will. Comm. Scholt." 9:24,1925.
    Pestalotiopsis monochaetioides (Doyer) Stey., Bull. Jard. Bot. État Bruxelles 19:309–310,1949.

Pustules black, erumpent, punctiform. Conidia 5-celled, elongate, fusiform, 26 (22–30) × 8 (5–10) μ; 3 intermediate colored cells, the upper 2 cells somewhat darker than lowest colored cell, constricted at the septa; wall of the two lowest colored cells warty and uneven; setulae slender, mostly 2, sometimes 1 or 3, rarely 4, usually up to 30 μ long; when 1, up to 60 μ long or longer.

On dead twigs of *Chamaecyparis lawsoniana* (Murr.) Parl., Naarden, Holland. According to Steyaert's study the conidia are 26–31 × 8–10 μ, colored cells 18–22 μ long, olivaceous and concolorous, 1 to 3 setulae, 11–43 μ (pl. 11, fig. B). Steyaert's second specimen (pl. 10, fig. E) isolated from *Picea excelsa* L. [=*P. abies* (L.) Karst.] by Van Beverwijk has monosetulate conidia, 26–33 × 9–11.5 μ, concolorous intermediate cells 18–23 μ, setulae 30–55 μ, pedicels 3–8 μ long. According to the present author's study of *P. monochaetioides* Doyer from Centr. Bur. Schimmelcultures, the conidia are 25–32 × 9.5 μ, colored cells 19–22 μ long, the upper 2 umber, the lowest pale brown, 1 apical appendage 45–75 μ long. Another specimen on dead twigs of *Juniperus virginiana* L., Belmont, Mass. June 22, 1938, leg. Guba, features conidia 22–29 × 7–9.5 μ; intermediate colored cells olivaceous, equally colored, 15.5–19.5 μ long; apical hyaline cells tapering, usually crowned with one appendage, 25–40 μ long or with 2–3, rarely 4 or 5 setulae and shorter; pedicels broad-conic up to 9 μ long [Fig. 45]. The species is a borderline form having the essential features of both *Monochaetia* and *Pestalotia*. The warty character of the two lowest cells may not be significant.

148. **Pestalotia subsessilis** Speg., Anal. Mus. Nac. Buenos Aires, Ser. III, 13:413,1911; Syll. Fung. 22:1225,1897,

Spots amphigenous, orbicular, somewhat pellucid, 2–6 mm diam, determinate, whitish. Acervuli few, innate, erumpent, epiphyllous, sublenticular, small, black. Conidia 5-celled, fusiform or subclavate, 20–30 × 8–11 μ; intermediate colored cells olivaceous, concolorous, exterior cells hyaline, the superior cells crowned with 3 strongly divergent setulae, 20 μ, long, inferior cells conoid; pedicels short, 2–3 μ, hardly developed.

On living leaves of *Rivina laevis* L. [= *R. humilis* L.] Metan Salta, Argentina.

The species is not to be confused with *Pestalozziella subsessilis* Sacc. & Ell. (Michelia 2:575,1882; Syll. Fung. 3:737,1884) on leaves of *Geranium carolinianum* L., Newfield, N. J., in Ellis N. Am. Fungi No. 1223 and Fungi Col. No. 444; moreover, it should not be confused with *Pestalotia sessilis* Sacc. [= *Robillarda sessilis* Sacc.] on leaves of *Rubus caesius* L. or with *P. sessilis* Sacc. [= *P. saccardensis* Guba] on leaves of *Diospyros mespiliformis* Hochst.

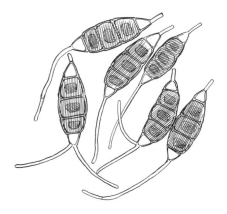

FIG. 45 [147]. *Pestalotia monochaetioides* Doyer.

149. **Pestalotia macrochaeta** (Speg.) Guba, Mycologia 24:369,1932.

 P. funerea Desm. var. *macrochaeta* Speg., Anal. Mus. Nac. Buenos Aires,
 Ser. III, 13:412,1911; Syll. Fung. 22:1226,1913.

Pustules sparse and scattered without order, 100–200 in diam, globose-
lenticular, innate, erumpent at maturity. Conidia 5-celled, straight, fusiform, tapering toward the base or somewhat elliptic-fusoid, 22–31 × 8–10 μ;
intermediate cells usually equally colored, olivaceous or umber, or the two
upper cells slightly darker, 15–20 μ long; apical hyaline cells cylindric or
conic, rather short, the basal cells conic, abruptly contracted or sometimes
attenuated; setulae 3, 15–32 μ long; pedicels 3–10 μ long.

 On decaying needles of *Pinus sylvestris* L., Villa Elisa, Argentina, Aug.
1908, Spegazzini [Fig. 46]. According to the original description, the
conidia are 28–30 × 8–9 μ, setulae 30 μ and the pedicels 7–10 μ long. The
emended description supplied by Guba (Mycologia 24:369,1932) is in error.
The present description, based on the study of type material, conforms
closely to Spegazzini's conception of the fungus.

 On palm leaves (*Palmaceae*), Australia, intercepted at San Francisco,
Cal., March 19, 1916, Geo. Compere, Plant. Quar. Insp., U.S.D.A. No,
90288.

150. **Pestalotia funerea** Desm. Ann. Sci. Nat. Bot. II, 19:335–336,1843;
 Mem. Soc. Roy. Sci. Agr. Arts, Lille 1842:108–109,1843; Syll. Fung.
 3:791, 1884.

 P. abietina Roum. Fungi Galliae Exs. 735, 1880, nom. nud.

 P. cesati Rabh., Fungi europ. Exs. 1932, 1875.

 P. cupressina Niessl, Hedwigia 22:188,1883; Syll. Fung. 3:792,1884.

 P. inquinans Cooke & Harkn. Grevillea 12:94,1884; Syll. Fung. 3:784,
 1884.

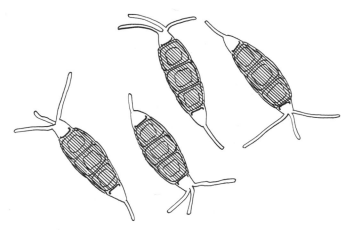

   Fɪɢ. 46 [149]. *Pestalotia macrochaeta* (Speg.) Guba.

P. polychaetia Cooke & Harkn., Grevillea 12:94,1884; Syll. Fung. 3:785, 1884.

P. funerea Desm. var. *taxodii* C. Roum.   Fungi Galliae Exs. 3385, 1885, nom. nud.

P. funerea Desm. var. *cryptomeriae* D. Sacc., Myc. Ital. 1569, 1905, nom. nud.

P. aomoriensis Sawada, Bull. Govt. For. Exp. Sta., Japan 45:52,1950.

Pestalotiopsis funerea (Desm.) Stey., Bull. Jard. Bot. État Bruxelles 19: 340–342,1949, pl. 17, fig. C.

P. funerioides Stey., Bull. Jard. Bot. État Bruxelles 19:345–346,1949, fig. 28.

Pustules amphigenous, 100–300 μ in diam, scattered or confluent, puncti-form, globose-lenticular, subepidermal then erumpent, surrounded by the torn epidermis, the sooty contents staining the matrix.   Conidia clavate-fusoid, broad, tapering toward the base, 5-celled, straight, 21–29 × 7–9.5 μ; intermediate colored cells guttulate, umber or olivaceous, equally colored or the lowest colored cells sometimes slightly paler, usually 15–20 μ long, slightly constricted at septa; superior hyaline cells short-conic bearing a crest of 3 to 6, usually 4 to 5 simple, straight setulae, 5–20 μ long; basal hyaline cells usually short, rather obtuse or broad-conic; pedicels 2–7 μ, sometimes up to 12 μ long.

On leaves, bark and cones of members of the *Coniferales*, the type on dead leaves of *Thuja*, near Paris, France, 1841.

Specimens examined: On *Abies lanceolata* Poir. [= *Cunninghamia lanceo-tala* Hook.] (leaves), Roumeguère, Fungi Galliae Exs. 735, Angers, France, leg. Guepin, sub *P. abietina* Roum. (*P. guepini* Desm. var. *abietina* Guepin) [Fig. 47a]; on *Araucaria bidwellii* Hook. (leaves), in Briosi and Cavara, Funghi par., VII–VIII, no. 200 [Fig. 47b].

On *Chamaecyparis lawsoniana* (Murr.) Parl. (leaves and twigs), Sydow Myc. Germ. No. 839, Tamsel, Brandenburg, Germany, Apr. 1, 1909, leg. P. Vogel, (Klebahn, Myc. Centralbl. 4:5,1914, fig. 34, 3a) [Fig. 47c]: Kabat and Bubak, Fungi Imperfecti Exs. 739, same locality, Feb. 7, 1911.

On *Cryptomeria japonica* D. Don (leaves and cones), D. Saccardo, Myc. Ital. No. 1569, Padua, Italy, Apr. 1904, sub *P. funerea* Desm. var. *cryptomeriae* D. Sacc.; (twigs), in herb. Berlin Bot. Mus., Parma, Italy, leg. Passerini (Klebahn, Myc. Centralbl. 4:5,1914, fig. 34, 3b).

On *Cupressus flavescens* (cones), in herb. Grove No. 4119, East Cornwall, England, leg. Rhodes and Rilstone, July 21, 1929, sub *P. conigena* Lév.; on *C. glauca* Lam. (dead twigs), Coimbra, Portugal No. 687 (IV Ser.) in herb. Jard. Bot., Univ. Coimbra, No. 1132 sub *P. cupressina* Niessl; on *C. macro-carpa* Gord. (bark), in Ellis, N. Am. Fungi No. 634, California, leg. Harkness; on *Cupressus* sp. in Rabenhorst, Herb. Myc. Fung. I: 63, Brixia, Italy, Cesati sub *P. funerea* Desm. var. *heterspora* Desm.

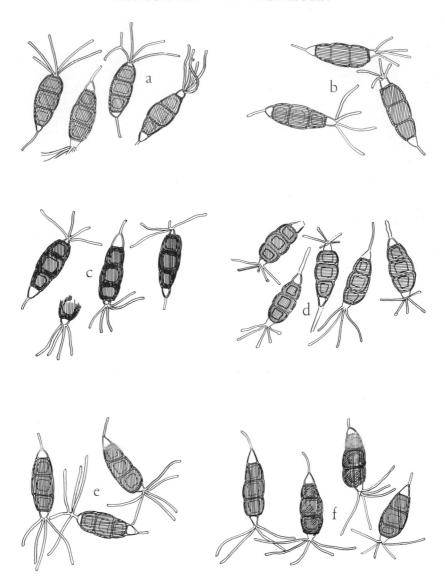

Fɪɢ. 47 [150]. *Pestalotia funerea* Desm.

On *Juniperus* (leaves), in herb. Grove, Stratford-on-Avon, England; on *J. chinensis* L. (leaves and twigs), Shiloh, N. J., Sept. 9, 1927, leg. R. P. White.

On *Retinospora squarrosa* Sieb. & Zucc. [= *Chamaecyparis pisifera* (Sieb. & Zucc.) Endl. var. *scriarrosa* (Endl.) Beiss. & Hochst.] (leaves), Sydow, Mycotheca Marchica No. 4440, Bellevue Garten, Berlin, Oct. 1895, leg. P. Sydow.

On *Pinus taeda* L. (cones), herb. Curtis No. 3797 in herb. Farlow, Society Hill, S. C., June, 1857.

On *Podocarpus latifolia* Hort. (leaves), Rabenhorst, Fungi europ. Exs. 1932, Naples, Italy, leg. Cesati, sub *P. cesati* Rabh. [Fig. 47d].

On *Sequoia sempervirens* Endl. (leaves), Angers, France, leg. Guepin, herb. crypt. Tulasne, in herb. Mus. d'Hist. Nat. Paris; (wood) Trinidad, California, 1932, leg. H. E. Parks.

On *Thuja occidentalis* L. (twigs and leaves), West Manchester, Mass., July 1936, Guba; Wellesley, Mass., Aug. 1938, Guba; Concord, Mass., Sept. 1949, A. MacDougall; (leaves), in Rabenhorst, Fungi europ. Exs. No. 2898, Padua, Italy, Aug. 1881, P. A. Saccardo; ex. herb. Dearness No. 3325 and Ellis & Everhart Fungi Col. No. 3535, London, Ont., Canada, Aug. 1911, leg. Dearness; (cones), in Ravenel, Fungi Am. Exs. No. 700, Aiken, S. C.; Ellis, N. Am. Fungi No. 527, Sept. 1880 sub *P. conigena* Lév.; on *T. occidentalis* L. var. *ellwangeriana* Beiss. in Krieger, Fungi Saxonici, Shandau, Germany, Aug. 28, 1901, W. Krieger; on *T. orientalis* L. (cones), in Otto Jaap, Fungi sel. Exs. 443, Brandenburg, Germany, leg. Jaap, 1910, sub *P. conigena* Lév.; on *T. orientalis* L. var. *elegantissima* (Gord.) Vos. (leaves), Shiloh, N. J., Sept. 9, 1927, leg. R. H. White; on *T. pyramidalis* Ten. [= *T. orientalis* L. var. *stricta* Loud.], Shiloh, N. J., Sept. 9, 1927, leg. White.

On *Thuja* and *Juniperus* (leaves), Angers, France, leg. Guepin, herb. Dr. Roussel in Mus. d'Hist. Nat. Paris.

On *Thuja* and *Cupressus* (leaves), Nov. and Dec. 1841 in herb. Desmazières No. 8 in Mus. d'Hist. Nat. Paris.

Desmazières' description of *P. funerea* is incomplete. The setulae are given as 3, 4 or rarely 5, straight, slender, about half as long as the conidia which were given as 22.2 μ long. In the absence of an adequate description, the fungus has come to be badly misunderstood. The fungus is restricted to the *Coniferales*. Both Saccardo and Rabenhorst listed host plants in many families and Doyer (Med. Phytopath. Lab. "Will. Comm. Scholt." 9:1–72,1925) asserted that the species is omnivorous. Likewise, numerous varieties of *P. funerea* on widely scattered and unrelated hosts have been described. Gleisberg (Ber. Deut. Bot. Ges. 39:63–72,1914) and Doyer doubted the genetic relationship of these varieties, and my examination of many types shows no analogy to the nominal species. Nevertheless *P. funerea* has been used in a very general way. The status of *P. conigena* Lév. is quite similar. The type was described on *Thuja occidentalis* L. and *Pinus sylvestris* L. but the fungi on the two hosts are distinct, that on *Thuja* being *P. funerea*. Reference in the type description to the obtuse apical cell and 4 short setulae is suggestive of *P. funerea* and *Thuja* is a common host plant. Reference to the long attenuated conidia and 4 setulae in the description of *P. conigena* Lév. is not characteristic of *P. funerea* and suggests the fungus on *Pinus*. The type on *Pinus* in Mus. d'Hist. Nat. Paris is not *P. funerea* Desm.

It is accepted as the type of *P. conigena* Lév.   Steyaert (Bull. Jard. Bot. État Bruxelles 19:340,1949, pl. 17, fig. D, tab. IV), regarded *P. conigena* Lév. a synonym.   The author prefers to keep the two species separate.

Pestalotia cesatii Rabh., on leaves of *Podocarpus*, Rabenhorst, Fungi europ. No. 1932, is a synonym.   The conidia measure $22-27 \times 8-8.5 \mu$, colored part olivaceous or umber, $15.8-19.5 \mu$, setulae 3–6, usually 5, $6-15 \mu$ long; pedicels $3-12 \mu$.

P. aomoriensis Sawada is a synonym.   The fungus has clavate-fusiform, 5-celled conidia, $27-28 \times 6.5-7 \mu$, colored cells $16-19 \mu$, 3–5 setulae $15-26 \mu$, exterior hyaline cells conoid.   On leaves and stems of *Cryptomeria japonica* D. Don, Japan.

Pestalotia funerea Desm. var. *heterospora* Desm. (Ann. Sci. Nat. Bot. II, 19:336,1843) on dead leaves of *Cupressus*, France, embraces two distinct species.   One has 5-septate, long pedicellate conidia destitute of apical setulae, the other 4-septate short pedicellate conidia crested with several setulae and typical of *P. funerea* Desm.   *P. funerea* Desm. var. *heterospora* Desm. in Desmazières' Plantes Crypt. Fr., fasc. 27, no. 1326, is a *Coryneum* with 5-septate conidia and no other conidial form is present.   Apparently cotype material was issued in Roumeguère Fungi Galliae Exs. 432 under the same name and inscribed "Ad folia emortua *Cupressorum, Juniperi communis, Thujarumque* in hortis, Spec. dedit amice Desmazières."   Klebahn (Myc. Centralbl. 4:18,1914) stated that the fungus probably is a *Hendersonia*.   The specimen in Rabenhorst, Klotzsch Herb. Myc. Fung. I: 63,1855, on *Cupressus* from Brixia, Italy, leg. Cesati, bearing the name *P. funerea* Desm. var. *heterospora* Desm., is *P. funerea* Desm.

Thuemen (Fung. Austriaci No. 1062, 1874) published the epithet *Pestalotia heterospora* Desm. var. *cupressi* Cesati on leaves of *Cupressus lawsoniana* A. Murr. [= *Chamaecyparis lawsoniana* (Murr.) Parl.], Tetschen, Bohemia, 1873.   The material lacks the fungus.   The name suggests *P. funerea* Desm. var. *heterospora* Desm.   The type bearing the latter name is a mixture of two distinct species, one of them being *P. funerea* Desm.

P. funerea Desm., var. *taxodii* C. Roum. (Fungi Galliae Exs. 3385, 1885) was reported on dead leaves of *Taxodium distichum* H.B.K. Forest of Fontainebleau, Seine et Marne, France, Feb. 1884, Feuilleaubois.   The specimen is empty.   Klebahn (Myc. Centralbl. 4:18,1914) reported the same circumstances.

Pestalotia inquinans Cooke & Harkn. was originally described on dead leaves of *Eucalyptus*, California, herb. Kew No. 2094 [Fig. 47e].   The species is identical with *P. funerea* Desm.

P. polychaetia Cooke & Harkn. was described on twigs of *Cytisus*, California, herb. Kew [Fig. 47f].   The fungus has all of the characters of *P. funerea* Desm.   The original description mentioned 3-celled conidia and it is vague in other respects.

The species *Pestalotiopsis funerioides* Stey. is based on a culture of a fungus from *Cupressus* sp., collected by Branquhinho d'Oliveira, Azores Islands, and originally named *P. funerea* Desm. var. *macrochaeta* Speg. One setula is in line with the axis of the conidium, the others diverge by 45–90 degrees. Steyaert reported that the conidia are longer and the setulae longer, more slender and flexuous than those of *P. funerea* Desm. Spegazzini distinguished *P. funerea* var. *macrochaeta* from *P. funerea* by the length of the setulae which measure 15–32 μ and by 3 setulae. The number of setulae would also distinguish it from *Pestalotiopsis funerioides* Stey. (Bull. Jard. Bot. État Bruxelles 19:1949, fig. 28). *P. funerioides* is the same as *Pestalotia funerea* except that it has longer and flexuous setulae, but the difference does not seem significant and could be the result of artificial culture.

A fungus having the characters of *P. funerea* was reported as the cause of the brown leaf diseases of *Phlox* in Austria by Wenzl (Z. Pflanzenkr. 48:346–347,1938). No infection studies were undertaken.

There are differences of opinion concerning the biology of *Pestalotia funerea* Desm. Böhm (Z. Forstw. Jadgw. 26:63–71,1894) reported this species causing the blighting of shoots of *Thuja menziesii* Dougl. [=*T. plicata* D. Don]. He was successful in obtaining infection with conidia applied to wounds on living twigs of *Thuja menziesii* Dougl., *Chamaecyparis lawsoniana* (Murr.) Parl. and *Pseudostuga douglasii* Carr. [=*P. menziesii* (Mirb.) Franco], but after five months no conidia developed. The extensive dying of junipers at Eberswalde which Böhm attributed to *P. funerea* was claimed by Danckelmann to be due to temperatures of −30C to −32C in the winter of 1892–1893. Gleisberg (Ber. Deut. Bot. Ges. 39: 63–72,1914) inoculated living parts of *Thuja occidentalis* L. with conidia of *P. funerea* obtained from that host but without success, and he concluded that *P. funerea* was a saprophyte which developed only after a change in the nature of the bark.

Spaulding (Science 26:220–221,1907) reported a serious needle blight of *Pinus ponderosa* Laws. and *P. divaricata* Dum.-Cours. [=*P. banksiana* Lam.] on two-year-old seedlings from which he recovered *P. funerea*. He succeeded in infecting healthy seedlings of *Pinus ponderosa* Laws. A similar disease was reported from South Africa by Fisher (Agr. Jour., Union South Africa 3: 389–391,1912) on *Pinus pinaster* Ait., *P. canariensis* C. Smith, *P. longifolia* Salisb. [=*P. palustris* Mill.], *P. insignis* Dougl. [=*P. radiata* D. Don], *P. massoniana* Lamb., *Cupressus lusitanica* Mill., *Chamaecyparis lawsoniana* (Murr.) Parl., and *Casuarina leptoclada* Miq. The organism was identified as *P. funerea* but no proof of its pathogenicity was established. Hartley *et al.* (Jour. Agr. Research 15:521–558,1918) reported *P. funerea* prevalent on dead coniferous needles throughout the United States. With cultures obtained from Jack and Rocky Mountain yellow spines, inoculations of white pine were without result. Attempts to infect green shoots of *Thuja occidentalis* L. injured by puncturing or heating, failed.

Hartley (U.S.D.A., Bur. Plant Industry Bull. 44,1913) reported having isolated forms of *Pestalotia* with 4- and 5-celled conidia from dead coniferous seedlings, but the cultures were not sufficiently frequent to indicate parasitism. Smith (Gard. Chron. III, 26:354,1899) found *P. funerea* associated with withered distal portions of shoots of *Biota orientalis* Endl. [=*Thuja orientalis* L.] in England, and reported a similar phenomenon on species of *Thuja*, *Cupressus*, *Chamaecyparis*, and *Juniperus*. He assumed the fungus to be parasitic because Tubeuf (Beitr. Kennt. Baumkr. 1888) regarded *P. hartigii* as the cause of the "Einschnürungskrankheit" of forest tree seedlings in Germany. Wenner (Phytopathology 4:375–383,1914) isolated *P. funerea* from bark and needles of *Pinus strobus* L. and his inoculation experiments proved that this species is parasitic, especially under moist conditions. The fungus was shown to be capable of attacking leaves and stems of white pine, Norway spruce, and hemlock. Studhalter (Science 55:547,1922) artificially infected the needles of *Pinus radiata* D. Don, apparently with *P. funerea*. Graves (Phytopathology 4:63–72,1914) found a *Pestalotia* on needles of withered shoots of Norway spruce, and the manner of the appearance of the disease suggested a parasitic relationship. Doyer (Med. Phytopath. Lab. "Will. Comm. Scholt." 9:1–72,1925) inoculated seedlings of *Pinus sylvestris* L. and *Picea excelsa* Link [=*P. abies* (L.) Karst.] with *P. funerea* from *Thuja* and *Chamaecyparis*, with a form from *Taxus*, *Biota*, and *Retinospora* named *P. macrotricha* Kleb., with a form from *Thuja* named *P. versicolor* Speg., and with Fischer's strain of *P. hartigii* Tubeuf. In no case was infection obtained. Negative results were also obtained on the same plants with Brown's strain of *P. scirrofaciens* Brown, *P. monochaetioides* Doyer, *P. virgatula* Kleb., and *P. theae* Sawada. Further inoculations of conifers under various conditions and at different times of the year failed.

White (New Jersey Agr. Exp. Sta. Rep. 1930, 267–268,1931) isolated *P. funerea* Desm. from many host plants among the *Coniferales* and considered it a contributing factor in the death of the leaves. It was observed on grafted stock and cuttings. Crandall (Phytopathology 28: 227–229,1938) isolated the fungus from diseased roots of *Pinus resinosa* Ait. and his inoculations of seedlings at and below the soil line killed the plants through injuries within 20 days. Davis *et al.* (U.S.D.A. Forest Path. C.C.C., lit. cit. p. 26, mimeogr. ed., Dec. 1938) associated the fungus with girdled lesions on stems of pine seedlings in nurseries, accompanied by a swelling above the lesions.

Christensen (Bull. Torrey Bot. Club 59:525–554,1932) with a *Pestalotia* misdetermined *P. funerea*, obtained from needles of *Pinus palustris* Mill. killed by *Septoria acicola* Thuem., failed to infect uninjured seedlings of many types of conifers and concluded that the fungus is saprophytic. The description of his races of the fungus and microphotographs of spores show nothing in common with *P. funerea*.

Birch (N. Z. Jour. For. 3:3,108–113,1933) reported the association of *P. funerea* with the damping-off disease of coniferous seedlings and gummosis of *Cupressus macrocarpa* Hartw. and *C. lawsoniana* A. Murr. [= *Chamaecyparis lawsoniana* (Murr.) Parl.]. Infection was associated with contaminated soil, bark injuries about the roots and high humidity under abnormally crowded conditions in the nursery. Loss of vigor following transplanting contributed to the further growth of the pathogen and the death of the transplants. Salisbury (Bimonthly Prog. Rep., Div. For. Biol., Dept. Agr., Canada 13,6,4,1957) reported heavy damage to Chinese juniper, *Juniperus chinensis* L. associated with *P. funerea* in British Columbia. Gibson (E. African Agr. Jour. 24:1,47–52,1958), in a survey of pine plantations in Kenya, reported on the prevalence of a pine disease known as "dead top." As the shoots die they become colonized by insects and fungi, and most frequently by species of Pestalotia which were not specifically identified. Proof of their pathogenicity was not established, thus leaving the subject in doubt.

151. **Pestalotia multiseta** (Speg.) Guba, comb. nov.

   P. funerea Desm. var. *multiseta* Speg., Michelia 1:479,1879; Syll. Fung. 3:791,1884.

Conidia 5-celled, long-fusiform, elongate, elliptic, 22–26 × 7.5–9.5 μ, hardly constricted at the septa; intermediate colored cells umber, equally colored, 15–19 μ, guttulate, apical hyaline cells long conic-cylindric, obtuse or hemispherical, basal cells hyaline or dilute yellow with contents, narrow to broad-conic; setulae 3–5, simple or one of them usually branched, 9–16 μ long, apical; pedicels up to 6 μ long.

On fallen leaves of *Iris germanica* L., Conegliano, Italy, 1877, Spegazzini [Fig. 48]. The type description is quite inaccurate. The conidia are given as 25–30 × 9–10 μ, the setulae as 5–10 μ long. The fungus is distinct from *P. funerea* Desm. in the branching setulae and long exterior hyaline cells.

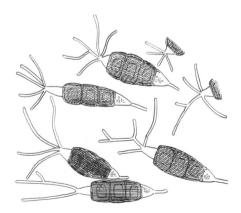

F𝚒ɢ. 48 [151].   *Pestalotia multiseta* (Speg.) Guba.

152. **Pestalotia thujae** Sawada, Rep. Govt. For. Exp. Sta., Japan 46:140,1950.

Pustules epiphyllous, sparse or crowded, borne under the epidermis, at length dehiscing at the apices.   Conidia elliptic-fusiform, 5-celled, 25–31 × 6.5–10 μ; intermediate cells equally colored, 18–19 × 6.5–10 μ; exterior cells hyaline; apical cells conic, 4.5–6 μ long; 3–6 setulae, 2 of them at apex, 1–4 radiating from slope and base of apical cells, 19–22 μ long; basal cells obconic, 3.5–13 μ long; pedicels short.

On leaves and young twigs of *Thuja standishii* Carr.   Foliage and young shoots are killed by the fungus.

On cone scales of *Thuja occidentalis* L., Oneida, N. Y., June 6, 1923, H. D. House, sub *P. conigenoides* Dearn. & House in Myc. Fairmanii No. 4733 and herb. N. Y. State Mus. [Fig. 49a].

On withered shoots of *Picea abies* Karst., Weston, Mass., June 13, 1938, Guba [Fig. 49b].   Conidia 24–27 × 6–7.5 μ, setulae 3–4, rarely 5 or 2, 20–31 μ long, 1 setula at base of apical cell, others from apex or side of apical hyaline cells; pedicels 6–15 μ long.

153. **Pestalotia caudata** Syd., Bull. Herb. Boiss. II: 1,84,1900; Syll. Fung. 16: 1017,1902.

Pustules amphigenous, subglobose or lenticular, subepidermal, erumpent, black, scattered, later disposed in a series, confluent or hysteriform, up to 1 cm long.   Conidia long-fusiform, erect, tapering at the extremities, 5-celled, 28–35 μ long; intermediate cells olivaceous, the central ones umber, not constricted at the septa, 18–21 × 6–7 μ; apical hyaline cells long-cylindric, bearing usually 3, sometimes 2 or 4 filiform setulae, 18–24 μ, rather uniform in length, divergent and reflexed; basal hyaline cells long, acute or attenuated.

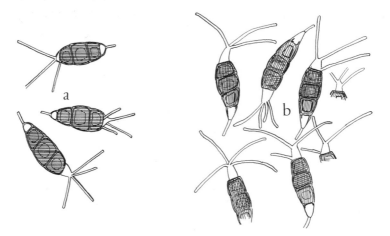

F𝗂ɢ. 49 [152].   *Pestalotia thujae* Sawada.

On stems of *Cladium ensifolium* Benth., Serra do Itatiaia, Brazil, E. Ule, No. 2143 in herb. Sydow, Mus. Bot., Stockholm, Sweden. This is a characteristic species having long, narrow conidia and prolonged tail-like inferior cells.

Grove (British Stem and Leaf Fung. II, 350,1937) reported this species on leaves and stems of *Cladium mariscus* (L.) R. Br. in England.

154. **Pestalotia heterospora** Griff. & Maubl., Bull. Soc. Mycol. Fr. 29:248–249,1913, fig. 2; Syll. Fung. 25:606,1931.

Pustules pycnoid, epiphyllous, scattered, erumpent, punctiform, black, seated on dry pale smoky spots. Conidia polymorphic, some normal, regular, fusiform, 5-celled, $25 \times 6\,\mu$; intermediate cells brown, exterior cells conoid, hyaline; setulae 4, short, divergent; lower hyaline cells attenuated into filiform pedicels. Other conidia irregular, 2–4-celled, allantoid, flexuous, curved, $25\text{–}40 \times 5\text{–}7\,\mu$, with or without exterior hyaline cells, often moderately constricted at the septa, the superior cells naked or bearing 3 or 4 setulae, the base often truncate, pedicels broad-fusoid, $15\text{–}20 \times 5\,\mu$.

On living leaves of *Butyrospermum parkii* Kotschy, Koulikora (Haut Senegal and Niger), Africa, Vuillet. The species is characterized by peculiar polymorphic conidia. The fungus follows leaf spots caused by a species of *Fusicladium*.

155. **Pestalotia nattrassii** (Stey.) Guba, comb. nov.
   Pestalotiopsis nattrassii Stey. Trans. Brit. Mycol. Soc. 36:82,1953, fig. 1.
   P. guepini (Desm.) Stey. var. *major* Stey. Trans. Brit. Mycol. Soc. 36:237, 1953, fig. 1.

Conidia fusiform, 5-septate, $27\text{–}33 \times 8\text{–}9\,\mu$; intermediate cells brown, concolorous, slightly constricted at septa, $17\text{–}23\,\mu$ long, guttulate; exterior hyaline cells conoid; setulae $18\text{–}32.8\text{–}46\,\mu$ long, 1–4, branched above the apices, $24\text{–}35.4\text{–}44\,\mu$ long, sometimes sub-branched; basal hyaline cells conoid or rotundate; pedicels lacking, short or deciduous.

Culture from leaves of *Thea sinensis* L. [= *Camellia sinensis* (L.) Kuntze], Sotik, Kenya, East Africa, Dec. 1949, R. M. Nattrass.

According to Steyaert, this species is remarkable for its branched setulae, for which it resembles *Pestalotiopsis karstenii*. The branches arise at different levels on the short stalks 1 to $2\,\mu$ above the apical cells. The pedicels are lacking. The species is a large form of *Pestalotia guepini* Desm., a familiar inhabitant of *Camellia* and *Thea*, and both fig. 1 (Trans. Brit. Mycol. Soc. 36:237,1953) and the characters reported by Steyaert show a close relationship to this species. *Pestalotia karstenii* is a synonym of *P. guepini* Desm. *Pestalotiopsis guepini* (Desm.) Stey. var. *major* Stey. was described with long conidia $28\text{–}36 \times 7\text{–}9\,\mu$, 1–4, usually 3 setulae, branched, $20\text{–}45\,\mu$ long, pedicels $3\text{–}13\,\mu$ long, on dead leaves of *Encephalartos barteri* Carruth., Gold Coast,

West Africa, May 1949, S. J. Hughes. *Pestalotia guepini* Desm. and *Pestalotiopsis nattrassii* Stey. could not belong to the section Monosetulatae (*Pestalotiopsis*) = *Monochaetia*, as reported by Steyaert. *Pestalotia guepini* Desm., or it synonyms, has never been associated with the genus *Monochaetia*.

156. **Pestalotia betazamiae** Guba sp. nov.

Pustulae amphigenae, globoso-lenticulares usque hysteriformes, separatae vel confluentes, innato-erumpentes, 150–600 × 125–225 μ, atrae; conidia 5-cellularia, longa, fusiformia, ad basim attenuata, 28–35 × 7.5–9.5 μ, aequilateralia; cellulae basales acutae, apicales longae, cylindricae; cellulae mediae coloratae aequaliter umbrinae vel duae superiores paulo obscuriores, 19–24 longae; setulae 3, ad apicem extremam orientes, 19–38 μ longae, divergentes; pedicelli 6–10 μ longi.

Pustules amphigenous, globose-lenticular to hysteriform, separate or confluent, innate-erumpent, tearing the epidermis in a linear manner, 150–600 × 125–225 μ, black, the sooty contents ejecting and staining the matrix. Conidia 5-celled, long fusiform, tapering to the base, 28–35 × 7.5–9.5 μ, equilateral; basal cells long, acute, apical cells long, cylindric; intermediate colored cells umber throughout or the upper 2 colored cells somewhat darker, 19–24 μ long; setulae 3, arising at the apical extremity, 19–38 μ long, divergent; pedicels 6–10 μ long.

On brown weathered leaves of *Zamia* sp., Coconut Grove, Fla., 1897–98, Roland Thaxter, in herb. Farlow.

157. **Pestalotia oryzae** Hara.   Diseases of Rice, 1918, p. 200; 2nd ed., 1939, p. 176; Shirai, List of Japanese Fungi (K. Hara, 3rd ed., 1927, p. 253).

Acervuli punctiform, scattered, borne under the epidermis, erumpent, the contents oozing, pulvinate, brown, with very small stromata. Conidia ellipsoidal or fusoid, 5-celled, 25–35 × 7–10 μ, acuminate at apices, exterior cells small and short; intermediate colored cells yellowish brown, concolorous, constricted at the septa; setulae 3, filiform, 20–45 μ long; pedicels linear, 15–20 μ.

On dry stems and leaves of *Oryza sativa* L. Kawakami-mura, Pref. Gifu, Sept. 1914, 1920, K. Hara.

158. **Pestalotia trevoae** Speg. Rev. Facult. Agron. Vet., Argentina 6: Pt. 2, 178,1910; Syll. Fung. 22:1220,1913.

Pustules globose-lenticular, black, free or numerous and coalescing, 150–300 μ in diam., subepidermal, then erumpent, surrounded by torn cortex and epidermis, the black contents staining the matrix.

Conidia 5-celled, subcylindric, long and broad ellipsoid, rather strongly constricted at septa, 25–35 × 9–12 μ, three large intermediate colored cells, 21–26 μ long, guttulate, fuliginous or chocolate brown, subopaque, equally

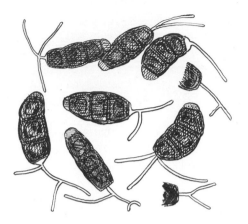

FIG. 50 [158]. *Pestalotia trevoae* Speg.

colored, surmounted by an obscure, obtuse or hemispherical, hyaline papilla or membrane, basal cells hemispherical, pale yellow-brown; apical appendages 2–4, usually 3, often branched, sometimes 1 and branched, 13–33 μ long, filiform, arising abruptly from the hyaline membranous papilla surmounting the conidia; pedicels deciduous, indefinite or absent.

On dead decaying branches of *Trevoa trinervia* Miers, San Bernardo, near Santiago, Chile, Spegazzini [Fig. 50].

The apical membrane or cell is collapsed, concealed or very short, acute or filiform, covering the superior colored cell. The pedicels according to Spegazzini are 30–50 μ long.

159. **Pestalotia macrospora** Ces., Fres. Beitr. Myk. 54–56,1852; Klotzsch, Herb. Myc. Fung. 17:1663,1852, nom. nud.; Syll. Fung. 3:796,1884; Klebahn, Myc. Centralbl. 4:3,1914.

    P. pteridis Sacc. in Thuemen, Myc. Univ. 83,1875; Syll. Fung. 15:242, 1901.

    P. funerea Desm. var. *typica* Sacc., Michelia 1:479,1879; Syll. Fung. 3:791, 1885.

    Pestalotiopsis macrospora (Ces.) Stey., Bull. Jard. Bot. État Bruxelles 19: 344–345,1949, fig. 27.

Pustules globose-lenticular, mostly epiphyllous, sparse or crowded, sometimes coalescing, subepidermal, erumpent on maturity, darkening the substratum, 140–275 μ in diam. Conidia 5-celled, straight, long clavate, 30–40 × 7–9 μ; intermediate colored cells 20–29 μ, cylindric, olivaceous, equally colored or slightly contrasted; apical hyaline cells small, obtuse, bearing a crest of 3–5, or usually 4–5 setulae, arising separately or in pairs and often branched, 15–22 μ; basal hyaline cells long, acute, tapering into rather long pedicels, 6–11 μ.

On blighted fronds of *Pteris aquilina* L. [= *Pteridium aquilinum* (L.) Kuhn]. The fungus is characterized by long clavate conidia, small apical cells and a crest of numerous setulae which are sometimes branched.

Specimens examined: Klotzsch, Herb. Myc. Fung. 17:1663,1852, Cesati; D. Saccardo, Myc. Ital. No. 1175, Montello, near Treviso, Italy, Sept. 1902; Saccardo, Mycotheca Veneta No. 326, Montello, Italy; Petrak, Fungi Albanici et Bosniaci Exs. 33, Sept. 29, 1918, F. Petrak [Fig. 51a]; Rabh. Herb. Myc. Fung. No. 66 ex. herb. Thuemen and Thuemen, Myc. Univ. 83, Montello, Italy, Sept. 1874, P. Saccardo, sub *P. pteridis* Sacc. [Fig. 51b]; herb. Patouillard in herb. Farlow, Honnet, France, Trabut, sub *P. funerea* Desm. var. *typica* Sacc.

Accurate illustrations of this species were published by Voglino (Atti. Soc. Ven.-Trent, Sci. Nat. Padova 9: pl. 4, fig. 22, 1885), Saccardo (Fung. Ital., aut. del. Patavia, 1876–1886, Table 1114) and Klebahn (Myc. Centralbl. 4: fig. 34, 1914). Saccardo (Michelia 1:479,1879) reported *P. funerea* Desm. var. *typica* Sacc. on *Pteris aquilina* L. [= *Pteridium aquilinum* (L.) Kuhn], *Photinia serrulata* Lindl., *Eucalyptus stuartiana* F. Muell., *Rubus fruticosus* L., *Euonymus chinensis* Lindl., *Thuja* and *Cupressus*, but Saccardo's assertion of such wide host range is incorrect.

160. **Pestalotia hughesii** (Stey.) Guba, comb. nov.

Pestalotiopsis hughesii Stey., Trans. Brit. Mycol. Soc. 36:237,1953, fig. 2.

Spots indefinite. Pustules circular or oval, 250–300 μ diam. Conidia fusoid, straight or somewhat curved, 5-celled, 34–45 × 7–11 μ; 3 intermediate cells brown, concolorous, guttulate, 18–32 μ long; exterior cells hyaline, apical cells long conoid, setulae 2 to 3, broad, with conspicuous lumen, 9–29 μ long, basal cells conoid, tapering; pedicels 3–8 μ long.

On stems of *Cyperus articulatus* L. Gold Coast, West Africa, April 1949, S. J. Hughes. The setulae are thick at the base with a thick membrane that

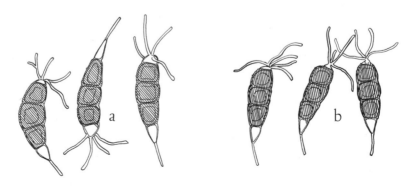

Fig. 51 [159].   *Pestalotia macrospora* Ces.

thins out abruptly towards the middle.   This gives the setulae a more or less bulbous appearance at the base.   A wide lumen is visible in the whole length of the setulae.   The setulae are sometimes branched near the bases (suggestive of a starfish with 3 rather than 5 appendages).   The species was dedicated to S. J. Hughes, Commonwealth Mycological Institute, Kew, England, in recognition of his mycological explorations in the Gold Coast and Togoland.

Versicolorae, Umbrae-Olivae

Species Nos. 161–201

161. **Pestalotia paraguayensis** Speg., Ann. Soc. Ci. Argent. 26:68,1888; Syll. Fung. 10:491,1892.

Spots amphigenous, orbicular, small, 0.5–1 mm in diam, often margined, determinate, becoming white and surrounded by purplish zones.   Pustules amphigenous, solitary in central portion of spots, some gregarious, 80–100 μ in diam, black, erumpent.   Conidia 5-celled, obovate or sub-clavate, $20 \times 7 \mu$; exterior hyaline cells small, 3 intermediate colored cells brown-olivaceous, the lowest of them pale or lighter; setulae 2–3, short, coarse, $5–10 \times 1.5 \mu$, divergent; pedicels short, $5 \times 1 \mu$, hyaline.

On living leaves of *Euphoria* sp., sometimes in association with a species of *Phyllosticta*, Caa-Guazu, Brazil, Jan. 1882.

162. **Pestalotia palmarum** Cooke, Grevillea 4:115,1875; 5:102,1876, pl. 86, fig. 3; Syll. Fung. 3:796,1884; Klebahn, Myc. Centralbl. 4:9,1914; Guba, Phytopathology 19:210–212,1929.

P. brevipes Prill. & Del., Bull. Soc. Mycol. Fr. 10: 84–85,1894; Syll. Fung. 11:578,1895.

P. fuscescens Sor., Z. Pflanzenkr. 2nd ed., 2:399–400,1886, figs. 18–19; Syll. Fung. 22:1227,1917.

P. palmicola Sacc. & Syd., Syll. Fung. 14:1030,1899.

P. arengae Lund, Bot. Tidsskr. 43:306–308,1935, fig. 2.

P. taslimiana Mund. & Kheswalla, Mycologia 34:310,1942.

Pestalotiopsis palmarum (Cooke) Stey., Bull. Jard. Bot. État Bruxelles 19:322,1949.

Pustules subepidermal, erumpent, punctiform, scattered or gregarious, globose-lenticular to hysteriform, $125–425 \times 100–250 \mu$, often coalescing, sooty at maturity, seated on brown or ashen-gray spots with determinate margins or generally on discolored areas and dead matrix.   Conidia straight or curved, 5-celled, $16–22 \times 5–7 \mu$; intermediate colored cells usually versicolorous, the upper two umber, the lowest olivaceous, sometimes equally colored, $11–15 \mu$, only slightly constricted at septa; exterior cells tapering;

setulae 2, usually 3, up to 16 μ, sometimes slightly longer, divergent; pedicels short, up to 6 μ long.

On *Cocos nucifera* L. and other species of *Palmaceae*.

On *Cocos nucifera* L. (sprout), Bengal, India, Jan. 27, 1870, in herb. Kew; (leaves), Demerara, British Guiana, subm. by M. C. Cooke, Roumeguère Fungi Galliae Exs. 5166, Thuem., Myc. Univ. to 1676 and herb. P. A. Saccardo; Santurce, Puerto Rico, Nov. 20, 1911, J. R. Johnston [Fig. 52a]. *Cocos plumosa* Hook. (bark), Los Angeles, Cal., Dec. 15, 1926, O. A. Plunkett. *Acrista monticola* O. F. Cooke, Luquillo Forest, Puerto Rico, F. L. Stevens No. 5553, Dec. 2, 1913. *Archontophoenix alexandrae* Wendl. & Drude (rotting petiole), Paget East, Bermuda, J. M. Waterston, No. 509, Feb. 3, 1943. *Areca cathecu* L. (dead sheaths), herb. University of California, No. 411963; Los Baños, Philippine Islands, C. F. Baker, Oct. 1914.

Arenga saccharifera Labill. (leaves), Djoeloe, Toba, Sumatra, Sept. 6, 1916, sub *P. arengae* Lund (type). *Calamus* sp., Chittagong, India, Dec. 15, 1907, No. 2250, Pusa, Aug. 24, 1916, M. Taslim, sub *P. taslimiana* Mund. & Kheswalla, in herb. Crypt. Ind. Orient. *Chamaerops humilis* L. (spathes), Cavara Fung. Longobard. Exs. No. 193, in Bot. Gard., Pavia, Italy. Klebahn (Myc. Centralbl. 4:12–13,1914) reported that the conidia measure 22–27 × 8–9μ. He regarded the fungus as *P. versicolor* Speg. *Corypha elata* Roxb. (leaves), Los Baños, Philippine Islands, O. A. Reinking No. 161, 1917. *Howea forsteriana* (F. Muell.) Becc. (leaves), Florida, sub *P. discoidea* Ell. nom. nud. in Nat. Fungus Coll., U.S.D.A. *Licuala* sp. (leaves), Kabat et Bubak, Fungi Imperfecti Exs. 686, Bot. Gard., Buitenzorg, Java, 1908, F. von Hoenhel [Fig. 52b]. *Litsea glutinosa* C. B. Rob, (leaves), Los Baños, Philippine Islands, C. F. Baker Fungi Malayana No. 375 associated with *P. gibberosa* Sacc. [Fig. 52c]. *Livistona chinensis* R. Br. greenhouse, State College, Pa., May 22, 1929, L. O. Overholts. *Lucuma caimito* DC. [=*Ponteria caimito* (Ruiz. & Pav.) Radlk.] (fruit), Rio de Janeiro, Brazil, Jan. 6, 1910, A. Puttemans, in herb. Inst. Biol. Veg. No. 92. *Persea gratissima* Gaertn. [=*P. americana* Mill.] (culture from twigs), University of California, Feb. 1954, H. N. Hansen (with ascogenous stage *Leptosphaeria* sp.). *Phoenix* sp. (leaves), Pusa, May 16, 1906 and Poona, India, Aug. 21, 1903, E. J. Butler. *P. sylvestris* Roxb., Jala, Darbhanga, India, Oct. 12, 1915, M. Taslim; Wasai, near Bassein, Bombay, India, J. H. Burkill sub *P. pinnarum* Butl. (unpublished species); *P. dactylifera* L., Rio de Janeiro, Brazil, March 20, 1914, E. Rangel, No. 1085.

On *Poinciana regia* Bojer [= *Delonix regia* (Boj.) Raf.], Philippine Islands, July 1927, Cult. No. 2820 from bark, H. W. Wollenweber, Biol. Reichsanstalt, Berlin, sub *P. sonsensis* P. Henn. On *Ptychosperma macarthurii* Nichols [= *Actinophloeus macarthurii* (Wendl.) Becc.] (leaves); Fungi Malayana No. 172 sub *P. pauciseta* Sacc., Mt. Maquiling, near Los Baños, Laguna, Philippine Islands, Sept. 1913, C. F. Baker, det. P. A. Saccardo (type) [Fig. 52d]; similar material in herb. P. A. Saccardo, Los Baños, Luzon, Sept. 1913, S. A.

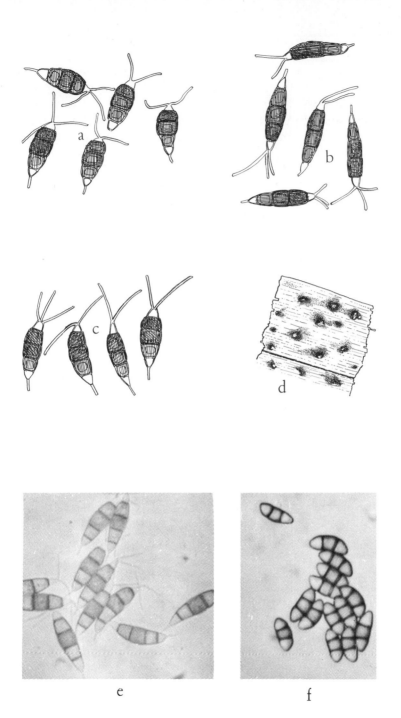

FIG. 52 [162]. *Pestalotia palmarum* Cooke. (*d*) fruiting pustules. (*e*) conidia and (*f*) ascospores (Leptosphaeria) from culture.

Reyes. *Sequoia gigantea* DC. [= *Sequoiadendron giganteum* (Lindl.) Buch.] (culture from dead twig), University of California, Feb. 6, 1954, H. N. Hansen (conidia with ascogenous stage *Leptospheria* sp.) [Fig. 52e,f].

The fungus was described by Cooke, first on a dead sprout of germinating coconut from Bengal, India, and later on dead leaves of *Cocos nucifera* from Demerara, British Guiana. *P. brevipes* Prill. & Delacr. is synonymous with *P. palmarum* Cooke. *P. brevipes* (Syll. Fung. 11:788,1895) was replaced with *P. palmicola* Sacc. & Syd. (Syll. Fung. 14:1030,1899). Since it was a later homonym of *P. brevipes* Cooke described on *Aralia spinosa* L.

The inscription with the specimen on *Licuala* in Kabat & Bubak, Fungi Imperfecti Exs. No. 686 implies that *P. coffeae* Zimm. is a synonym of *P. palmarum* Cooke, but Klebahn (Myc. Centralbl. 4:10–11,1914) included this fungus on *Licuala* with others in his species *P. gracilis* on the basis of his opinion that the conidia and substratum are distinct (fig. 34, 9e). This disposition of the fungus is unacceptable. Kabat and Bubak noted that their specimen agrees with the type of *P. palmarum* in Roumequère Fungi Galliae Exs. 5166 from Demerara, British Guiana.

Klebahn based his description of *P. palmarum* Cooke on specimens on leaves of *Cocos nucifera* as issued in Thuemen, Myc. Univ. No. 1676 and Vize, Microf. Exot. No. 7. The latter has setulae with knobbed extremities and is *P. phoenicis* Vize. The former has conidia with 3 simple setulae.

P. discoidea Ell. on *Howea forsteriana* Becc. (leaves) and *P. pinnarum* Butl. on *Phoenix* sp. (leaves) are herbarium names. The latter name appeared as a nomen nudum in Uppal, Patel, and Kamat (Fungi of Bombay, p. 28, 1935), and as a synonym of *P. palmarum* Cooke (Mycologia 34:314,1942). Further particulars and literature review concerning the biology and nomenclature of *P. palmarum* were reported by Guba (Phytopathology 19:210–212, 1929), and are not repeated here.

Pure cultures of *P. palmarum* Cooke from twigs of *Persea* and *Sequoia*, California, submitted by H. N. Hansen and determined by the author were accompanied by the perfect ascus form *Leptosphaeria*. Under extremely high humidity the form of the ascus stage was modified to agree with the genus *Rhyncosphaeria* (Letter, Dec. 17, 1953 and Phytopathology, 46:637,1956).

White (New Jersey Agr. Exp. Sta. Rep. 1928–29, pp. 277–278, 1930, pp. 264–265, 1931) reported successful infections of *Kentia* only in sunscalded leaf spots. The organism caused an enlargement of the spots. Roepke (Med. Landb. Wageningen 39 (1):3–40,1935) reported the appearance of *Pestalotia* following injury to coconut palm leaves by the insects *Chalcocoelis albiguttata* and *Thosea moluccana*, which caused the eventual death of the leaves. Wollenweber and Hochapfel (Z. Pflanzenkr. 46:406–408,1936) reported that *P. palmarum* Cooke is capable of causing a fast decay of apples through wound inoculations. The measurements of the conidia as given would indicate a misdetermination of the species. Ciferri (Riv. Pat. Veg. 17:

209–294,1927) obtained negative results in attempts to infect leaves of *Cocos nucifera* with *P. palmarum* Cooke and *P. canangae* Koord., the latter isolated from leaves of *Cananga odorata* Hook. f. & Thoms.

This widespread disease of plants of the *Palmaceae* reported in British and German literature in the time of Cooke, De Bary, and Smith was associated with the fungus *P. palmarum* Cooke. Sorauer named the fungus *P. fuscescens*. The latter fungus was found on leaf spots and petioles of *Corypha australia* R. Br. [= *Livistona australis* (R. Br.) Mart.], and was assumed to cause the death of young cultivated plants. The measurements of the conidia as reported by Sorauer were greatly exaggerated. Klose (Deut. Gart. Obstbau Ztg. 164, 1878) reported that young palms are frequently destroyed without in the beginning showing any injury in the roots. The plants assumed a gray appearance. Individual leaves turned yellow and died as root infection became apparent. Spots on the leaves became dark brown and those at the base of the petioles were sunken and dotted with fruiting bodies of the fungus. Infection experiments always gave negative results. Klose concluded that a weakening of the plant was necessary for infection. Frank (Pilzpar. Krankh. Pflanz, 2:441,1896, 2nd ed.) considered *P. fuscescens* as a saprophyte.

163. **Pestalotia stellata** Berk. & Curt., Grevillea 2:155,1874; Syll. Fung. 3: 787,1884.

  P. myricae Ell. & G. Martin, Am. Naturalist 18:70,1884; Syll. Fung. 3: 785,1884.

Spots pale, definite. Acervuli stellate, black, punctiform, sparse, amphigenous, flat, 140–280 μ in diam, seated on definite pale, circular spots or irregularly shaped dead areas with black borders. Conidia 5-celled, straight or sometimes slightly curved, broad-fusiform or broad-elliptic, only slightly constricted at septa, 17–20 μ; 3 intermediate colored cells cask-shaped, guttulate, 12–16 × 6.5–9 μ, the 2 upper umber, the lowest olivaceous; exterior hyaline cells small, short-conic, the apical cells bearing a crest of 3, broadly divergent setulae, 4–11 μ or somewhat longer; pedicels attenuated downwards.

On living leaves of *Ilex opaca* Ait., usually secondary and associated with other fungi. Specimens examined: Society Hill, S. C., April 1855, herb. Curtis in herb. Farlow, and herb. Berkeley No. 4921 in herb. Kew [Fig. 53a]; Liberty, Texas, Nov. 6, 1914, H. Jolivette sub *P. funerea* Desm., Nat. Fungus Coll., U.S.D.A. [Fig. 53b].

Cooke and Ellis (Grevillea 6:85,1878) reported this species on *Quercus tinctoria* Bartr. [= *Q. velutina* Lam.] in Ellis, Fungi of New Jersey No. 2640, and Saccardo (Syll. Fung. 3:787,1884) subsequently cited both hosts. The form on *Quercus* is not associated with pale white leaf spots and is distinct from *P. stellata* Berk. & Curt. The material in Ellis & Everhart, Fungi Col. No. 1352, labelled *P. stellata* on leaves of *Quercus tinctoria* Bartr. and

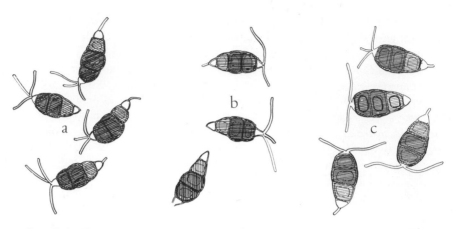

FIG. 53 [163].   *Pestalotia stellata* Berk. & Curt.

Vaccinium arboreum Marsh., consists of two distinct species.   According to Voglino (Atti Soc. Ven.-Trent, Sci. Nat. Padova 9:209–243,1885), *P. stellata* in Ravenel, Fungi Am. Exs. 254 on leaves of *Nerium* and in Ellis & Everhart, N. Am. Fungi No. 34 on leaves of *Ilex opaca* Ait. belong to this species.   Both are different species; the latter is *P. annulata* Berk. & Curt. and the former *P. oleandri* Guba.

White (New Jersey Agr. Exp. Sta. Ann. Rep. 1930:266–67,1931) described leaf spots attributed to this fungus which are at first epiphyllous, brown, roughly circular, then gray and surrounded by a reddish brown margin. Sporulation is abundant on the upper leaf surfaces.   Successful infection was obtained by scalding leaves and applying a heavy spore suspension.

P. myricae Ell. & G. Martin was described on *Myrica cerifera* L. (partly fresh leaves), Ellis, N. Am. Fungi 1222, Green Cove Springs, Fla., Dec. 1882, G. Martin [Fig. 69c].   The fungus was wrongly described with 2-septate conidia and the dimensions are inaccurate.   The authors reported pustules 75 μ in diam, seated on brown spots, 5–10 mm diam and conidia 9–12 μ long. A study of type material shows that the fungus is *P. stellata* Berk. & Curt.

164. **Pestalotia langloisii** Guba sp. nov.

Pustulae amphigenae, gregariae, punctiformes, 120–200 μ in diam, globoso-lenticulares, coalescentes, erumpentes; conidia 5-cellularia, recta vel elliptico-fusoidea, subconstricta, 17–22 × 6.5–8 μ; cellulae mediae coloratae, 12–15 μ longae, olivaceae, duae superiores saepe leniter obscuriores, guttu-latae; cellulae apicales hyalinae, breves, late conicae usque cylindricae; setulae 3, interdum 2, longitudine aequales, 15–20 μ vel interdum paulo longiores, late divergentes; cellulae basales hyalinae, latae, longe conicae; pedicelli recti, breves.

Pale gray areas with definite narrow purplish borders. Pustules amphigenous, gregarious, punctiform, 120–200 μ diam, globose-lenticular, coalescing, erumpent and surrounded by pale torn shreds of the epidermis. Conidia 5-celled, straight to elliptic-fusoid, only slightly constricted at septa, 17–22 × 6.5–8 μ; intermediate colored cells 12–15 μ long, olivaceous, upper 2 colored cells frequently or usually slightly darker, guttulate; apical hyaline cells short, broad-conic to cylindric; setulae 3, sometimes 2, equally long, 15–20 μ or sometimes slightly longer and widely divergent; basal hyaline cells broad and long conic; pedicels erect, short.

In spots and dead areas on living leaves of *Eriobotrya japonica* Lindl., Louisiana, Aug. 29, 1890, A. B. Langlois, No. 837 inscribed *Pestalotia eriobotryae* Ell. & Ev., Point à la Hache, La., Dec. 1886, herb. Ellis I: 13, in herb. Farlow [Fig. 54a]. The fungus was named *Pestalotia eriobotryae* without description in Langlois, Cat. Prov. Plantes de la Basse-Louisiane p. 32, 1887. On dead concentric areas in leaves of *Paeonia moutan* Sims [= *P. suffruticosa* Andr.], Chiba College, Matsudo, Chiba-Ken, Japan, Sept. 6, 1925, C. Kurada. On *Quercus* sp. (leaves), St. Martinsville, La., Sept. 1888, A. B. Langlois sub *P. maura* Ell. & Ev. (Jour. Mycol. 4:123,1888) in Nat. Fungus Coll., U.S.D.A. [Fig. 54b]. The type of *P. maura* was reported on *Psychotria rufescens* H.B.K. collected in Florida. It is a 4-celled conidial

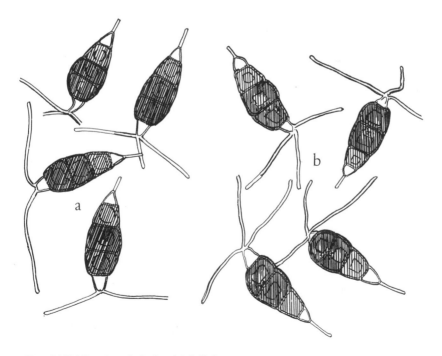

FIG. 54 [164]. *Pestalotia langloisii* Guba.

form.   Ellis and Everhart applied the same name to many distinct 5-celled conidial forms on *Persea, Quercus* and other host plant material collected by Langlois in Louisiana (Jour. Mycol. 5:159,1889).

165. **Pestalotia westerdijkii** (Stey.) Guba comb. nov.
    Pestalotiopsis westerdijkii Stey., Bull. Jard. Bot. État Bruxelles 19:329–
        330,1949, pl. 15, fig. A.

Pustules irregular in form and size, dense, punctiform, black, carbonaceous 75 μ and more in diam.   Conidia 5-celled narrow-fusiform, straight, or slightly curved, usually 20–25 × 6–7 μ, tapering to the base; intermediate colored cells 14–18 μ, concolorous or upper 2 of them umber or usually darker; exterior hyaline cells conoid; setulae aborted or rudimentary, papillaeform, 1 to 3, short, 2–9 μ long or only as a short projection from apex, of unequal length; pedicels 3 μ long.

On leaves of *Cocos nucifera* L. in culture in herb. Jard. Bot. État Bruxelles, Belgium, and herb. Guba from Celebes, Dutch East Indies, sub *P. breviseta* Sacc.   Steyaert's description of the fungus features conidia, 20–27 × 5.5–9 μ, intermediate colored cells 14–18 μ long, 2–4, usually 3 setulae, 3–15 μ long. Steyaert's pl. 15, fig. A (Bull. Jard. Bot. État 19:1949) shows narrow fusiform conidia, short setulae and contrasted colored cells.

166. **Pestalotia cruenta** Syd., Mem. Bull. Herb. Boiss. 4; 5,1900; Syll. Fung.
        16:1017,1902.
    Pestalotiopsis cruenta (Syd.) Stey., Bull. Jard. Bot. État Bruxelles 19:318–
        319,1949, pl. 12, fig. A.

Spots circular, oblong, blood-colored, middle area at length pale, amphigenous, 0.5–1 cm in diam.   Pustules epiphyllous, punctiform, black, 120–180 μ diam, gregarious, borne below the cuticle.   Conidia, fusiform, 5-celled, 18–24 × 5–7 μ, hardly constricted at septa; colored cells 12–15 μ, central or upper 2 umber, lowest olivaceous, guttulate; exterior cells hyaline conoid; setulae 1–4, usually 2–3 and 10–20 μ long, divergent, pedicels up to 8 μ long, usually 4–5 μ long.

On living leaves of *Polygonatum lasianthum* Maxim., Musashi Province, Japan, Kusano.   The fungus is associated with a pycnidial fungus with ovate 1-celled conidia, probably *Phyllosticta cruenta*.   Sydow described oblong-fusoid, 5-celled conidia, 18–24 × 5–6.5 μ, 1–4 diverging setulae, 12–20 μ long. On branch of *Prunus persica* (L.) Stokes, Shikukawara, Pref. Kanagawa, Japan, July 21, 1950, Harada.   The fungus on *Poinciana* (*Delonix*) from the Philippine Islands designated *P. cruenta* Syd. and used by Wollenweber and Hochapfel (Z. Pflanzenkr. 46:408–409,1936) for infecting apples is *P. palmarum* Cooke.   This fungus, after 28 days following wound inoculations, caused a rot of apple of 0.5 cm in diam and finally of the entire apple.   The progress of the rot was slow, reaching a diameter of 4.5 cm in 56 days.   The assertion by the authors that *P. sonsensis* P. Henn. described on leaves of *Ceratonia* is a synonym of *P. cruenta* is incorrect. Steyaert (Trans. Brit. Mycol. Soc. 36:83,1953) identified Wollenweber's fungus from *Delonix regia* (Boj.) Raf. as *Pestalotiopsis neglecta* (Thuem.) Stey. He asserted that *Pestalotiopsis cruenta* is similar to *Pestalotia neglecta*.

167. **Pestalotia foedans** Sacc. & Ell., Michelia 2:575,1882; Syll. Fung. 3:792, 1884; Voglino, Atti Soc. Ven.-Trent. Sci. Nat. Padova 9:209–243,1885, table IX, fig. 13.

   P. ramealis Fries, Summa Veg. Scand., p. 416, 1846, nom. nud.; Syll. Fung. 3:801,1884.

   P. peregrina Ell. & G. Martin, Jour. Mycol. 1:100,1885; Syll. Fung. 10: 490,1892.

   P. shiraiana P. Henn., in Engler., Jahrb. Bot. 37:164,1906; Syll. Fung. 22: 1226,1913.

   P. chamaecyparidis Sawada, Bull. Govt. For. Exp. Sta. (Japan) 46:122, Dec. 1950.

   Pestalotiopsis foedans (Sacc. & Ell.) Stey., Bull. Jard. Bot. État Bruxelles 19:329,1949, pl. 13, fig. C.

Pustules densely gregarious, innate-erumpent, coalescing freely, tearing the woody matrix longitudinally, sooty at maturity, 200–425 × 170–340 μ. Conidia 5-celled, rather slender-fusiform, tapering toward the base, erect, 19–24 × 5.5–7 μ, sometimes wider, slightly or hardly constricted at the septa; intermediate colored cells guttulate, 14–17 μ long, the upper two umber, the lowest olivaceous, the walls usually darker; apical hyaline cells conic, cylindric and narrow, basal cells acute; setulae 3, rarely 4, divergent, slender, 6–18 μ long; pedicels 4–9 μ long.

On decaying bark of white cedar, *Thuja occidentalis* L., Newfield, N. J., Oct. 1880, Ellis and Harkness, in Ellis & Everhart N. Am. Fungi No. 954, 1883, and Rabenhorst, Fungi europ. Exs. 2997 [Fig. 55a]; Ellis & Everhart Fungi Col. No. 81, same collection, but host is designated *Cupressus thyoides* L. [=*Chamaecyparis thyoides* (L.) B.S.P.].

On *Cryptomeria japonica* D. Don (needles), Philadelphia, Pa., Oct. 1938, J. P. Griffith in herb. L. O. Overholts No. 21360; on *C. japonica* D. Don var. *lobbii* Carr. (leaves and twigs), Princeton, N. J. Feb. 1928, R. P. White. On *Chamaecyparis thyoides* (L.) B.S.P. (dead twigs), Society Hill, S. C., April 1849, sub *P. funerea* Desm., in herb Curtis, No. 2610 in herb. Farlow. On *Juniperus chinensis* L. var. *pfitzeriana* Spaeth. (needles), Shiloh, N. J., Sept. 9, 1927, R. P. White. On *Juniperus* sp., New Haven, Conn., Nov. 9, 1934, G. Hahn; Dundee, Illinois, 1922, Guba [Fig. 55b].

On *Pinus mugo* Turra (needles), Pennington, N. J., Aug. 2, 1927, R. P. White. On *P. radiata* D. Don (needles), greenhouses, Washington, D. C., May 1, 1928, G. G. Hedgcock, in herb. Forest Path, U.S.D.A. No. 46740.

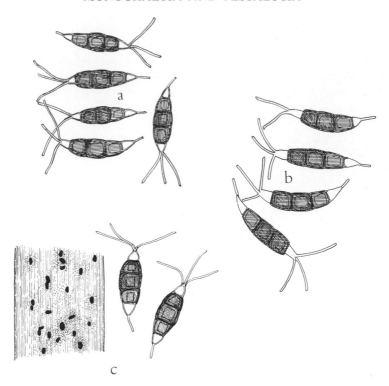

FIG. 55 [167].   *Pestalotia foedans* Sacc. & Ellis.   (*c*) fruiting pustules in matrix.

On *P. palustris* Mill. (needles) in herb. Forest Path. U.S.D.A. Nos. 49308, 49309.   On *Pinus strobus* L. (needles), Rock Creek Park, Washington, D.C., Sept. 3, 1923, G. G. Hedgcock in herb. Forest Path., U.S.D.A., No. 27230.

On *Prunus persica* (L.) Stokes (branch), Shikukawara, Pref. Kanagawa, Japan, July 21, 1950, Harada, in herb. Agr. Inst. Yokohama Nat. Univ.

On *Thuja pyramidalis* Ten.   [=*T. orientalis* var. *stricta* Loud.] (blighted needles), Shiloh, N. J., Sept. 9, 1927, R. P. White.

According to the original description the 5-celled conidia measure 22 × 5.5–6.5 μ, the setulae 15–17 μ, the pedicels 5–8 μ long.   The pustules follow the grain of the bark.   The character of the pustules is of doubtful specific value since on other substrata they are subglobose.

P. ramealis Fries, collected in Scandinavia, was named "nom. nud." without host.   A portion of a twig from the Fries herbarium, University of Uppsala, was identified as of the *Cupressaceae*.   The conidia are essentially like *P. foedans* Sacc. & Ell.

P. peregrina Ell. & G. Martin is another synonym.   The pustules are globose-lenticular and rupture the epidermis in a linear manner.   The conidia have the same dimensions as *P. foedans*, the setulae 3, 8–17 μ long. On dead needles of cut-off branches of *Pinus austriaca* Link [$=P. nigra$ Arn.], Newfield, N. J., May 1885, in Ellis & Everhart N. Am. Fungi, 2nd ser. No. 1627 [Fig. 55c]. In contrast, the original description reported oblong-elliptic conidia, colored part 12–16 × 6–7 μ, setulae 3, 7–10 μ long, the pedicels about as long as the conidia.

Pestalotia shiraiana P. Henn. was described on needles of *Cryptomeria japonica* D. Don, collected at Yoshino, Prov. Yamato, Japan, July, 1903, M. Shirai No. 35. The type specimen in herb. Berlin Bot. Mus. is the same as *P. foedans*. According to Hennings, the oblong-fusoid conidia measure 13–17 × 4–6 μ and the setulae 10–15 μ. Study shows slender fusiform conidia, 19–24 × 5–6.5 μ, intermediate colored cells 14–18 μ long, upper two usually umber, lowest one olivaceous, setulae 3, rarely 4, 10–22 μ long. The acervuli are punctiform, globose-lenticular, 75–150 μ in diam. In contrast, the acervuli of *P. foedans* grow in a linear manner between the bark fibers, which could hardly have significance. *P. chamaecyparidis* Sawada described on leaves and stems of *Chamaecyparis obtusa* (Sieb. & Zucc.) Endl., Japan, is the same fungus. The fungus, according to Ito and Kontani (Bull. Govt. For. Exp. Sta. Japan 76:63–72,1954), caused a blighting of seedlings at Meguro. The fungus infected the seedlings only through wounded tissue.

168. **Pestalotia gaultheriae** Dearn. & House, Ann. Rep. N. Y. State Mus. 1924, Bull. 266:94,1925.

Pustules subglobose, amphigenous, mostly hypophyllous, generally distributed and seated without order, erumpent, breaking the epidermis irregularly and margined by the ruptured cuticle, 90–225 μ in diam. Conidia narrow-fusoid, 5-celled, curved or angled, 20–25 × 5–7 μ, slightly constricted at the septa; intermediate colored cells olivaceous to umber, the two upper of them somewhat darker than the lowest one, 14–16 μ long; exterior cells dilute yellow, prominent, the apical cells long cylindric or conic, bearing 3, occasionally 4 setulae, 6–16 μ, the basal cells acute, tapering into erect pedicels, 4–10 μ long.

On brown languishing leaves of *Gaultheria* sp., summit of Piedro de Lino, Panama, E. P. Killip, Feb. 24, 1918, herb. N. Y. State Mus. [Fig. 56].

169. **Pestalotia coffeae** Zimm., Med. uit's. Lands-Plantentium 67:74–75, 1904, fig. 45; Syll. Fung. 22:1223,1913.

Pustules subcuticular, erumpent, black. Conidia oblong-fusiform, 5-celled, 25 × 5–6 μ, the intermediate colored cells umber or dark, the lowest of the three pale brown, constricted slightly at the septa; setulae 3, hyaline, divergent, 15–20 μ; apical hyaline cells long conic to cylindric; basal hyaline cells conic, tapering; pedicels 4 μ long.

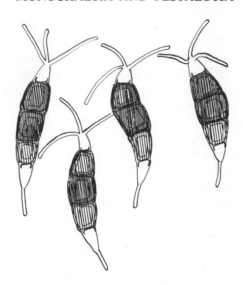

Fig. 56 [168]. *Pestalotia gaultheriae* Dearn. & House.

On fruits of *Coffea arabica* L., Java, associated with a species of *Colleto-trichum*. Kabat and Bubak, Fungi Imperfecti Exs. No. 686, regarded *P. coffeae* Zimm. as a synonym of *P. palmarum* Cooke.

Roger ("Phytopathologie des pays chauds," Ency. Mycol. XXVIII, 1953, pl. 876) published a description of *P. coffeicola* Averna–Saccá, on coffee leaves in Sao Paulo, Brazil, as follows: "conidia 5-celled, narrow fusiform, 16–27 × 7.5–9.5 μ, setulae 2, 24–29 μ long." The fungus is seated in irregular reddish brown spots about the apices and margins of the coffee leaves. Finally the whole leaf is affected and it dries up almost completely. The acervuli are amphigenous, small, hemispherical or conical and the contents issue in cirrhi. The fungus was originally reported without formal description by Averna-Saccá (Segunda Contr. Para Estud. Molesti Crypt. Cafeeiro, Sao Paulo II, 21–23, fig. 7, 1925) and is distinct from *P. coffeae* Zimm. *P. coffeicola* Averna-Saccá is a dubious species and has been placed in synonymy under *P. guaranitica* (Speg.) Guba.

170. **Pestalotia eusora** (Sacc.) Guba comb. nov.
    Pestalotia funerea Desm. var. *eusora* Sacc., Ann. Mycol. 6:568,1908; Syll. Fung. 22:1227,1913.

Pustules loosely arranged or gregarious, dense, hypophyllous, erumpent, black, surrounded by adherent epidermis, up to 250 μ in diam. Conidia 5-celled, equilateral, narrow-fusiform, straight, 19–25 × 5.5–7 μ; intermediate colored cells 15–16 μ long, guttulate, upper two colored cells usually dark or umber, lowest colored cells olivaceous or pale, sometimes olivaceous throughout; basal cells acute, pointed, apical cells narrow cylindric to acute, setulae 3, arising from apex, widely divergent, 12–19 μ long, usually 12–16 μ; pedicels short, up to 6 μ long.

On withering leaves of *Heptapleurum barteri* Hiern, Roca Sandade, Island of St. Thomé, West Africa, A. Moller, Dec. 1907, in herb. P. A. Saccardo.   Saccardo (Syll. Fung. 22:1913) described 5-celled conidia, 20–22 × 5.5–6 μ and 3 setulae, 11 μ long.   The fungus has nothing in common with *P. funerea* Desm. and is considered a distinct species.

171. **Pestalotia gracilis** Kleb., Myc. Centralbl. 4:10–11,1914; Syll. Fung. 25: 609,1931.
  P. sassafras Ell. & Ev., Ellis, N. Am. Fungi No. 1376, 1885 (nom. nud.).
  Pestalotiopsis gracilis (Kleb.) Stey., Bull. Jard. Bot. État Bruxelles 19: 310–312,1949, pl. 11, fig. D.

Fruiting bodies mostly hypophyllous, globose-lenticular or hemispherical, 75–200 μ diam, subepidermal then erumpent, surrounded by the torn epidermis, densely gregarious and confluent, blackening the matrix.   Conidia 5-celled, straight, fusiform, sometimes slightly curved, slightly constricted at septa, 19–23 × 6–7 μ; intermediate colored cells 12–15 μ long, the upper two umber, the lowest olivaceous; basal hyaline cells long conic, tapering; the apical hyaline cells large, conic to cylindric, bearing a crest of 2–4, usually 3, widely divergent setulae, 13–25 μ long; pedicels erect, 4–7 μ long.

On dead leaves of *Sassafras variifolium* (Salisb.) Kuntze [= *S. albidum* (Nutt.) Nees], Newfield, N. J., Oct. 1884, in Ellis, N. Am. Fungi No. 1376 [Fig. 57] on leaves of *Laurus sassafras* L. [= *Sassafras albidum* (Nutt.) Nees], Newfield, N. J., Oct. 1883, sub *P. guepini* Desm. in Ellis & Everhart Fungi

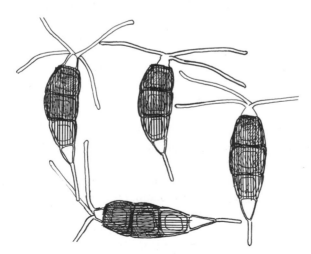

F<small>IG</small>. 57 [171].   *Pestalotia gracilis* Kleb.

Col. No. 370b. Sooty mats of spores cover both surfaces of the brown leaves. On leaves of *Paeonia* sp., Arlington, Va., Aug. 31, 1920.

Klebahn described *P. gracilis* from many specimens on unrelated hosts of which Ellis & Everhart Fungi Col. No. 370b on *Laurus sassafras* [= *Sassafras albidum* (Nutt.) Nees], designated *P. guepini* Desm., is the first listed. This specimen and the type of *P. sassafras* Ell. & Ev. are identical. Klebahn described the conidia 20–27 × 5.5–7 μ, 3 setulae 10–26 μ, pedicels 3–10 μ. His species embraced the following specimens:

a. Ellis & Everhart, Fungi Col. No. 370b as *P. guepini* Desm. on *Laurus sassafras* L. [= *Sassafras albidum* (Nutt.) Nees].

b. Thuemen, Myc. Univ. No. 884 as *P. funerea* Desm. var. *euonymi-japonici* Thuem., on fallen decaying leaves of *Euonymus japonicus* L. This fungus is *P. neglecta* Thuem.

c. D. Saccardo, Myc. Ital. No. 181 as *P. funerea* Desm. on dead leaves of *Ilex aquifolium* L. Padua, Italy. This fungus is *P. neglecta* Thuem.

d. D. Saccardo, Myc. Ital. No. 183 as *P. guepini* Desm. on *Cocculus laurifolius* DC., Bot. Gard., Padua, Italy. This fungus is *P. cocculi* Guba.

e. Kabat & Bubak, Fungi Imperfecti Exs. 686 as *P. palmarum* Cooke, on leaves of *Licuala* sp., Buitenzorg, Java, F. von Hoehnel. This fungus is *P. palmarum* Cooke.

Gallucci-Rangone (Ann. Sper. Agraria Roma (n.s.) 8, 5, 1437–1457, 1954) reported a full description of *P. gracilis* on *Laurus nobilis* L.

172. **Pestalotia pauciseta** Sacc., Ann. Mycol. 12:311,1914; Syll. Fung. 25, 608, 1931.

Pustules amphigenous, black, scattered, sometimes gregarious, globose-lenticular, hemispherical, 80–200 μ in diam. coalescing, forming sooty black spots. Conidia 5-celled, not constricted at septa, erect or slightly curved, 19–24 × 6–7.5 μ; intermediate colored cells 13.5–16 μ long, the upper 2 umber, lowest olivaceous, the walls darker, broadest at septa dividing 2 upper colored cells; exterior hyaline cells conspicuous, apical cell broad-conic, turbinate, bearing 2–3, usually 3 setulae, 21–32 μ long, filiform, widely divergent, basal hyaline cells broad-conic, obtuse or attenuated; pedicels up to 5 μ long.

On leaves of *Litsea glutinosa* C. B. Rob., Mt. Maquiling, near Los Baños, Laguna Province, Philippine Islands, Oct. 1913, in Baker, Fungi Malayana No. 172, Suppl. 1 [Fig. 58].

The original description of this species is a heterogenous characterization of five forms on five host plants, two distinct forms appearing on one and one form appearing on two host plants as follows:

P. phoenicis Vize and *P. fici* (Stey.) Guba. On leaves of *Connarus*, Los Baños, Philippine Islands, S. A. Reyes, No. 1782.

P. phoenicis Vize. On leaves of *Uvaria*, Taytay, Palawan, Philippine Islands, E. D. Merrill, No. 8749.

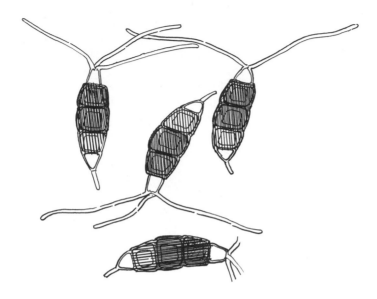

FIG. 58 [172]. *Pestalotia pauciseta* Sacc.

P. pauciseta Sacc. On leaves of *Litsea glutinosa* C. B. Rob., Los Baños, C. F. Baker, No. 1779.

P. palmarum Cke. On leaves of *Ptychosperma macarthurii* H. Wendl. [=*Actinophloeus macarthurii* (Wendl.) Becc.], Los Baños, S. A. Reyes, No. 1843.

P. virgatula Kleb. On leaves of *Guioa* [=*Cupania*], Taytay, Palawan, E. D. Merrill, No. 8867.

The salient characters of the original description are: Acervuli orbicular, 200–250 μ diam. Conidia fusiform, acute, 20–24 × 4.5–5 μ, setulae usually 2, filiform, 8–15 μ long.

173. **Pestalotia vaccinii** (Shear) Guba Phytopathology 19:201–202,1929.

P. guepini Desm. var. *vaccinii* Shear, Bull. Torrey Bot. Club 29:456–457, 1902; U.S.D.A. Tech. Bull. 258:9:1931.

Pustules amphigenous, punctiform, subepidermal, erumpent, black, coalescing, sooty at maturity, 100–250 μ diam, sparsely scattered over the leaf blade. Conidia 5-celled, narrow-fusiform, usually straight, 21–25 × 5–7 μ, not constricted at septa; intermediate colored cells guttulate, 15–16 μ, long, olivaceous or usually the two upper ones umber, the lowest olivaceous; apical hyaline cells long-cylindric, bearing 3, rarely 4, setulae, 20–34 μ long; pedicels 4–14 μ.

On dead leaves of *Vaccinium macrocarpon* Ait., Parkdale, N. J., Sept. 1901, C. L. Shear, sub *P. guepini* Desm. var. *vaccinii* Shear in Nat. Fung. Coll., U.S.D.A. [Fig. 59]. On *Andromeda floribunda* Pursh. [=*Pieris floribunda* (Pursh) Benth. & Hook.] (brown leaves), Rockland, Mass., July 19, 1931, K. S. Chester. On *Andromeda* sp. (leaves), Angers, France (Guepin), sub *P. guepini* Desm. in herb. Mus. d'Hist. Nat. Paris, M. L. R. Tulasne, 1873. On *Kalmia latifolia* L. (leaves), Boskoop, Holland, Apr. 7, 1919, Plant Introduction, U.S.D.A. No. 4460, on brown spots with purple borders.

There is nothing in the type description of *P. guepini* Desm. (Ann. Sci. Nat. II. 13:182–184,1840, pl. 4, fig. 1–3), which might be construed as being in agreement with *P. guepini* var. *vaccinii*. Desmazières' description and figure of the conidia are worthless as a basis for comparison, since they do not fit the type specimen of the fungus on leaves of *Camellia* (Desmazières' Plantes Crypt. 22:1084) or any other of the numerous later specimens of *P. guepini* on *Camellia*. The trinomial by Shear is untenable (Guba and Linder, Mycologia 24:415–418,1932). *P. vaccinii* is characterized by slender conidia, contrasted colored cells and long simple setulae.

174. Pestalotia lambertiae Petr., Sydowia 8:219,1954.

Pustules amphigenous, sometimes epiphyllous, irregularly distributed, solitary or aggregated, then more or less confluent, formed in the epidermis, depressed-globose, broad-ellipsoid, at first closed, thereafter breaking apart irregularly and widely exposed, usually 180–250 μ in diam, the walls membranous, 6–10 μ, the sides up to 18 μ thick, context pseudoparenchymatic, cells angulate-rotundate, pale yellow brown. Conidia 5-celled, 18–27 × 5–8 μ, fusiform, attenuated in both directions, straight, rarely unequilateral; intermediate cells olivaceous-brown, lowest of the three colored cells lighter; exterior cells hyaline, conoid, not or only slightly constricted at septa;

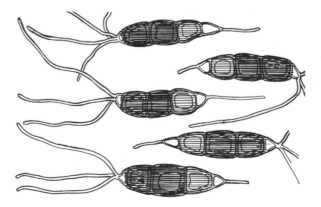

Fig. 59 [173].   *Pestalotia vaccinii* (Shear) Guba.

setulae 2, rarely 3 or 4, vertically directed, straight, or curved, filiform, 13–16 μ long; pedicels short, filiform, 3–5 μ long.

On dead leaves of *Lambertia formosa* Sm., Jervis Bay, Australia, A. C. T. 25, II, 1953.

175. **Pestalotia canangae** Koord., Verh. K. Akad. Wetenschappen Amsterdam 13:224,1907; Syll. Fung. 22:1219,1913.

Dead patches brown, large. Pustules distributed without order, epiphyllous, subglobose, subepidermal, erumpent on maturity, sooty, 75–150 μ in diam. Conidia 5-celled, straight, curved or angled, tapering to the base, clavate-fusoid, 19–25 × 6–8 μ, only slightly constricted at septa, colored part 12.5–14.5 μ long, the upper 2 colored cells umber or slightly darker than the lowest one; apical hyaline cells prominent, sometimes hidden, conic or acute, bearing 2, usually 3, rarely 4, short setulae, 6–15 μ long; basal cells often inflated, pedicels short, 2–4 μ.

On living leaves of *Cananga odorata* Hook. f. & Thoms., Prov. Purworedjo, Central Java, leg. Koorders, Aug. 1905, in herb. Berlin Bot. Mus. According to Koorders, the fungus kills large parts of old and young leaves.

On leaves of *Bladhia sieboldii* Naki [= *Ardisia sieboldi* Miq.], Chutung, Sinchu, Taiwan, Feb. 10, 1908, R. Suzuki in herb. Univ. Imp. Taihokuensis and Nat. Fungus Coll., U.S.D.A.

176. **Pestalotia oleandri** Guba sp. nov.
   P. stellata Berk. & Curt. var. *nerii* Cooke, Grevillea 7:45,1878, nom. nud.
   P. stellata Berk. & Curt. var. *oleandri* Cooke. Ravenel, Fungi Am. Exs. 254, 1879, nom. nud.

Pustulae globoso-lenticulares, 300–400 μ in diam, dispersae punctiformes, plerumque epiphyllae; conidia 5-cellularia, aequilateralia, vulgo recta, ad septam inter cellulas duas coloratas superiores latissima, vix constricta, 21–24 × 6–8 μ; cellulae mediae coloratae guttulatae, duae superiores umbrinae, infima olivacea, 14.5–16 μ longae; cellulae hyalinae extimae prominentes, apicales conicae usque cylindricae, usque 4.5 μ longae, setulis 2 vel saepius 2 usque 15 μ longis vel interdum longioribus cristatae, basales late conicae; pedicelli recti, 2–4 μ longi.

Pustules globose-lenticular, 300–400 μ diam, distinct, scattered, punctiform, largely epiphyllous, black, generally distributed over the matrix. Conidia 5-celled, usually equilateral, broadest at the septa dividing the 2 superior colored cells, hardly constricted at the septa, 21–24 × 6–8 μ; intermediate colored cells guttulate, the 2 upper umber, the lowest olivaceous, 14.5–16 μ long; exterior hyaline cells prominent, the apical cells conic to cylindric, up to 4.5 μ, bearing a crest of 2 or usually 3 setulae, up to 16 μ long or slightly longer, the basal cells broad conic, resting on erect pedicels, 2–4 μ long.

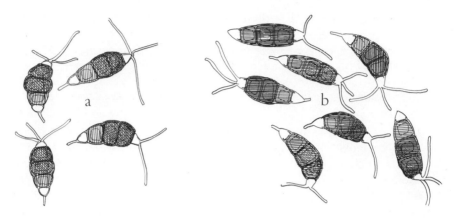

FIG. 60 [176].   *Pestalotia oleandri* Guba.

On dead fallen leaves of *Nerium oleander* L., Darien, Ga. 1877, in Ravenel, Fungi Am. Exs. 254, sub *P. stellata* Berk. & Curt. var. *oleandri* Cooke [Fig. 60a].   The fungus is distinct from *P. stellata*, for which reason the new name is suggested.

On spots in leaves of *Coccoloba uvifera* L., Haiti, West Indies, March 15, 1922, V. K. Charles, Nat. Fungus Coll., U.S.D.A. sub *P. coccolobae* Ell. & Ev.   On decaying fruits of *Rosa* sp., South Carolina, H. W. Ravenel, herb. Atkinson, Dept. Plant Path., Cornell University, and Santee Canal, South Carolina, H. W. Ravenel No. 1370, herb. Curtis in herb. Farlow, sub *P. bullata* Berk. & Rav. (nom. nud.) [Fig. 60b].   The 5-celled fusiform conidia are 19–25 × 6.5–9 μ, the upper 2 colored cells umber, the lowest olivaceous, setulae 3, sometimes 4, usually 7–16 μ, sometimes up to 20 μ long.

177. **Pestalotia acaciae** Thuem.   Inst. Rev. Sci. Litt. Coimbra 28:41–42, 1880; Thuemen, Myc. Univ. No. 1777, 1880; Syll. Fung. 3:786,1884.
    P. acaciicola Speg., Anal. Soc. Ci. Argent. 93:115,1922.
    P. truncata Lév. var. *septoriana* Fairman, Mycologia 5:245,1913; Syll. Fung. 25:605,1931.

Spots papery white, along the margins of the leaves, irregularly shaped with broad rust colored borders.   Pustules amphigenous, usually hypophyllous, irregularly distributed, solitary, rarely gregarious, hemispherical or globose-lenticular, black, borne below the papery epidermis, usually 150 μ diam.   Conidia elliptic-ovate, 5-celled, 19–23 × 7–8.5 μ, straight, hardly constricted at septa; intermediate colored cells 14–19 μ long, the upper two umber, the lowest olivaceous, broadest at the middle dark cell; apical hyaline cells hidden, the basal hyaline cells obtuse; setulae 3, filiform, divergent, 12–22 μ long; pedicels 3–6 μ long.

On living leaves of *Acacia longifolia* Willd., Bot. Gard., Coimbra, Portugal,

Aug. 1879, A. Moller, in Thuemen, Myc. Univ. No. 1777, in herb. Berlin Bot. Mus., associated with other fungi. Material deposited in Berlin Bot. Mus. and Univ. Coimbra as No. 576, Ser. III on *Acacia longifolia* Willd., Aug. 1879, A. Moller No. 646 and as No. 576, Ser. III on *A. saligna* Wendl., May, 1879, A. Moller No. 544, lacks the fungus. Thuemen reported the conidia 24 × 9–10 μ, acute at both ends, setulae 2 or 3.

On living leaves of *Ribes rubrum* L. Takoma Park, Md., Sept. 3, 1905, C. L. Shear in Bartholomew Fungi Col. No. 2441, sub *P. guepini* Desm. [Fig. 61]. Klebahn (Myc. Centralbl. 4:12–13,1914) referred this specimen to *P. versicolor* Speg. On leaves of a shrub probably of the *Rubiaceae*, Pueblo Viejo, Mexico, June 1911, H. Q. Morton, sub *P. truncata* Lév. var. *septoriana* Fairman. The pustules are 45–90 μ in diam and appear like *Septoria*. Fairman reported 2 and 3 simple or branched setulae, and 2–4-septate conidia, which the author did not find in his study of the type specimen. On brown spots on leaves of *Thea sinensis* L. [= *Camellia sinensis* (L.) Kuntze], Minas Gerais, Brazil, May 1, 1933, A. S. Müller No. 526.

178. **Pestalotia zahlbruckneriana** P. Henn., Annal K. K. Nat. Hist. Hof. Mus. (Wien.) 15:3,1900; Syll. Fung. 16:1017.

    P. versicolor Speg. var. *vagans* Speg., Rev. Mus. La Plata 15:42,1908; Syll. Fung. 22:1226,1913.

Pustules epiphyllous, scattered or somewhat gregarious, at first pulvinate, covered by pale or gray epidermis, then erumpent, the contents protruding,

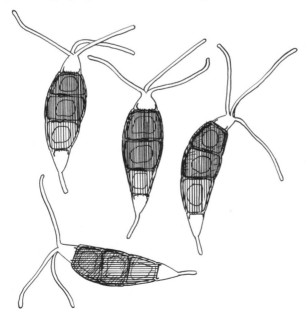

Fig. 61 [177]. *Pestalotia acaciae* Thuem.

subglobose and surrounded by the torn papery epidermis or the fragments covering the black mass, 150–900 μ diam.   Conidia 5-celled, 20–26 × 6.5–8.5 μ, curved, angulate, fusoid-clavate, tapering to the base, slightly constricted at the septa; upper 2 of the 3 median colored cells umber, the lowest olivaceous, 15–18 μ; apical cells conic or cylindric and turned to one side, the basal hyaline cells acute, tapering into short pedicels, 3–5 μ; setulae 3 or sometimes 4, divergent, curved, 14–22 μ long.

On inflorescence of *Strelitzia angustifolia* Dryand [= *S. parvifolia* Ait.], Port Alfred (Kowie), South Africa, A. Penther.   Hennings gave the conidial measurements as 17–20 × 6–8 μ, the setulae 15–21 μ, and the pedicels 8–15 μ.

On dead weathered leaves of *Acer negundo* L., Great Falls, Md., Oct. 7, 1939, J. A. Stevenson, Nat. Fungus Coll., U.S.D.A.   In spots on leaves of *Ailanthus* sp., Shreveport, La., Oct. 10, 1913, E. Bartholomew, herb. Dearness No. D 4576.

On *Cornus florida* L. (twigs), Ridgefield, N. J., Aug. 18, 1935, R. P. White.

On *Eucalyptus kirtoniana* F. Muell. (leaves), Brooksville, Fla., Jan. 17, 1917, J. W. Morrow, Nat. Fungus Coll., U.S.D.A. No. 2898.

On *Marantaceae* (leaves), Wumbali, Belgian Congo, Aug. 1913, H. Vanderyst No. 2037, herb. Jard. Bot. État Bruxelles, No. 369–14 sub *P. mangiferae* P. Henn.

On brown weathered leaves of *Podocarpus chinensis* Teijsm. & Binn. [= *P. macrophylla* var. *makei* Sieb.], Nanking, China, Apr. 2, 1930, S. D. Teng, No. 720 sub *P. funerea* Desm. [Fig. 62a]; on leaves of *Podocarpus* sp., Bot. Gard., Washington, D. C., Dec. 10, 1920, J. A. Stevenson No. 5312, sub *P. guepini* Desm. [Fig. 62b].

On *Psidium guajava* L. (leaves) Plant Introduction Garden, Brooksville, Fla., Feb. 13, 1922 and Feb. 19, 1924, J. A. Stevenson; Belleview, Fla., Sept. 29, 1902, Mrs. C. Kelsey.   On *Psidium pumilum* Vahl (leaves), Yarrow, Md., Jan. 29, 1919, J. A. Stevenson & J. T. Rogers Nos. 4407, 43762, 3740.

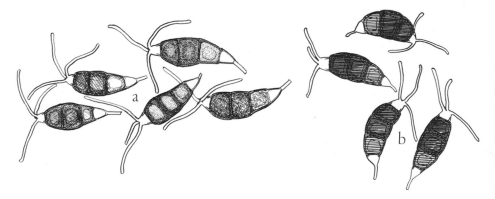

Fig. 62 [178].   *Pestalotia zahlbruckneriana* P. Henn.

On *Rhizophora mangle* L. (leaves), Miami, Fla., Apr. 9, 1910, L. L. Harter, Forest Path, U.S.D.A. No. 20421.

On fruits of *Stillingia sebifera* Mich. [= *Sapium sebiferum* Roxb.], Washington Insp. House, U.S.D.A., J. F. Rogers, Atlanta, Ga., Sept. 31, 1916, Nat. Fungus Coll., U.S.D.A. No. 19374.

On wilting leaves of a shrub-like tree, Ipiranga, Sao Paulo, Brazil, A. Usteri, Jan. 1905, sub *P. versicolor* Speg. var. *vagans* Speg. My study shows 5-celled, fusiform conidia, 20–26 × 6.5–9 μ, setulae 3, rarely 2, 10–20 μ. Spegazzini's measurements are 20–30 × 8–10 μ, setulae 20 μ. Type material from Spegazzini is good but similar material from Berlin Bot. Mus. (Dahlem), reported by Klebahn (Myc. Centralbl. 4:18,1914), lacks the fungus.

179. **Pestalotia aquatica** Ell. & Ev., Jour. Mycol. 5:157,1889; Syll. Fung. 10: 492,1892.

Pestalotiopsis aquatica (Ell. & Ev.) Stey. Bull. Jard. Bot. État Bruxelles 19: 334–335,1949, pl. 25, fig. B.

Spots amphigenous, chestnut brown, definite, irregular in shape and area, as much as 3 × 2 cm, concentrically wrinkled, surrounded by a purplish or dark border. Acervuli epiphyllous, sparse, scattered, erumpent, circinate, black, 80–130 μ in diam. Conidia 5-celled, straight or slightly curved, elliptic-fusoid, not constricted at septa, 20–24 μ long; intermediate cells guttulate, olivaceous and equally colored or the upper 2 colored cells often darker, 13–16 × 7–8.5 μ; exterior hyaline cells short and broad conic; crest of 3 broad or stout setulae 10–20 μ long, unequal in length, widely divergent; pedicels erect, 2–4 μ long.

Saprophytic on living leaves of *Peltandra virginica* (L.) Kunth., Newfield, N. J., Aug. 27, 1889, Nat. Fungus Coll., U.S.D.A. [Fig. 63]. The authors reported this fungus also on *Sarracenia purpurea* L. The type description reported the conidia as 18–20 × 6–7 μ, setulae 15–20 μ long.

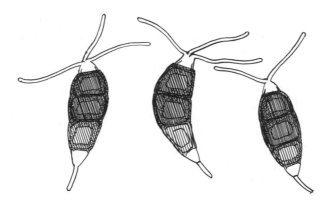

FIG. 63 [179]. *Pestalotia aquatica* Ellis & Ev.

180. **Pestalotia crassiuscula** (Stey.) Guba comb. nov.

> *Pestalotiopsis crassiuscula* Stey., Bull. Jard. Bot. État Bruxelles 19:338–340,1949, pl. 16, fig. D.

Conidia 5-celled, elliptic to clavate fusiform, straight, $22-26 \times 7-9 \mu$; 3 intermediate colored cells 14–18 μ long, upper two umber or darker, lowest one olivaceous, sometimes concolorous; apical hyaline cells conoid-cylindric, basal hyaline cells conoid and pointed; setulae 3, sometimes 2, filiform, flexuous, spreading 13–32 μ long.

On leaves of *Eucalyptus globolus* Labill., Tanganyika Terr., Africa, 1934, Biol. Reichs. Anst. Land. u. Forstw. Berlin, culture No. 5300, Wollenweber sub *P. disseminata* Thuem.

Wollenweber and Hochapfel (Z. Pflanzenkr. 46:401,1936) reported conidia $24-33 \times 6.7-9 \mu$; colored part 16–21 μ; setulae 2–4, usually 3, 15–41 μ long; pedicels 5–8 μ. The fungus produced a slow decay in apple fruits and was designated *P. disseminata* Thuem. Steyaert (Bull. Jard. Bot. État Bruxelles 19:1949) reported clavate-fusiform conidia $23-28 \times 7-10 \mu$, intermediate colored cells 15–19 μ, central one or upper two of them often opaque, obscuring the dividing septa; setulae 3 sometimes 4, coarse and very thick, usually 22–30 μ long. These characters were not recognized by Wollenweber or the present author in their study of the original culture no. 5300.

On *Salix* sp. (bark), Columbus, Ga. Aug. 9, 1911 in herb. Forest Path., U.S.D.A. No. 2480. On dead leaves of *Salix nigra* Marsh., Tuskegee, Ala., Nov. 3, 1926, G. W. Carver, associated with *P. bicolor* Ell. & Ev. Species differs from *P. bicolor* by longer setulae and strongly contrasted color of the dark intermediate cells.

181. **Pestalotia conigena** Lév. Ann. Sci. Nat. Bot. III, 5:285,1846; Syll. Fung. 3:792,1884.

> *P. funerea* Desm. var. *conigena* (Lév.) Grove, British Stem and Leaf Fungi II, p. 348, 1937.

Pustules globose-lenticular, innate-erumpent, surrounded and partly covered by the torn epidermis, gregarious and sometimes confluent. Conidia 5-celled, equilateral, slender fusiform, $19-26 \times 7-8.5 \mu$ or longer, tapering toward the ends, only slightly constricted at septa; intermediate colored cells 14–18 μ long, upper two of them umber or dark, lowest colored cell olivaceous; apical hyaline cells long conic to cylindric, basal cells long, acute or conic; setulae 2 to 4, usually 3, rarely 5, filiform, 12–42 μ long; pedicels erect, filiform, 9–16 μ long.

On cones of *Pinus sylvestris* L. near Paris, France, Léveillé, herb. Mus. d'Hist. Nat. Paris (type). The type description embraces another fungus on cones of *Thuja occidentalis* L. agreeing with *P. funerea* Desm. No measurements are given in the original description. The conidia are reported as elongate, attenuated, crowned with 4 setulae and the septa either 3 or 4.

Klebahn (Myc. Centralbl. 4:6,1914) from a study of unauthentic specimens, failed to obtain a satisfactory understanding of the fungus and was confused by the inadequacy and indefiniteness of the type description.

The genus *Thuja* is a common host for *P. funerea* and the earliest collections of the fungus are deposited in the Muséum d'Histoire Naturelle, Paris. Léveillé's original description is a vague characterization of two distinct species, that is, *P. conigena* and *P. funerea*, the former on cones of *Pinus sylvestris*, the latter on dead leaves of *Thuja*. The specimen in Ellis, N. Am. Fungi No. 527 on *Thuja occidentalis* cited by Voglino as the basis of *P. conigena* and the specimen in O. Jaap, Fungi sel. Exs. 443 on *Thuja orientalis* (cones) cited by Klebahn (Myc. Centralbl. 4:1914, fig. 4a) as his conception of *P. conigena*, both distributed under that name, and the specimen in D. Saccardo, Myc. Ital. No. 1569 on *Cryptomeria japonica* (Klebahn, Myc. Centralbl. 4:1914, fig. 4b) bearing the name *P. funerea* Desm. var. *cryptomeriae* D. Sacc., should be designated *P. funerea* Desm. Klebahn's figures of the conidia of the two specimens cited are not typical. The clavate-fusiform conidia of *P. funerea* Desm. usually are crested with 5 setulae extending in a narrow arc beyond the apices of the conidia.

Specimens examined: On leaves of *Araucaria brasiliensis* Loud., [= *A. angustifolia* (Bertol.) Kuntze], Esav, Minas Gerais, No. 1375. Conidia equilateral, fusiform, 22–26 × 7–8.5 μ, intermediate colored cells 14–16 μ long, upper two darkest, setulae 3 or sometimes 4, 15–27 μ. On leaves of *Araucaria brasiliensis* Loud. [= *A. angustifolia* (Bertol.) Kuntze], Angers, France, Dr. Guepin in herb. M.L.R. Tulasne, Mus. d'Hist. Nat. Paris, sub *P. guepini* Desm.

On *Chamaecyparis obtusa* Sieb. & Zucc. var. *gracilis* Rehd. (needles) and *C. pisifera* (Sieb. & Zucc.) Endl. var. *filifera aurea* Beiss. (needles), Shiloh, N. J., Sept. 9, 1927, R. P. White; *C. thyoides* (L.) B.S.P. var. *ericoides* (Carr.) Sudw. (needles), Beverley, N. J., Sept. 2, 1927, R. P. White.

On *Juniperus bermudiana* L. (culture from needles), Bermuda, Apr. 20, 1942, J. M. Waterston; on *Juniperus excelsa* Bieb. var. *stricta* Gord. (needles), Shiloh, N. J., Sept. 9, 1927, R. P. White. On *Juniperus* sp. (needles and twigs), Hill's Nursery, Dundee, Ill., in herb. Dept. of Bot., University of Illinois; on *J. virginiana* L. (needles and twigs), Washington, D. C., Dec. 1907, P. Spaulding, herb. Forest Path., U.S.D.A. No. 2140.

On *Pinus palustris* Mill. (needles), herb. Forest Path., U.S.D.A. No. 49304, Washington, D. C., Apr. 3, 1919, G. G. Hedgcock. On *Pinus rigida* Mill. (needles), Takoma Park, Md., Apr. 19, 1908, herb. Forest Path., U.S.D.A. No. 2153, P. Spaulding; cultures from needles, Nos. 10, 11, Washington, D. C., 1935. On *Pinus strobus* L. (needles), Petersham, Mass., Nov. 1907, herb. Forest Path., U.S.D.A. No. 2151. On *Pinus sylvestris* L. (needles), herb. Forest Path., U.S.D.A. No. 2143, Burlington, Vt., Oct. 1907, P. Spaulding. On needles and twigs of *Sequoia gigantea* DC. [= Sequoiadendron giganteum (Lindl.) Buch.], Paget, Bermuda, Dec. 12, 1940, J. M. Waterston. On needles of *Thuja occidentalis* L. var. *globosa* Gord. and numerous other varieties of *Thuja orientalis* L., Shiloh, N. J., Sept. 9, 1927, R. P. White.

182. **Pestalotia vismifolia** Guba sp. nov.

Pustulae discoideae, globoso-lenticulares, 75–150 μ in diam., plerumque epiphyllae, punctiformes, in maculis definites marginatis brunneis, dein erumpentes effusaeque; conidia 5-cellularia, fusiformia, aequilateralia, 22–26 × 7.5–9.5 μ; cellulae mediae coloratae vesicolores, duae superiores umbrinae, infima olivacea, 14–16 μ longae, vix constrictae; cellulae hyalinae apicales late conicae usque cylindricae, basales hyalinae attenuatae; setulae 3, crassae, flexuosae, 9–16 μ longae; pedicelli 3–6 μ longi.

Pustules discoid, globose-lenticular, 75–150 μ diam, largely epiphyllous, punctiform on definitely bordered brown spots, the erumpent contents black, effuse. Conidia 5-celled, fusiform, equilateral, 22–26 × 7.5–9.5 μ; intermediate colored cells contrasted, upper two umber, lowest olivaceous, 14–16 μ, only slightly constricted at septa; apical hyaline cells broad-conic to cylindric, basal hyaline cells tapering; setulae 3, coarse, flexuous, 9–16 μ long; pedicels 3–6 μ long.

On leaves of *Vismia acuminata* Pers., Caracas a Colonia Tovar, Venezuela, March 19, 1939, Whetzel, Müller, Tamayo, No. 3039.

183. **Pestalotia japonica** Syd., Hedwigia 38:144,1899; Syll. Fung. 16:1013, 1902.

Pestalotiopsis japonica (Syd.) Stey., Bull. Jard. Bot. État Bruxelles 19: 335–336, 1949.

Pustules globose to lenticular, numerous, sparse, punctiform, amphigenous, 85–175 μ in diam, seated on dead brown marginal areas. Conidia short, oblong or elliptic-fusoid, 5-celled, not constricted at septa, 19–24 μ long; intermediate colored cells 14–16 × 8–10 μ, the two upper ones umber, the lowest one olivaceous; apical hyaline cells short conic, basal cells short obtuse or rounded; setulae 3, frequently 4, straight, 12–20 μ; pedicels erect, short, 2–5 μ.

On living leaves of *Cedrela sinensis* Juss., Bot. Gard., Tokyo, Japan, Oct. 31, 1898, M. Miyoshii, in herb. Sydow, Mus. Bot., Stockholm, Sweden.

184. **Pestalotia eriobotrifolia** Guba sp. nov.

Pustulae atrae, globoso-lenticulares, punctiformes, epiphyllae, subepidermalicales, elevatae, erumpentes, 150–300 μ in diam, conidia 5-cellularia, recta, late fusoidea, tantum leniter constricta, 19.5–25 × 7.5–9.5 μ; cellulae mediae coloratae, 13–16 μ longae, cellula infima olivacea, duobus superioribus obscurioribus vel umbrinis; cellulae apicales hyalinae, breves, conicae usque cylindricae, setulis 3, interdum 2, late divergentibus, 17–27 μ longis coronatae; cellulae basales hyalinae, conicae, attenuatae; pedicelli usque ad 7 μ longi.

Dead brown areas circular, rectangular or variable, often involving half of leaf. Pustules black, globose-lenticular, punctiform, epiphyllous, sub-epidermal, raised, erumpent, surrounded by torn epidermis, exposing the black contents, 150–300 μ in diam. Conidia 5-celled, straight, broad fusoid, only slightly constricted at septa, 19.5–25 × 7.5–9.5 μ; intermediate colored cells 13–16 μ long, lowest olivaceous, upper two darker or umber; apical hyaline cells short, conic to cylindric, crowned with 3, sometimes 2 widely divergent setulae, 17–27 μ long; basal hyaline cells conic, tapering; pedicels up to 7 μ long.

On leaves of *Eriobotrya japonica* Lindl., Bot. Gard., Washington, D. C., J. T. Rogers, Oct. 24, 1916, Nat. Fungus Coll., U.S.D.A., No. 2415 [Fig. 64].

185. **Pestalotia natalensis** van Beyma, Antonie van Leeuwenhoek, Jour. Microbiol. Serol. 6:263–290,1940, fig. 15.

Pestalotiopsis natalensis (van Beyma) Stey., Bull. Jard. Bot. État Bruxelles 19:344,1949, pl. 27, fig. B.

Conidia 5-celled, elliptic-fusoid, broadest at middle colored cell, 25–33 × 8–9 μ (van Beyma), 20–26 × 8–9.5 μ (Steyaert); colored cells 14–19 μ long, the upper two umber and darker than the lowest colored cell; setulae 3–5 and 30–40 μ long (van Beyma), 2–5 usually 4 and 15–32 μ long (Steyaert), sometimes one of them branched; pedicels none (van Beyma), occasional and 2–7 μ long (Steyaert).

On pods of *Acacia mollissima* Willd. [= *A. decurrens* Willd. var. *mollis* Lindl.] Natal, Union of South Africa. Culture, Dr. Marie Ledeboer, Centr. Bur. Schimm. Cult., Baarn, Netherlands.

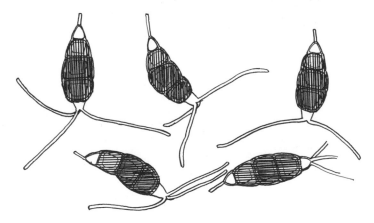

FIG. 64 [184]. *Pestalotia eriobotrifolia* Guba.

186. **Pestalotia longiseta** Speg., Michelia 1:478,1879; Syll. Fung. 3:787,1884.

Pustules sparse, epiphyllous, punctiform, lenticular or subspherical, black, 100–200 μ in diam, seated on reddish or brown spots not exceeding 0.5 cm in diam, surrounded by purple or black margins.   Conidia straight or curved, 5-celled, fusiform, hardly constricted at the septa, 22–25 × 7.5–9 μ; colored cells 13–18 μ long, guttulate, the two upper umber, the lowest olivaceous, end cells hyaline, prominent, the apical cells conic, bearing 3, or rarely 4 coarse and widely divergent setulae, 18–38 μ; basal cells conic, abruptly contracted into narrow pedicels, 4–11 μ.

On living leaves of *Rubus caesius* L., Susegana, Conegliano, Italy, Nov. 1876, Spegazzini [Fig. 65].

The collection studied bears the date and locality of the type, but the host given is *Rubus fructicola*, an error.   The long setulae are characteristic of this species.

187. **Pestalotia batatae** Ell. & Ev., Jour. Mycol. 8:65,1902; Syll. Fung. 18: 481,1906.

Pustules numerous, gregarious, and coalescing, subcuticular, raising cuticle in hemispherical manner, roughening and blackening the surface of the tuber, forming thick black crusts or cushions.   Conidia oblong-clavate constricted at septa, 5-celled, straight, 23–28 μ; median cells guttulate, 15–18

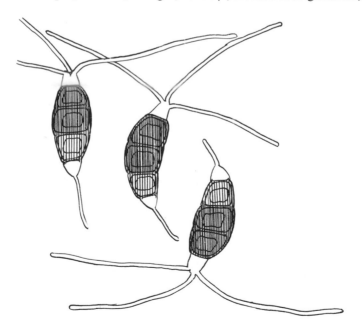

Fig. 65 [186].   *Pestalotia longiseta* Speg.

× 7–8 μ, sometimes up to 20 μ long, the two upper umber or only slightly darker than the lowest colored cell; apical hyaline cells long, conic or cylindric, basal long, conic, dilute olivaceous; setulae 3, spreading, 7–16 μ, sometimes slightly longer; pedicels short, 2–4 μ.

On tubers of *Batatas edulis* Choisy [= *Ipomoea batatas* (L.) Lam.], Tuskegee, Ala., Sept. 1900, G. W. Carver, herb. Ellis, N. Y. Bot. Gard.; on fruit of *Vitex* (Moosooku-Kiloko), Elizabethville, South Africa, Sept. 31, 1919, J. Burt Davy in Nat. Fungus Coll., U.S.D.A. No. 28231 sub *P. guepini* Desm.

188. **Pestalotia matildae** Richatt, Agri Tecnica (Chile) 13:89–92, Dec. 1953.

Pustules amphigenous, subepidermal, coalescing in dense carbonaceous layers under epidermis, the black masses here and there tearing through the epidermis in irregular order. Conidia narrow-fusiform, 5-celled, equilateral, tapering toward both extremities, 22–32 × 6–8 μ, usually 25–29 μ long; intermediate colored cells umber, 15–19 μ long, the lowest colored cell lighter brown, clear, the upper two or the center ones darker, slightly constricted at septa; basal hyaline cells long narrow, acute; apical hyaline cells long narrow, conic-cylindric, often oblique; setulae 2 or usually 3, 13–22 μ long, filiform, often awkwardly arranged about the crest of apical cells, 2 or 3 joined at crest of apical cells or sometimes distinct, when 2, one of them stronger, attenuated, the other filiform, one setula often subapical arising along the slope of apical cells; pedicels 2–5 μ long.

On leaves of *Boldoa boldus* (Mol.) Looser [=*Peumus boldus* Mol.], Rihue y Canete, Bio-Bio Province, Chile, Fernando Celedon, July 25, 1952, No. 495, Dept. Agr., Santiago, Chile [Fig. 66]. The fungus was reported to cause irregular brown spots on leaves. The author's study of type material reveals that the fungus is present only in dead decaying leaves. The dark spots on living leaves are quite distinct and appear to be sterile. A pathogenic relationship of the fungus with the spots is questionable.

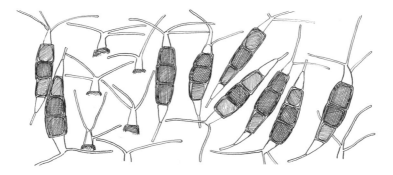

FIG. 66 [188]. *Pestalotia matildae* Richatt.

189. **Pestalotia paeoniae** Servazzi, Boll. Lab. Sper. R. Osserv. Fitopat. Torino XVI, 32–39, 1938, pl. I–II.

P. carbonacea Stey., Bull. Jard. Bot. État Bruxelles 19:183–184,1948, pl. 5, fig. E.

P. cassinis Laughton, Bothalia 4:822,1948.

P. ocoteae Laughton, Bothalia 4:826,1948.

Pestalotiopsis angusta Stey., Trans. Brit. Mycol. Soc. 36:241,1953, fig. 3a,b.

P. carbonacea (Stey.) Stey., Bull. Jard. Bot. État Bruxelles 19:335,1949.

P. paeoniae (Servazzi) Stey., Bull. Jard. Bot. État Bruxelles 19:312,1949, pl. XI, fig. C.

Pustules sparse, scattered, small, punctiform, $80 \times 100 \mu$, subepidermal, at first globose, expanding under the epidermis, erumpent, expelling the contents, raised like a dome. Conidia 5-celled, narrow, elongate-fusoid, $20–28 \times 6–8 \mu$, often constricted at septa, intermediate colored cells guttulate, $14–18 \mu$ long, olivaceous, concolorous, or central or upper two colored cells usually umber or darker, walls and septa dark; apical hyaline cells conic-cylindric or turbinate, $3–5 \mu$ long; setulae 3, sometimes 2 or 4, filiform, flexuous, $16–26 \mu$ long, usually distinct at point of origin; basal hyaline cells conic, acute, attenuated, $3–6.5 \mu$; pedicels filiform, deciduous, $3–10 \mu$ long.

On branches of *Paeonia arborea* Donn. [$=P. suffruticosa$ Andr.], Italy, Bertola, 1936.

The fungus is associated with enlarging brown constricted spots eventually girdling the branches. The disease is alleged to kill shoots and leaves in 7 to 8 days after the first appearance of the spots. Servazzi also noted aberrant conidia with 2 and 4 intermediate colored cells but rarely with 5 or 6 colored cells. Steyaert studied an original culture of *P. photiniae* Servazzi and found conidia $22–28 \times 6–8 \mu$, setulae 2–3, usually 2, $9–18 \mu$ and pedicels $3–6 \mu$ long. He reported that this fungus is *P. paeoniae*.

On *Euphorbia dawei* N. E. Brown, Nioka, (Terr. Djugu, Dist. Ituri), Lac Albert, Belgian Congo, Monteny, Oct. 1941, in herb. Hort. Bot., Bruxelles, Belgium, sub *P. carbonacea* Stey., which is a synonym. This fungus has narrow fusiform conidia, $22–29 \times 6–8 \mu$, colored cells $15–19 \mu$, the upper two umber, lowest olivaceous, setulae 3, sometimes 4, $15–28 \mu$ long.

Pestalotia cassinis Laughton and *P. ocoteae* Laughton are alike and similar to *P. paeoniae* Servazzi. *P. cassinis* was described on leaves of *Cassine sphaerophylla* O. Ktze. [$= Elaeodendron sphaerophyllum$ Presl.], coastal scrub, Brenton, Knysna, South Africa, Laughton, Nos. 34914, 34916. *P. ocoteae* was described on immature fruits of *Ocotea bullata* E. Mey., Deep Walls Forest, Knysna, South Africa, J. Phillips, No. 17824. The specimens differ only in the larger fructifications, reported as $240–300 \mu$ diam.

Pestalotiopsis angusta Stey. was described on leaves of *Borassus aethiopum* Mart. [$= B. flabellifer$ L.], Gold Coast, West Africa, Apr. 1949, S. J. Hughes and on *Bridelia ferruginea* Benth., Togoland, May 1949, S. J. Hughes.

190. **Pestalotia oxyanthi** Thuem. Inst. Rev. Sci. Litt. Coimbra 28:420,1880; Syll. Fung. 3:790,1884.

Pestalotiopsis oxyanthi (Thuem.) Stey., Bull. Jard. Bot. État Bruxelles 19: 329,1949, pl. 13, fig. D.

Acervuli largely hypophyllous, numerous, punctiform, hemispherical or applanate, subepidermal, erumpent and surrounded by the torn epidermis, generally distributed, 150–225 μ in diam. Conidia 5-celled, long, narrow-clavate, tapering toward the ends, straight or curved, 22–30 × 6–7 μ, usually 24–29 μ, intermediate cells 16–29 μ, guttulate, the upper two cells umber, the lowest olivaceous, only slightly constricted at the septa; apical hyaline cells long, narrow, cylindric or conic, the basal cells long, acute; setulae usually 3, rarely 2 or 4, flexuous, 13–30 μ, sometimes 6–35 μ long; pedicels short, erect, 3–10 μ.

On dead leaves of *Oxyanthus pubescens* (?), greenhouse, Bot. Gard., Coimbra, Portugal, August, 1879, A. D. Moller, No. 641; Contr. Myc. Lusit. 574 (Ser. III), herb. Jard. Bot. Univ. Coimbra.

191. **Pestalotia leucothoës** R. P. White, Mycologia 27:343–344,1935, pl. 32 B and C.

Pestalotiopsis leucothoës (R. P. White) Stey., Bull. Jard. Bot. État Bruxelles 19:319–320,1949, pl. 12D.

Pustules 75–150 μ diam, subglobose, largely hypophyllous, dense, punctiform, the black contents issuing in coils surrounded by the torn epidermis or oozing forth as a globose head. Conidia narrow-fusiform, 5-celled, only slightly constricted at septa, 23–28 × 5–7 μ; intermediate colored cells 14–18 μ long, guttulate, the central or upper two colored cells umber, lowest one olivaceous; apical hyaline cells long conic; setulae usually 3 or 4, rarely 2 or 5, typically 3, often arising from different points about the crown, one or two of them sometimes arising below it, rarely branched, usually 20–33 μ long; basal cells long, acute, attenuated; pedicels 6–16 μ long.

On discolored, sharply bordered dead areas on leaves of *Leucothoë catesbaei* Gray, Springfield, N. J., Aug. 1931, R. P. White, with other fungi.

192. **Pestalotia subcuticularis** Guba nom. nov.

P. aucubae R. P. White, Mycologia 27:342–343,1935, pl. 32A.

Pustules black, carbonaceous, subepidermal, 150–300 μ in diam, usually epiphyllous, scattered, the contents issuing in coils surrounded by the torn epidermis or as compact pyramidal cones. · Conidia 5-celled, narrow fusiform, erect or slightly curved, only slightly constricted at the septa, 22–27 × 6–7 μ (White, 23–32 × 7–9 μ); intermediate colored cells usually 15–18 μ long, the walls and septa dark, the upper two colored cells umber or darker than lower colored cells, becoming darker with age, guttulate; walls between two upper colored cells usually very dark; apical hyaline cells conic; setulae commonly 3, rarely 2, 4, or 5, united or arising at the apex of the superior cell, rarely arising from different points, widely divergent, slender, filiform, 22–38 μ, usually 22–31 μ long (White, 21–51 μ); basal hyaline cells typically long conic, acute; pedicels filiform, 2–17 μ long (usually 2–9 μ), generally erect.

On foliage of *Aucuba japonica* Thunb. var. *variegata* D'Ombr., following infections caused by *Colletotrichum pollaccii* Magn. or injuries due to sun scald, Rutherford, N. J., Aug. 20, 1932, R. P. White. The original description reported long, slender fusiform conidia, 25–30 × 7–8 μ, olivaceous colored cells, acute hyaline exterior cells, setulae usually 3, generally 29–41 μ long.

Gutner (Acta Inst. Bot. Acad. Sci. U.S.S.R., Ser. II: I: 291,1933, tab. 1, fig. 12), used the same specific name to designate a *Pestalotia* on the same host. The new name, *P. subcuticularis*, is proposed for *P. aucubae* R. P. White.

193. **Pestalotia cibotii** R. P. White, Mycologia 27:344–345,1935, pl. 32D.

Pustules largely epiphyllous, subglobose, punctiform, the black contents issuing in coils or cones, subglobose, 120–175 μ diameter. Conidia 5-celled, slender fusiform, tapering to the base, usually equilateral, sometimes slightly curved, slightly constricted at septa, 19–30 μ long (usually 21–28 μ) × 5–7 μ wide (usually 5–6 μ); intermediate colored cells 14–18 μ (mostly 15.5–18 μ) olivaceous, upper two slightly darker than the lowest, sometimes umber; apical hyaline cells conic, rounded at the summit; basal cells acute. Setulae 3 or 4, typically 4, rarely 2 and 5, arising from different points about the crown of the apical cell, 6–28 μ long (usually 15–20 μ); pedicels short, straight, up to 6 μ long.

Parasitic on living fronds of *Cibotium schiedei* Schlecht. & Cham., Rutherford, N. J., Aug. 20, 1932 and June 26, 1934, R. P. White. On *C. regale* Lind., Rutherford, N. J., R. P. White, Aug. 20, 1932. On seeds of *Araucaria imbricata* Pav. [= *A. araucana* Koch], Glasgow, Scotland, intercepted at Plant Quar. Insp. House, U.S.D.A., Washington, D. C., Nov. 4, 1929, D. P. Limber.

194. **Pestalotia aceris** P. Henn., Bot. Jahrb. (Engler) 29:152,1900–1901; Syll. Fung. 16:1014,1902.

Spots pale or dark, dried out, effuse, forming dead areas on lobes of leaves. Pustules amphigenous, small, scattered, punctiform, black, globose-lenticular, not exceeding 140 μ in diam, usually less than 100 μ, rupturing the epidermis and exposing the black contents. Conidia usually equilateral, elliptic-fusoid, 5-celled, 22–29 μ; upper two intermediate colored cells umber, the lowest olivaceous, 13–18 × 7.5–9.5 μ, slightly constricted at septa; apical hyaline cells cylindrical, bearing 3, rarely 2, short setulae 3–13 μ long; basal hyaline cells slightly obtuse or somewhat narrow, tapering into short hyaline pedicels, 3–7 μ long.

On living leaves of *Acer palmatum* Thunb., Bot. Gard., Tokyo, Japan, (Kusano), Nov. 1899, ex. herb. Kusano, in Berlin Bot. Mus. Hennings reported conidia 15–18 × 7–8 μ, setulae 5–8 μ long and fruiting pustules, 70–80 μ in diam.

195. **Pestalotia maculiformans** Guba & Zeller, Mycologia 24:370–371,1932, fig. 4.
   Pestalotiopsis maculiformans (Guba & Zeller) Stey., Bull. Jard. Bot. État Bruxelles 19:329,1949.

Acervuli epiphyllous, subglobose, punctiform, subepidermal, becoming erumpent by an asteroid rupture of the epidermis, 175–300 μ in diam, sooty at maturity from the discharged contents, seated on circular spots 1–4 mm in diam, wood brown to ashen gray on upper surface, with purplish or reddish brown border, almost concolorous below. Conidia fusoid, straight, 5-celled, 22–28 × 7–9 μ, slightly constricted at the septa; 3 intermediate colored cells guttulate, the lowest olivaceous, the upper two darker, 15–18 μ; exterior hyaline cells prominent, the basal conic, the apical cylindric; setulae 3, rarely 2 or 4, irregular in length, 9–20 μ; pedicels erect, 3–7 μ.

On living leaves of *Vaccinium ovatum* Pursh, west of the Coast Range, Ore. Specimens examined: Several collections near Waldport, Lincoln County, Ore., S. M. Zeller, Aug. 15, 1929 and Oct. 1929, in herb. Oregon Agr. College, No. 4879, in herb. Zeller No. 7565. Steyaert (Bull. Jard. Bot. État Bruxelles 19:178–179, 1948, pl. 3, fig. E) reported this species on *Elaeis guineensis* Jacq.

196. **Pestalotia populi-nigrae** Sawada & K. Ito, Bull. Govt. For. Exp. Sta. Tokyo 45:135–144, Sept. 1950.
   P. lignorum Gambogi. Publ. Inst. Pat. Veg. Microbiol. Agr. Univ. Pisa no. 332, 15, 1956. Ann. Sper. Agraria Roma (n.s.) 11, 4, Suppl. LXXVII-XCVI, 1957.

Lesions on shoots pale brown, centered about dead nodes or buds, enlarging and girdling the twigs. Pustules punctiform, globose-lenticular, numerous and distributed without order, erumpent, surrounded by torn shreds of the epidermis, 150–290 × 90–150 μ.

Conidia 5-celled, clavate-fusiform, erect or sometimes slightly curved, slightly constricted at septa, 21–30 × 7–9 μ; 3 intermediate colored cells 13–18 μ long; upper two colored cells darker than the lowest one; exterior cells hyaline, apical cells narrow, conic; setulae 3, rarely 2 or 4, unequal, widely divergent, 25–35 μ long; basal hyaline cells turbinate, 3–6 μ long; pedicels short, generally obscure, 3–7 μ long.

On shoots of *Populus nigra* L., *P. monilifera* Ait. [= *P. deltoides* Marsh.],

P. nigra L. var. *italica* DuRoi, and *P. simoni* Carr., Japan, K. Ito, S. Kimura, K. Sato, 1948 and 1949, herb. Govt. For. Exp. Sta., Tokyo. Disease was described by K. Ito, "Shoot blight of poplars caused by a new species of *Pestalotia*." The fungus is associated with black blighted lesions on current season's shoots of *Populus nigra* L. and was first observed in many localities in Tohuku district of northern Japan. The lesions are usually centered about a dead bud. The leaves are not attacked. The constriction of the shoot causes wilting and death of the leaves. The disease also appears on nursery stock and cuttings. Infection readily follows burned incisions in black poplar but it develops slowly in unburned wounds. The fungus gains entrance through dead tissue. In the field, dead buds and injured leaf scars are considered favorable infection courts for the fungus. *Populus monilifera* Ait. [=*P. deltoides* Marsh.] and *P. simoni* Carr. are moderately susceptible. *P. maximowiczii* Henry is resistant.

Further observations on the pathogen were reported by Chiba and Kobayashi, Jour. Japanese For. Soc. 41:146–147,1959, and Ito, Parasitic Dis. of Poplars in Japan, Ministry of Agr. and For., Tokyo, pp. 9–10, June 1959, fig. 14. The fungus causes a shoot blight of black poplar, *Populus nigra* L. in Italy. It was originally isolated from felled poplar wood and named *P. lignorum* Gambogi. Further study (Gambogi, Nuovo G. bot. ital. n.s. 63, 2–3, 248–256, 1956; Gambogi & Verona, Ann. Sper. Agrarla Roma (n.s. 12), 4, Suppl. I–II, 1958) identified the fungus as *P. populi-nigrae*.

197. **Pestalotia sydowiana** Bres., Hedwigia 35: Beibl. 32–33, 1896; Syll. Fung. 14:1027,1899.
> *P. epigaeae* P. Henn. Notizbl. K. Bot. Gard. Mus., Berlin, 3:40,1900; Syll. Fung. 18:482,1906.
> *P. macrotricha* Kleb., Myc. Centralbl. 4:6,1914; Syll. Fung. 25:601,602, 1931.
> *P. cavendishiae* Chardon & Toro, Jour. Dept. Agr. Porto Rico 14:279, 1930.
> *P. guepini* Desm. var. *rhododendri* Cooke. J. E. Vize, Microf. Brit. 509, 512, 1888, nom. nud.

Acervuli globose-lenticular, epiphyllous, sparse or densely gregarious, erumpent, surrounded by torn epidermis, 150–300 μ in diam, seated in ash-gray or brownish spots with reddish margins. Conidia 5-celled, equilateral, fusiform, tapering to both ends, 23–29 × 8–9.5 μ; intermediate colored cells guttulate, 16–19 μ long, slightly or hardly constricted at the septa, the lowest colored cells olivaceous, the upper two darker or umber; apical hyaline cells long and broad cylindric, the basal hyaline cells broad-conic; setulae 3, rarely 4, divergent or recurved, flexuous, 23–40 μ long; pedicels 6–12 μ long.

On living leaves of *Gaultheria procumbens* L., Bot. Gard., Berlin, Germany, 1894–95, P. *Sydow* in Sydow, Mycotheca Marchica No. 4372 (type of *P.*

sydowiana Bres.).   On dry leaves of *Epigaea repens* L. Bot. Gard., Berlin, July 1899, P. Hennings (type of *P. epigaeae*).   The globose-lenticular pustules measure up to 225 μ in diam, the conidia are straight, 22–29 × 6.5–8 μ, colored cells 15–18 μ, pedicels 9–22 μ, setulae 3, slender, 19–32 μ long. Hennings described conidia 22–25 × 7–10 μ, setulae 30 μ, pedicels 20 μ long. On dead leaves of *Epigaea asiatica* Maxim., Is. Onda, Okitsu, Japan, intercepted at Plant Quar. Insp. House, U.S.D.A., Washington, D. C., J. T. Rogers, No. 23965.

P. *longiseta* Speg. described by Grove (Jour. Bot., 1886, p. 198), on leaves of *Azalea* is *P. macrotricha* Kleb. (Grove, British Stem and Leaf Fung. II, p. 350, 1937).   Grove furnished a good description of the fungus.   On leaves of *Cavendishia pubescens* (H.B.K.) Hemsl., Granizales, Antioquia, Colombia, Sept. 11, 1927, R. A. Toro (type of *P. cavendishiae* Chardon & Toro).   Pustules like pycnidia; conidia 22–29 × 7–10 μ, setulae 3, 20–42 μ; pedicels 3–10 μ.   According to the author's study, this fungus is the same as P. *sydowiana* but the original description reported conidia 20–24 × 4–6 μ, intermediate colored cells 15–17 μ, upper two umber, the lowest olivaceous; setulae 3, 10–12 μ long.

On stems and leaves of *Rhododendron maximum* L., Nuttallburg, W. Va., Nuttall, sub *P. guepini* Desm. in Ellis & Everhart Fungi Col. No. 370a (type of *P. macrotricha* Kleb.) [Fig. 67].

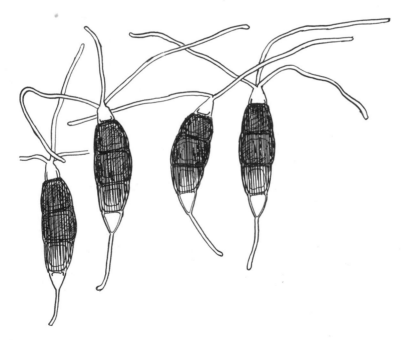

Fig. 67 [197].   *Pestalotia sydowiana* Bres.

On *Rhododendron maximum* from Holland, herb. J. A. Stevenson No. 1359, April 9, 1921; Coldfield, Warwickshire, England, Sept. 9, 1885, herb. Grove; Massachusetts, 1937, herb. Guba. On *Rhododendron ponticum* L. and *Rhododendron* hybrids intercepted at Plant Quar. Insp. House, U.S.D.A., Washington, D. C., from Holland, May 26, 1920, J. A. Stevenson; from Belgium, Oct. 28, 1915, J. T. Rogers, No. 471 sub *P. guepini*; Naarden, Holland, Apr. 10, 1921, A. J. Bruman and H. F. Bain; Dedemsvaart, Holland, April 4, 1923, A. J. Bruman. On *Rhododendron* sp., Westchester, Pa., Dec. 14, 1914 by F. Windle; on *Rhododendron* leaves, Kew, England, in Vize, Microf. Brit. Nos. 509, 512, sub *P. guepini* Desm. var. *rhododendri* Cooke.

Lihnell (Med. Vaxtsky., Stockholm, 40, 1943), described a defoliation disease of azaleas from Belgium. The leaves were infected with numerous species of *Pestalotia* and possibly a new species (p. 53) having conidia $19 \times 8 \mu$, two dark brown cells 13μ long and setulae $13–25 \mu$. The pathogenicity of the organisms could not be established by inoculation tests.

Inoculation of apple fruits with *P. sydowiana* caused total rotting in 60 to 90 days (Wollenweber and Hochapfel, Z. Pflanzenkr. 46:401–411,1936) and numerous fructifications after three weeks. They used cultures of the fungus from twigs of *Rhododendron*, Westphalia, Germany, Aug. 1933, from *Erica gracilis* Salisb., Berlin, Nov. 1936, and from stems of *Erica* sp., Giessen, Germany, Dec. 1933.

Servazzi (Boll. Lab. Sper. R. Osserv. Fitopat. Torino 13:72–79,1936) reported that *P. macrotricha* is a weak parasite. The fungus produced atypical conidia on inoculated *Kalmia latifolia* leaves, with 2 and 3 setulae, $17–27 \mu$ long, also typical conidia with 2 to 4, usually 3 setulae, $25–40 \mu$ long. Typical conidia appeared almost exclusively on leaves of *Rhododendron maximum*. Cultures of the fungus from *Kalmia latifolia* gave atypical conidia but fourth generation cultures produced typical conidia. Modifications in the composition of nutrient culture media produced changes in atypical conidia and fruiting bodies.

The stem and leaf blight of *Rhododendron* and *Azalea* is frequently encountered in shipments of stock from Europe. The disease causes considerable damage to *Rhododendron* in nurseries according to Clinton (Rep. Conn. Agr. Exp. Sta. 1915, 443, 1916), and Flachs (Blumen u. Pflanzenbau 42:94, 1927). The fungus follows injuries to the foliage by aphis, according to Schmitz (Phytopathology 10:273–278,1920), and a positive parasitic habit was demonstrated by Schmitz and Tengwall (Med. Phytopath. Lab. "Will. Comm. Scholt." 6:58–61,1924). Doyer (Med. Phytopath. Lab. "Will. Comm. Scholt." 9:1–72,1925) reported negative results from inoculating *Rhododendron* with a species of *Pestalotia* from *Cocos* (not *P. guepini* Desm.), with *P. vaccinii* (Shear) Guba from cranberry, with forms from *Juniperus* and *Rhododendron* named *P. funerea* and from *Retinospora* (not *P. macrotricha*). Also included in Doyer's studies were forms isolated from *Rhododendron* (not *P. guepini*), from *Thuja* named *P. funerea*, from *Taxus* (not *P. macrotricha*), and from *Altingia* (not *P. theae*). Doyer's forms from *Taxus*, *Retinospora* and *Biota* are not *P. macrotricha*. White (Florist's Exch., May 25, p. 32, 1929; N. J. Agr. Exp. Sta. Rep., June 30, pp. 277–278, 1928–29; Jour. Econ. Ent. 26:631–640,1933) and White and Hamilton (N. J. Agr. Exp. Sta. Circ. 350, 1935) presented a description of the disease on *Azalea* and *Rhododendron* and reported that weakened or injured tissue is necessary for infection; otherwise the fungus is harmless. Servazzi (Boll. Lab. Sper. R. Osserv. Fitopat. Torino 13:72–92,1936) obtained positive infection without wounding only at the axils of the leaves of *Kalmia latifolia* and *Rhododendron maximum*. He considered the fungus a weak parasite, able to adapt itself to various species of *Ericaceae*. Seaver (Mycologia 34:298–301,1942) named the apothecial stage of the fungus on *Rhododendron*, *Pestalopezia rhododendri* Seaver. The alleged apothecial stage on *Rhododendron* has been distributed under the name *Dermatea lobata* Ell., a fungus described on *Quercus alba* L. in Ellis & Everhart, Fungi Col. No. 331, and also as *Lachnella rufo-olivacea* (Alb. & Schw. ex Fr.) Sacc.

198. **Pestalotia caffra** Syd., Ann. Mycol. 12:266,1914; Syll. Fung. 25:606–607,1931.

Spots or areas dry, brown, spreading, largely of insect origin, with yellowish elevated margins. Pustules largely epiphyllous, irregularly distributed, small, erumpent, contents raised like a cone, surrounded by torn shreds of the epidermis, collapsing, the sooty contents spreading over the matrix. Conidia broad-clavate, 5-celled, hardly constricted at the septa, 21–28 × 8–11 μ; intermediate cells 16–19 μ, upper two colored cells umber, the lowest olivaceous; setulae 3, widely divergent, 20–26 μ, superior hyaline cells short, basal hyaline cells tapering; pedicels erect, 2–7 μ.

On living leaves of *Mimusops caffra* E. Mey., Isipingo, Natal, Nov. 1913, E. M. Doidge, in herb. Sydow, Mus. Bot. Stockholm, I. B. Pole Evans, No. 6630. According to Sydow the conidia measure 19–24 × 9–11 μ.

The characterization of the fungus by Laughton (Bothalia 4:822,1948) agrees with that of Sydow. Steyaert (Bothalia 6:381,1954) considered the species a synonym of *Pestalotiopsis glandicola* (Cast.) Stey. [=*Pestalotia glandicola* (Cast.) Guba].

199. **Pestalotia staticis** Moskoveta, Bull. Jard. Bot. Kyiv 16:71–87,1933.

Pustules epiphyllous, black, punctiform, globose, at first immersed then erumpent, 135–150 μ in diam, seated in irregular or orbicular spots, gray or gray-brown, sometimes purple margined, 1–10 mm in diam. Conidia fusiform or clavate, straight or somewhat curved, 5-celled, somewhat constricted at the septa, 15–30 × 7–12 μ; 3 intermediate colored cells, the two upper ones dark olivaceous, the lowest pale olivaceous; exterior cells hyaline; setulae 3, rarely 2 or 4, equal, occasionally unequal, 26–33 μ long; pedicels erect or curved, 4–8 μ.

On leaves of *Statice limonium* L. [=*Limonium vulgare* Mill.] Dist. Cherson, near Snigirivka, Ukraine, Russia.

200. **Pestalotia ardisiae** P. Henn., Hedwigia 41:116,1902; Syll. Fung. 18:482, 1906.

Spots on dead areas, gray or dark, weathered, marginate, dry, distinct. Pustules for the most part epiphyllous, subglobose to lenticular, subepidermal then rupturing the epidermis, surrounded by torn shreds and exposing the black contents, 70–150 μ in diam. Conidia 5-celled, straight, rather long fusiform, tapering at both ends, 25–31 × 8.5–9.5 μ, hardly constricted at the septa, basal hyaline cells long acute, apical hyaline cells long conic; intermediate colored cells 15.8–19.3 μ, the upper two umber, the lowest one olivaceous; setulae 3; diverging at right angles to the conidia, 15–30 μ long; pedicels 3–5 μ long.

On leaves of *Ardisia grandis* Seem. Bot. Gard., Sao Paulo, Brazil, July, 1901, Puttemans, in herb. Berlin Bot. Mus. Hennings' description of the fungus is very different; pustules 60–80 μ in diam; conidia subclavate or subpyriform, 18–20 × 6–9 μ, setulae 14–18 μ long, the apical hyaline cells subhemispherical, 3.5–5 μ in diam, basal hyaline cells subconic, 3.5 μ long.

201. **Pestalotia planimi** Vize, Grevillea 5:109,1877; Syll. Fung. 3:788,1885.
  P. euonymi Vize, Bull. Cal. Acad. Sci. 2:161,1885; Syll. Fung. 15:242, 1901.
  P. spectabilis Kleb., Myc. Centralbl. 4:3,1914; Syll. Fung. 25:600,1931.
  P. pterocelastri Laughton, Bothalia 4:828–29,1948.
  Pestalotiopsis planimi (Vize) Stey., Bull. Jard. Bot. État Bruxelles 19:325–327,1949, fig. 25.

Pustules amphigenous, subglobose, numerous, gregarious, coalescing freely, subepidermal, then erumpent, rupturing epidermis in radiating manner, black, the sooty contents spreading over the matrix, 175–350 μ in diam, generally distributed. Conidia 5-celled, long fusiform, tapering to the base, straight, slightly constricted at the septa, 28–38 μ; intermediate colored cells guttulate, the upper two umber, cylindric, the lowest olivaceous, sometimes concolorous, 19–26 × 7–10 μ; exterior cells hyaline, large, the apical cells long cylindric, bearing a crest of 3 or sometimes 2 long curved setulae, 15–40 μ, the basal cells long, tapering into slender pedicels, 6–11 μ.

On dead weathered leaves of *Euonymus japonicus* L., associated with other fungi. The black, sooty masses of conidia stand out in striking contrast to the pale-brown-colored matrix.

Specimens examined: Ellis, N. Am. Fungi No. 758, San Francisco, Cal., 1881, H. W. Harkness [Fig. 68]; Thuemen, Myc. Univ. No. 2085, *ibid.*, sub

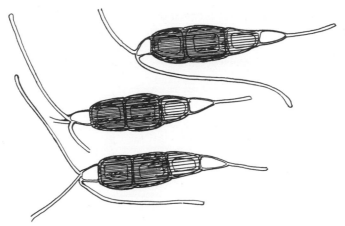

Fig. 68 [201].   *Pestalotia planimi* Vize.

P. planimi Vize var. *euonymi-japonici* Thuemen; Dept. Plant Path., N. Y. State Col. Agr. No. 6762, California, G. F. Meschutt; Thuemen, Myc. Univ. No. 884b, Coimbra, Portugal, Jan. 1879, A. Moller, sub *P. funerea* Desm. var. *euonymi-japonici* Thuemen.

The conidia of this species are unusually large.   The fungus was named *P. planimi* Vize and wrongly reported on dead stems of *Planimus*.   Harkness made known the error and stated that the name should be *P. euonymi* Vize and the host *Euonymus japonicus* L.   The original name, although based on the wrong host plant, must be retained.   Klebahn (Myc. Centralbl. 4:3,1914) made a new species, *P. spectabilis* Kleb., of the specimen in Thuemen, Myc. Univ. No. 884b, sub *P. funerea* Desm. var. *euonymi-japonici* Thuemen, but my study of this fungus shows that it is identical with *P. planimi* Vize. Steyaert placed this species among forms with spatulate setulae which he asserted are clearly visible in the specimen from Portugal (Thuemen, Myc. Univ. No. 884b).   He asserted that this character is occasionally present in the specimen from California (Thuemen, Myc. Univ. No. 2085).

Pestalotia pterocelastri Laughton was described on spots in leaves of *Pterocelastrus tricuspidatus* (Lam.) Walp. the "fynbos," Knysna, South Africa, Laughton, No. 35146.   There is nothing in the description of this species which distinguishes it from *P. planimi* Vize.

Versicolorae, Fulginae-Olivae

Species Nos. 202–258

202. **Pestalotia pandani** Verona, Nuovo Gior. Bot. Ital. 39 (3):473–474,1932, fig. 9.

Acervuli sparse or gregarious, subcutanous, black, distributed about the centers of pale spots with black margins.   Conidia fusoid-elongate, 5-celled,

13–16 × 4.8–6.5 μ; intermediate colored cells large, cuboid, dark, the exterior cells small, conoid, hyaline; setulae 2, 8–10 μ long, hyaline, divergent.

On dry fruits of *Pandanus tessellatus* Martelli, *P. pedunculatus* R. Br. var. *stradbrookeana* Martelli, and var. *lofuensis* Martelli, Australia.

203. **Pestalotia saccardensis** Guba nom. nov.

Pestalotia sessilis Sacc., Ann. Myc. 8:339,1910; Syll. Fung. 22:1224,1913.

Spots vague, epiphyllous, light grayish-yellow, narrow, black marginate. Acervuli punctiform, discoid, subcuticular, later erumpent, black, 120–130 μ in diam. Conidia 5-celled, sessile, elliptic-oblong, 17–19 × 7 μ, only slightly constricted at septa; 3 intermediate colored cells fuliginous, 13–16 μ long, exterior cells hyaline, acute; setulae 3, divergent, 6 μ long.

On withering or dead leaves of *Diospyros mespiliformis* Hochst., Mareb a Chenafena (Accehle-Guzzai), Eritrea, Africa. According to Saccardo, *Robillarda sessilis* Sacc. (Syll. Fung 3:408,1884) replaces *Pestalotia sessilis* Sacc., published in 1878. *Robillarda sessilis* Sacc. (Michelia II: 8,1882; Syll. Fung. 3:408,1884; 15:242,1901) is a different fungus. The latter fungus was originally named *Pestalotia sessilis* Sacc. The same name for another species is not valid; therefore the fungus on *Diospyros* is renamed *Pestalotia saccardensis* Guba.

204. **Pestalotia theobromae** Petch, Ann. Roy. Bot. Gard. Peradeniya 9:325–326,1925.

Spots irregular, more or less orbicular, dark brown to blackish brown, faintly zoned and surrounded by a narrow, pale-green border. Pustules epiphyllous, circular, 150 μ in diam, or elongate-lenticular, 300 × 150 μ. Conidia fusoid, 5-celled, 15–20 × 5–7 μ, 3 central colored cells, 12–16 μ long; setulae 3, 10–16 μ long; pedicels about 4 μ long.

On leaves of *Theobroma cacao* L., Pallekelle, Ceylon, April 1922, No. 6392.

On fruits of *Theobroma cacao* L., Philippine Islands, October 1925, R. O. Ocfemia. A culture submitted by H. H. Wollenweber, Berlin, featured 5-celled, clavate-fusiform conidia, 19–24 × 6.5–8 μ, setulae 3, rarely 4, 12–16 μ long, colored cells 12–16 μ the upper two umber to fuliginous, the lowest olivaceous; exterior hyaline cells short conic, rather acute. Wollenweber and Hochapfel (Z. Pflanzenkr. 46:401–411,1936) described conidia 21–24 × 6.9–8.8 μ, colored cells 14–16 μ, setulae 3, mostly 16–21 μ and pedicels 3–4 μ. Measurements are always greater in nutrient culture than in the natural substratum.

205. **Pestalotia coptospermae** P. Henn., Fungi Madagaskar, den Comoren und Ostafrika. Wissensch. Ergebnisse 3, pt. 1, 32, 1908, in Voeltz-kow, Reise in Ostafrika, 1903–1905; Syll. Fung. 22:1222,1913.

Spots effuse, pale, dried out. Acervuli scattered, epiphyllous, globose, lenticular, black. Conidia fusoid, 5-celled, intermediate colored cells dark,

13–15 × 5–6 μ, exterior cells hyaline, papilliform; 3 setulae, 10–14 μ, filiform; pedicels up to 10 μ long.

On leaves of *Coptosperma nigrescens* Hook. Nossi-Bé, Madagascar, J. M. Hildebrandt. The fungus is associated with *Coniothyrium coptospermae* P. Henn. and distinguished from it by the larger open fruiting bodies.

206. **Pestalotia briosiana** Montem., Atti Ist. Bot. Univ. Pavia II, Ser. 6:78–79, 1900, tab. XI, fig. 11; tab. XII, fig. 5; Syll. Fung. 16:1017,1902.

P. anthurii P. Henn., Hedwigia 41:116,1902; Syll. Fung. 18:484,1906.

Spots large, orbicular, for the most part zoned with concentric lines; pustules epiphyllous, punctiform, black, arranged in lines. Conidia 5-celled, fusiform, 17–20 × 6–7 μ; exterior cells hyaline, intermediate cells dark, the lowest one light-colored; setulae 3; spreading, 17–18 μ; pedicels short, 3 μ.

On living leaves of *Anthurium* sp., Bot. Gard., Pavia, Italy.

P. anthurii P. Henn. is characterized by globose-lenticular pustules up to 125 μ in diam seated on brown spots; elliptic-fusoid conidia 19–23 × 8–10 μ; the colored cells 14–16 μ, the upper two of them fuliginous, the lowest umber; pedicels 3–6 μ, setulae 3, 15–23 μ long. Reported on leaves of *Anthurium* sp., Bot. Gard., Sao Paulo, Brazil, Jan. 1900. Puttemans, No. 154, herb. Berlin Bot. Mus. (type). Hennings described conidia 18–20 × 4.5–5 μ, colored cells 16 μ, pedicels 6 μ long.

207. **Pestalotia pampeana** Speg., Anal. Mus. Nac. Buenos Aires III, 13:412, 1910; Syll. Fung. 22:1220,1913.

Acervuli black, sparse, innate in the cortex, later erumpent, circular, subglobose, 75–225 μ in diam, on pale spots girdling the twigs with distinct brown margins. Conidia 5-celled, broad elliptic to ovoid, erect, 17.5–20 μ, often strongly constricted at the middle septa; median cells thick walled, cask shaped, short, umber or fuliginous, equally colored, 11–13.5 × 7.7–9 μ; apical hyaline cells short conic, usually small, bearing a crest of 3, or rarely 4, straight setulae, 6–11 μ; basal hyaline cells small, short conic, abruptly contracted into the pedicels, 4–7 μ.

On living twigs of *Discaria americana* Gill. & Hook., Cordova, Argentina, April 1905, Spegazzini [Fig. 69].

The original description does not fit the type specimen. Illustrations of the conidia deposited with the type material show long, flexuous pedicels and long setulae. Author's study reveals short pedicels, short setulae, and 4-, rather than 3-, septate conidia.

208. **Pestalotia gibberosa** Sacc. Accad. Sci. Ven.-Trent. Istriana III, 10:83, 1917; Philippine Agr. 8:32–37,1919.

Pustules amphigenous, largely epiphyllous, distributed without order, circinate, 100–200 μ in diam, erumpent at maturity and carrying away the

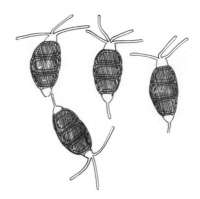

FIG. 69 [207]. *Pestalotia pampeana* Speg.

epidermis, exposing the black contents, the sooty masses covering the matrix. Conidia 5-celled, clavate to elliptic-fusoid, erect or curved and unequilateral, 14–20 × 6–8 μ, often gibbous; intermediate colored cells 10–15 μ long, upper 2 cask-shaped, umber to fuliginous, sometimes opaque, black at septa dividing the upper 2 colored cells, lowest colored cells pale brown or olivaceous, constricted at septa dividing contrasted colored cells; apical hyaline cells conoid to cylindric, narrow, sometimes hidden, crowned with 3 sometimes 2 or 4 divergent setulae, 8–18 μ long; basal hyaline cells obtuse, broadconic; pedicels 2–7 μ, erect.

On brown dead leaves of *Litsea glutinosa* Rob., Los Baños, Philippines, Dec. 1913, C. F. Baker, in Baker Fungi Malayana No. 375, herb. Farlow and herb. P. A. Saccardo, No. 2230.

On dead ashen and brown-colored spots and areas on weathered leaves of unidentified palm, Costa Rica Fungi, No. 177, Aug. 8, 1923, F. L. Stevens [Fig. 70a].

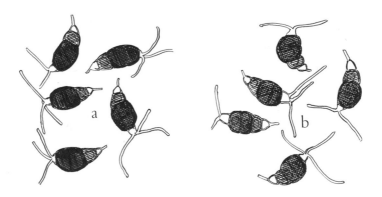

FIG. 70 [208]. *Pestalotia gibberosa* Sacc.

On dead leaves and twigs of *Cinnamomum camphora* Nees & Eberm., Taft, Fla., Aug. 23, 1915, C. Avery, Nat. Fungus Coll., U.S.D.A.

On leaves of *Cocos nucifera* L., Rio Piedras, Puerto Rico, May 18, 1923, R. A. Toro, No. 19 [Fig. 70b].

On *Kentia forsteriana* [=*Howea forsteriana* (F. Muell.) Becc.] (leaves), Rutherford, N. J., Oct. 27, 1927, R. P. White; on *K. forsteriana* and *K. balmoreana* [=*Howea balmoreana* (F. Muell.) Becc.] (leaves), greenhouse, Philadelphia, Pa., J. T. Rogers, Sept. 8, 1915, Nat. Fungus Coll., sub *P. palmarum*.

On *Persea* sp. (culture), Viscosa, Minas Gerais, Brazil, May 1, 1934, A. S. Müller.

209. **Pestalotia albo-maculans** P. Henn., Hedwigia 43:94,1904; Syll. Fung. 18:480,1906.

Spots round or oblong, irregular in shape, 0.2–1 cm in diam, white with narrow brown margin. Pustules dense, punctiform, gregarious and confluent, globose-lenticular, 120–180 μ in diam, subepidermal, erumpent, covered and surrounded by torn silvery shreds of the epidermis, the black sooty contents issuing and staining the matrix. Conidia 5-celled, clavate to elliptic-fusiform, unequilateral, 17–20 × 7.5–9 μ; intermediate colored cells 12–15 μ long, upper 2 of them fuliginous, almost black, opaque, together globose, the lowest ones umber; apical hyaline cells short conic, sometimes hidden, papillate bearing a crest of 2 or 3, usually 3 coarse or stout curved setulae, 12–22 μ long; basal hyaline cells short conic or obtuse; pedicels up to 5 μ.

On leaves of *Dalbergia* sp., Rio de Janeiro, Brazil, Dec. 1899, E. Uhle, associated with other fungi. Hennings described conidia, 15–18 × 7–8 μ and 2 setulae up to 15 μ long. On *Coffea liberica* Hiern (leaves), Rio de Janeiro, Brazil, Sept. 12, 1933, A. Bitancourt, Inst. Biol. Veg. No. 1832.

210. **Pestalotia conceptionis** Speg. Riv. Facult. Agron. Vet. de la Plata (Buenos Aires) 6: pt. 2, 177,1910; Syll. Fung. 22:1224,1913.

Spots none; pustules more or less lenticular, small, 100–120 μ in diam, subepidermal, black, arranged in series. Conidia ellipsoid, 5-celled, constricted at the septa, 16–20 × 8–9 μ, the 3 intermediate colored cells dark or olivaceous, rather large, the central one shorter than the other; exterior cells hyaline, small, the apical cells bearing 3 long, divergent setulae, 20–25 μ; pedicels 10–15 μ.

On dry decaying stems of *Asteriscium chilense* Cham. & Schlect., Cerro Caracol de Concepcion, Chile.

211. **Pestalotia stictica** Berk. & Curt., Curtis, Geol. & Nat. Hist. Survey,
    North Carolina, pt. III (Bot.), p. 118, 1867, nom. nud.   Grevillea
    2:155,1874; Syll. Fung. 3:793,1885.
  Pestalotiopsis stictica (Berk. & Curt.) Stey., Bull. Jard. Bot. État Bruxelles
    19:328–329,1949.

Pustules numerous, scattered irregularly over leaf surface, black, subepidermal then erumpent, often coalescing, globose-lenticular, largely hypophyllous, 70–140 μ diam.   Conidia 5-celled, unequilateral, 18–21 × 6.5–9 μ,
swollen in the middle and constricted at septa dividing the two lowest colored
cells; intermediate colored cells 12–15 μ long, guttulate, upper 2 fuliginous,
cask-shaped, lowest olivaceous; exterior cells hyaline, apical ones long conic,
the basal conic to hemispherical; setulae 3, curved and divergent, 20–31 μ
long, sometimes as short as 12 μ; pedicels short, straight, up to 9 μ.

On fallen leaves of *Platanus occidentalis* L., Santee River, S. C., No. 1638,
herb. Berk., 1879, in herb. Kew [Fig. 71]; San Antonio, Texas, Sept. 20, 1914,
Laura Broussard, Nat. Fungus Coll., U.S.D.A.; on leaves of *Cydonia
vulgaris* Pers. [= *C. oblonga* Mill.], Aug. 8, 1900, Tuskegee, Ala., G. W. Carver,
Aug. 8, 1900, sub *P. zonata* Ell. & Ev. var. *foliicola* Ell. & Ev., herb. Ellis in
herb. Farlow.

The original description clearly applies to this conidial form with 2
fuliginous colored cells.   According to the type description, the colored part
is 15 μ long and almost as much wide.   Saccardo (Syll. Fung. 3:793,1885)
asserted that conidia are 5 μ wide, but they are more properly 6.5–9 μ wide.
The fungus is distributed over the entire matrix without spots.   Two distinct
conidial forms occur on the type matrix; the other with narrow olivaceous

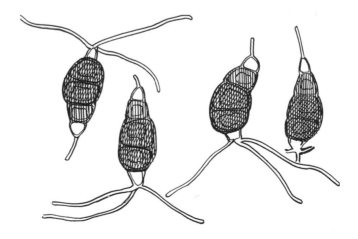

FIG. 71 [211].   *Pestalotia stictica* Berk. & Curt.

colored conidia is *P. microspora* Speg. The type description also embraces a fungus on large definite brown spots on leaves of *Tilia* (No. 4608, herb. Berkeley) collected by Beaumont in Alabama in 1879, which was designated new as *P. tiliae* Guba (Mycologia 24:383–384,1932).

212. Pestalotia cryptomeriaecoia Sawada, Bull. Govt. For. Exp. Sta., Tokyo 45:52,1950.

Pustules black, punctiform, at length erumpent, ostiolate. Conidia 5-celled, 13–16 × 8–9.5 μ; intermediate colored cells versicolorous, the upper two fuliginous, the lowest one pale; exterior cells hyaline, triangular, 3.4–4 μ long; setulae 3, 33–45 × 1.5–2 μ; pedicel 7–8 μ long.

On blighted reddish discolored leaves and twigs of *Cryptomeria japonica* D. Don.

The needle blight of "Sugi," *Cryptomeria japonica* D. Don, originally called "the red plague," is the most destructive disease of forest nurseries in Japan. Epidermic occurrences of the disease among *Cryptomeria* seedlings are common. The following species of *Pestalotia* are reported on blighted needles: *P. shiraiana* P. Henn.; *P. cryptomeriaecola* Sawada and *P. aomoriensis* Sawada.

The first two species attack only wounded leaves. *P. aomoriensis* attacks both wounded and healthy needles but the damage is not important. *Cercospora cryptomeriae* Shirai is considered the most destructive of the numerous fungi found on *Cryptomeria* in Japan. The needle blight of *Cryptomeria japonica* is described by Ito, Shibukawa, and Kobayashi (Bull. Govt. For. Exp. Sta., Tokyo 52:79–152,1952).

213. Pestalotia milletiae Laughton, Bothalia 4:825–826,1948.

Spots in foliage amphigenous, whitish-brown with dark margin, more or less circular, variable in size, spreading from margin or apex. Pustules epiphyllous, punctiform, scattered, 200–400 μ in diam, subepidermal, erumpent, acervuli or pseudopycnidia up to 300 μ in depth.

Conidia 5-celled, ellipsoid, straight or slightly curved, 19–22 × 7–8 μ; colored cells 14–18 μ long, upper two darker, fuliginous or central colored cell fuliginous; apical cells bluntly conical, bearing 2–3, usually 3, slender, delicate setulae, 10–15 μ long; basal cells conical, subhyaline, tapering into a slender erect pedicel, 4–5 μ long.

On living leaves of *Milletia sutherlandii* Harv., Eshowe Forest, Zuzuland, E. M. Laughton, No. 33437. Steyaert (Bothalia 6:381,1954) has placed this species in synonymy with *Pestalotiopsis glandicola* (Cast.) Stey. [=*Pestalotia glandicola* (Cast.) Guba], but in the author's opinion the conidia are too small to fit this species.

214. **Pestalotia virgatula** Kleb., Myc. Centralbl. 4:13,1914; Syll. Fung. 25: 599,1931.

　　P. funerea Desm. var. *mangiferae* Sacc., Atti Ist. Veneto Sci., Ser. VI: 2:461,1884.

　　P. microspora Speg. var. *philippinensis* Sacc. & Syd., Ann. Mycol. 11: 319,1913; Syll. Fung. 25:604,1931.

　　Pestalotiopsis virgatula (Kleb.) Stey., Bull. Jard. Bot. État Bruxelles 19: 336–337,1949, pl. 16, fig. B.

Pustules amphigenous, gregarious in places, rarely coalescing, small, 75–150 μ diam, subglobose, circinate, subepidermal then erumpent, the black contents staining the matrix. Conidia broad-clavate, pyriform, 5-celled, 17–23 × 6–8 μ, erect or curved; upper two colored cells swollen, fuliginous, lowest olivaceous or umber, only slightly constricted at the septa, 12–15 μ long; basal hyaline cells long conic, sometimes obtuse, apical hyaline cells conic, bearing 3, rarely 2, curved, widely divergent, rather stout appendages, 12–26 μ long; pedicels 3 μ long.

On dead weathered leaves of *Mangifera indica* L., in herb. Berlin Bot. Mus. sub " *Sphaerella tahitensis* in association with *P. funerea* Desm., on leaves of Manguier, Tahiti, A. Brunard." The fungus was originally briefly described by Saccardo with conidia measuring 22 × 6 μ. It has no connection with *P. funerea* Desm. Klebahn gave the name *P. virgatula* to this fungus.

On leaves of *Cocos nucifera* L., Ceylon, May 1927, sub *P. palmarum* Cooke. On dead leaves of *Eugenia* sp., Los Baños, Philippine Islands, Dec. 15, 1912, C. F. Baker, No. 558, sub *P. microspora* Speg. var. *philippinensis* Sacc. & Syd. There is no good reason for considering this fungus a variety of *P. microspora* Speg. On leaves of *Guioa* sp. [= *Cupania*], Palawan, Taytay, May 1913, E. D. Merrill, in herb. P. A. Saccardo, No. 886, sub *P. pauciseta* Sacc. This is the fifth host plant listed by Saccardo in his type description of *P. pauciseta*. The fungus on *Guioa* [= *Cupania*] belongs with *P. virgatula*. The forms on the other four hosts belong elsewhere (see *P. pauciseta*, p. 180). The specimen on leaves of *Litsea glutinosa* C. B. Rob. is considered the type of *P. pauciseta* Sacc.

215. **Pestalotia heucherae** Tehon & Daniels, Mycologia 19:126–127,1926, pl. 11, fig. 8.

Spots amphigenous, numerous, well defined, circular, 1–3 mm in diam, scattered, sometimes confluent, reddish-brown above with reddish-purple margins, dull brown below. Pustules 75–150 μ in diam, epiphyllous, subglobose, punctiform, subepidermal, erumpent and surrounded by torn shreds of epidermis, contents staining the matrix. Conidia 5-celled, elliptic-fusoid or elliptic-clavate, broad, straight, sometimes unequilateral, only slightly constricted at the septa, 17–23 × 7.5–9.5 μ; intermediate colored cells 12–16 μ long, walls and septa intensely dark, the upper 2 colored cells umber to fuliginous, at first translucent then opaque, the lowest olivaceous or the color contrast sometimes slight; apical hyaline cells short, broad-conic or rotundate, bearing 2 or usually 3, coarse, divergent setulae 6–16 μ long, usually up to 13 μ; basal hyaline cells broad-conic, obtuse; pedicels short up to 8 μ long.

On living leaves of *Heuchera parviflora* Bartl., Fountain Bluff, Jackson County, Ill., June 20, 1924, P. A. Young, Ill. State Nat. Hist. Survey, No. 2873.

On brown spots on leaves of *Byrsonima* sp., Llanos, Guarico, Venezuela, Apr. 7, 1939, C. E. Chardon, Myc. Exp. Venezuela, No. 3263, Dept. Plant Path. Cornell University. On dead leaves of *Dianella ensifolia* (L.) Rehd., Tsao Shan, Taipeh, Taiwan, Mar. 20, 1921, K. Sawada. On brown spots in leaves of *Psidium guajava* L., Paget, Bermuda, Feb. 21, 1929, H. S. Cunningham.

The original description of *P. heucherae* reported conidia 14–25 × 5–7 μ, concolorous, dilute brown, intermediate cells and 2, rarely 3, setulae, 10–20 μ long.

216. **Pestalotia versicolor** Speg. var. **polygoni** Ell. & Langl., nom. nud., Cat. Prov. Plantes de la Basse-Louisiane (Langlois) 1887, p. 32, No. 1064.

Pustules sparse, globose-lenticular to hysteriform, erumpent, openings elliptic to linnear, the black contents exposed and surrounded or partly covered by torn shreds of epidermis 150–450 × 120–175 μ. Conidia 5-celled, clavate or elliptic fusiform, 19–23 × 7.5–9.5 μ, frequently unequilateral; intermediate colored cells 12.5–16 μ long, upper 2 colored cells fuliginous, opaque, globose or swollen, lowest colored cells olivaceous, clear, constricted at the dividing septa; apical hyaline cells short, conic, cylindric, usually diverted sidewards, bearing 3 divergent setulae, 9–22 μ long; basal hyaline cells short, obtuse or conoid; pedicels up to 5 μ.

On stems of *Polygonum àcre* H.B.K., Louisiana, Mar. 14, 1887, A. B. Langlois, No. 1064, in Nat. Fungus Coll., U.S.D.A.

On fire-killed *Chamaecyparis* sp. Orlando, Fla., Feb. 9, 1938, C. L. Shear.

On dead spots in leaves of *Cinnamomum camphora* Nees & Eberm., Darien, Ga., Nov. 1943. On *Eriobotrya japonica* Lindl. (living leaves), Miami, Fla., Jan. 11, 1922, G. F. Moznette, Nat. Fungus Coll., U.S.D.A. [Fig. 72a]. On dead constricted areas on stems of *Jasminum primulinum* Hemsl., Winter Haven, Fla., Nov. 1946, J. W. Roberts. On leaves of *Mangifera indica* L., Espaillat, Moca, Dominican Republic, June 5, 1929, R. Ciferri, No. 113, sub *P. mangiferae* P. Henn. On fire-killed *Myrica* sp. (leaves), Orlando, Fla., March 3, 1932, C. L. Shear. On leaves of *Pandanus* sp., Rio State, Brazil, Dec. 23, 1912, E. Rangel in Inst. Biol. Veg. herb. Fitop., No. 610. On *Pyrus malus* L. (leaves), Louisiana, Aug. 18, 1887, A. B. Langlois, herb. Langlois, No. 1374, Nat. Fungus Coll., U.S.D.A. [Fig. 72b].

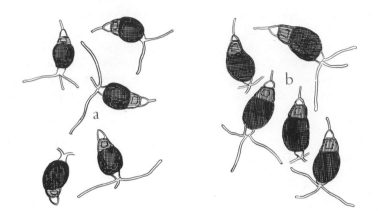

FIG. 72 [216].   *Pestalotia versicolor* Speg. var. *polygoni* Ellis & Langl.

217. **Pestalotia malicola** Hori, K. Hara in "A List of Japanese Fungi," 2nd ed. 1917, nom. nud.; K. Nakata and K. Takimoto, Jour. Chosen Gov. Agr. Exp. Sta., No. 15, 1928, p. 118, pl. 30, fig. 224 (Japanese).

P. thujopsidis Sawada, Rep. Govt. For. Exp. Sta., Japan, 46:144,1950.

Dead areas in leaves along margins, irregular in shape and size, at first brown, later ash-gray, the surface dotted and roughened with numerous black pustules. Conidia 5-celled, clavate fusiform, erect or unequilateral, slightly or more or less constricted at septa, $18.5–23 \times 7–9.5 \mu$, sometimes up to 25μ long; colored cells $13–16 \mu$ long, the upper two umber to fuliginous, the walls dark, rarely opaque, middle cells often the darkest, the two together cask-shaped, lowest colored cell pale brown, clear; apical hyaline cells short and broad, conic-cylindric with a crest of 3 divergent, coarse, setulae, $9–21 \mu$, sometimes up to 26μ long; basal hyaline cells conic to hemispherical, sometimes acute; pedicels short up to 5μ.

On leaves, twigs and fruit of *Malus pumila* Mill. var. *domestica* C. K. Schn. [= *M. sylvestris* Mill.], Korea; leaves, Daimon Village, Pref. Saitama, Japan, June 22, 1950, Y. Urasawa, in Imp. Central Exp. Sta., Nishigahara, Tokyo.

On *Eriobotrya japonica* Lindl. (seedling), Pref. Awa, Dec. 21, 1925, S. Sanekata; (leaves), Pref. Matsudo, Japan, Dec. 2, 1925, C. Kurada in herb. Chiba Col. Hort., Japan.

On *Pieris elliptica* Nakai (leaves), Toyotsumura, Miyako-gun, Fukuoka-ken, Japan, July 22, 1951, T. Hino.

On *Prunus* sp. (twigs), Amanogawa, Japan, Plant Quar. Insp. House, U.S.D.A., Washington, D. C., March 3, 1919, J. A. Stevenson in herb. Nat. Fungus Coll., U.S.D.A.

On *Photinia glabra* Maxim. (leaves), Myakuoji, Kyoto, Japan, Oct. 2,

1924, K. Togashi, in herb. Agr. Inst. Yokohama Nat. Univ. No. 2208.   On leaves of *Rhododendron degronianum* Carr. Mt. Ehiko, Pref. Fukuoka, Japan, Sept. 21, 1940, Y. Maki in herb. Agr. Inst. Yokohama Nat. Univ., No. 24125.

On leaves of *Thujopsis dolobrata* Sieb. & Zucc. var. *hondai* Makino, Japan.   Canes of *Vitis vinifera* L., Hyogo, Japan, Sept. 1930, T. Miki in Chiba Col. Hort., Matsudo, Japan, sub *P. uvicola* Speg.

The same fungus was reported as the cause of the brown spot disease of *Cydonia sinensis* Thouin [= *Chaenomeles sinensis* (Thouin) Koehne] in Korea and Japan.   The disease was described by various authors in the following literature: Nakata, Bull. Korean Agr. Soc. 11:9,1916 and Fukui, "Brown spot disease of *Cydonia sinensis*," Bull. Mie Imp. Col. Agr. For., Tsu, Japan, 3:19–20,1933.

218. **Pestalotia leprogena** Speg., Anal. Mus. Nac. Buenos Aires 23:109,1912;
    Syll. Fung. 25:604,1931.
    P. rhipsalidis Grillo, Inst. Biol. Veg., Rio de Janeiro 1:63–65,1934.

Spots repand-orbicular, 2–5 mm in diam, brown and circinate, gregarious or scattered, at length confluent, leathery, discoloring and involving entire fruit. Pustules loosely gregarious or scattered, black, conoid, erumpent, circinate, often confluent, sooty at maturity, 72–145 μ wide, blackening the matrix. Conidia 5-celled, clavate to elliptic-fusiform, curved or inequilateral, 18.5–23 μ; intermediate colored cells guttulate, the 2 upper ones usually fuliginous, swollen, opaque, the lowest ones olivaceous, 13–16 × 7.5–9 μ; exterior cells hyaline, broad conic, the basal ones rather acute; setulae 3, slender, spreading, 15–27 μ or usually up to 21 μ long; pedicels fragile, 4–8 μ.

On mature fruits of *Musa sapientum* Kuntze [= *M. paradisiaca* L. var. *sapientum* (L.) Kuntze], and other species, in Brazil and Argentina (Buenos Aires and La Plata).

On fruits of *Musa*, La Plata, Argentina, Nov. 1911, in herb. Spegazzini [Fig. 73]; on leaves of *M. paradisiaca* L. in F. L. Stevens, Fungi Puerto Rico, No. 122, sub *P. funerea* Desm.

On leaves of *M. cavendishii* Lamb., El Trompillo, Edo, Aragna, Venezuela, June 22, 1938, A. S. Müller, herb. Ministerio Agr., Venezuela.   On spots in living leaves of *Rhipsalis pachyptera* Pfeif., Bot. Gard., Rio de Janeiro, Brazil, No. 1790, sub *P. rhipsalidis* Grillo.   Grillo reported conidia 22–27 × 9–11 μ, intermediate colored cells olivaceous, 18–22 μ, setulae 13–27 μ, pedicels 7–11 μ.   Actually, the upper two of the 3 colored cells are fuliginous and opaque.

Becze (Rev. Appl. Mycol. 12:39,1933) reported *P. leprogena* Speg. on rotted bananas, *M. sapientum* L. [= *M. paradisiaca* L. var. *sapientum* (L.) Kuntze] and *M. cavendishii* Lamb., arriving at Hamburg, Germany. Tomkins (Trop. Agr. 8:255–264,1931) reported a *Pestalotia* among 86 per

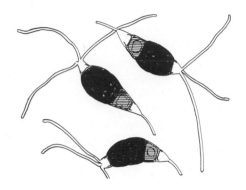

FIG. 73 [218].   *Pestalotia leprogena* Speg.

cent of his examinations of bananas.   When the fungus was used for inoculations of sound banana fingers it either failed to develop or produced only a very slight rot.

219. **Pestalotia ventricosa** Nann., Atti R. Accad. Fisiocr. Siena, Ser. 10, 2: 442,1927.

Pustules minute, suborbicular, sparse, 150–180 μ in diam, black.   Conidia oblong-fusiform, erect, 5-celled, constricted, 21–24 × 6–8 μ; the 3 intermediate colored cells olivaceous, brown, the upper 2 of them darker, swollen; inferior cells pale or subhyaline, subspherical, broad, 8 μ wide; superior hyaline cells short, conoid, setulae 2, 8–10 μ long.

On small dry twigs of *Lonicera implexa* Ait., near Chiatona, Tarentum, Italy, Sept. 1927.

220. **Pestalotia peyronelii** Verona, Nuovo Gior. Bot. Ital. 39 (3),474,1932.

Pustules sparse, gregarious, often confluent, black.   Conidia fusoid, 5-celled, 22–25 × 6.4–8.3 μ, the intermediate cells large, dark, the exterior cells small, hyaline; setulae 3, filiform, 6–8 μ long, divergent, hyaline.

On dry fruits of *Pandanus pedunculatus* R. Br. var. *stradbrookeana* Martelli, Australia.

221. **Pestalotia ixorae** Rangel, Bol. Agr., Ser. 16:321,1915, tab. 7, fig. 5; Syll. Fung. 25:605,1931.

Spots amphigenous, somewhat large, irregular, brick colored, with a limiting chestnut-brown border.   Pustules epiphyllous, black.   Conidia fusoid-clavate, 20–24 × 6–8 μ, 5-celled, not or only slightly constricted at septa; 3 intermediate colored cells constricted at septa, dark, the upper 2 fuliginous; exterior cells hyaline; setulae 2–3, divergent, filiform, up to 16 μ; pedicels filiform, hyaline, 2–3 μ long.

On living leaves of *Ixora* sp., Rio de Janeiro, Brazil, Aug. 1910, No. 122; culture from twigs of *Prunus triflora* Roxb., Lab. Biol. Agr., Porto Alegra, Rio Grande do Sul, Brazil, J. P. Da Costa Neto.

222. **Pestalotia pycnoides** Alm. & Camara, Rev. Agron., Soc. Sci. Agron., Portugal 4:60,1906, tab. 1, figs. 1–3; Bol. Soc. Broteriana 24:208, 1909; Syll. Fung. 22:1220,1913.

Pustules like pycnidia, epiphyllous, solitary, at first covered by the epidermis, then erumpent, sub-conic, 200–250 μ in diam. Conidia ovate-fusiform, 5-celled, 18–25 × 7–8 μ; the 3 intermediate cells dark chestnut colored, the exterior cells hyaline; setulae 3, 10–15 μ long.

On leaves of *Laurus nobilis* L. gardens of Institute Agronomica, Lisbon, Portugal, April to June, 1901, associated with *Phyllosticta laurina* Alm.

223. **Pestalotia zonata** Ell. & Ev., Proc. Acad. Nat. Sci. Phila. 1894:374, 1894; Syll. Fung. 11:578,1895.

P. ceratoniae Maubl., Bull. Soc. Myc. Fr. 21:92,1905, pl. 7, fig. 5; Syll. Fung. 18:480,1906.

P. versicolor Speg. var. *junci* Ell. & Langl., nom. nud., Langlois, Cat. Prov. Plantes de la Basse-Louisiane, p. 32, no. 1063, 1887.

Pustules subepidermal, globose-lenticular, punctiform, scattered on con-centrically zoned decaying spots, erumpent, surrounded by torn shreds of the epidermis, 75–175 μ in diam. Conidia 5-celled, long and narrow fusiform, erect or slightly unequilateral, hardly constricted at septa, 20–26 × 6–8.5 μ, tapering to the base; intermediate colored cells 12–18 μ long, usually 14–18 μ, upper 2 colored cells umber or sometimes fuliginous, opaque or becoming so, the walls and septa dividing the two upper colored cells blackening, obscured, the lowest colored cell olivaceous; apical hyaline cells conic or cylindric bearing a crest of 2–4, usually 3 setulae, 9–25 μ long, sometimes 15–27 μ; basal hyaline cells conic, vacuolate; pedicels 3–7 μ long.

On decaying fruit of *Cydonia* sp. Newfield, N. J., Sept. 20, 1890. The type description of *P. zonata* reported conidia 15–25 × 4–5 μ. On brown spots in leaves of *Posoqueria latifolia* (Lam.) Roem. & Schult., Davie, Broward County, Fla., Feb. 25, 1944. A. D. Rhoads. On living leaves of *Ceratonia* sp., São Paulo, Brazil, Puttemans, sub *P. ceratoniae* Maubl. Cultures from decomposed cellulose, U. S. Military Supplies, Pacific Area, World War II, W. H. Weston and D. W. Linder No. 57B5D [Fig. 74a] and 30 additional cultures identified as *Pestalotia virgatula* Kleb. (Research Rep., QMG Lab. Microbiol., Ser. 15, Q.M.C. Project 60, Aug. 3, 1949, p. 60).

On stems of *Juncus effusus* L., A. B. Langlois, No. 1063, Nat. Fungus Coll., U.S.D.A., sub *Pestalotia versicolor* Speg. var. *junci* Ell. & Langl. [Fig. 74b]. Conidia are 22–24 × 7–8.5 μ, upper 2 colored cells fuliginous, lowest colored cell olivaceous; setulae 3, 17–27 μ long.

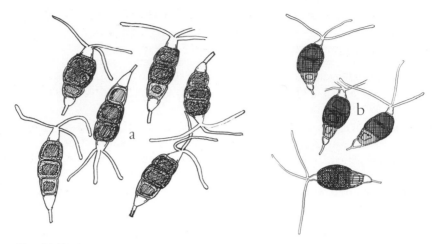

FIG. 74 [223].   *Pestalotia zonata* Ellis & Ev.

224. Pestalotia alöes Trinch., Rend. Napoli Soc. Reale Accad. Sc. Fisiche
Maten. Napoli 48:266–267,1909; Bull. Orto Bot. R. Univ. Napoli 2:
fasc. 4:503,1910; Riv. Patol. Veg. 4,101,1910; Syll. Fung. 22:1227,
1913.

Pustules rather large, gregarious, veiled by the ruptured epidermis, sublenticular, black, 170–245 μ in diam, 60–122 μ high. Conidia 5-celled,
fusoid or subpyriform, sometimes curved, not or slightly constricted at the
septa, 19–25 × 5–7 μ; the 3 intermediate cells broad, dark; exterior cells
small, subtriangular, hyaline; the apical cells with 3 setulae, long, filiform,
diverging from the acute apex, 17–25 μ long; pedicels hyaline, 4–10 μ
long.

On dry scapes of *Alöe virens* Haw. in botanic garden, Naples, Italy, Nov.
1908. The width of the conidia is unusually narrow and not consistent with
the broad intermediate cells implied in the description.

225. Pestalotia cinchonae Zimm., Ber. Land. u. Forstw. K., Gouv. Deut.
Östafrika 2:32,1904–1906, tab. 3, fig. 18; Syll. Fung. 18:481,1906;
Centralbl. Bakt. 12:316,1904 (Abstract).

Pustules small, apparent in the form of black spots, emitting black cirrhi
in a moist atmosphere. Conidia 5-celled, constricted at septa, 20–24 × 6 μ,
somewhat narrow, 3 intermediate cells dark, the upper 2 of them fuliginous,
the lowest lighter colored, extreme cells minute, subtriangular, hyaline;
setulae 3, spreading, 20–30 μ long; pedicels 4 μ long.

On dead twigs and brown leaf spots of hybrids of *Cinchona* sp. Amani,
East Africa.

226. **Pestalotia menezesiana** Bres. & Torr., Broteria (Bot.) 8:142,1909; Syll. Fung. 22:1222,1913.

Pestalotiopsis owenii Stey., Trans. Brit. Mycol. Soc. 36:88–89,1953.

P. owenii Stey. var. *major* Stey., Trans. Brit. Mycol. Soc. 36:89,1953.

Pustules amphigenous, black, numerous or densely gregarious, coalescing freely, sooty, spreading over the surface, at first subepidermal then erumpent, surrounded by the torn epidermis, 80–200 μ in diam. Conidia clavate-fusiform, 5-celled, 19–26 × 6.5–9 μ, curved, tapering into the conical basal cells; intermediate colored cells 13–17 μ long, the upper 2 colored cells umber to fuliginous, becoming opaque, cask-shaped, the lowest colored cells olivaceous, slightly constricted at the septa; basal cells long-conic, sometimes broad-conic, obtuse; crest of 3 setulae 9–31 μ, usually 15–26 μ long, divergent; pedicels short, straight, up to 6 μ long.

On desiccated leaves of *Vitis vinifera* L., Torrend, Fungi Sel Exs. 185, Porto Santo, Madeira Islands, A. de Noronha [Fig. 75]. According to Bresadola and Torrend, the conidia measure 25–27 × 8–9 μ, the setulae 28–30 μ, the pedicels 3–5 μ. On canes of *Vitis*, Vicosa Escala, Minas Gerais, Brazil, June 10, 1934, A. S. Müller in herb. A. S. Müller, No. 841.

Culture from lesions on *Theobroma cacao* L., Gold Coast, West Africa, Oct. 1949, H. Owen, sub *Pestalotiopsis owenii* Stey. *Pestalotiopsis owenii* var. *major* Stey. represents a sector of the type colony on malt nutrient agar. The fructifications are grouped in dense concentric rings in the sector or variant, while in the species they are effuse and loosely dispersed over the surface of the medium. Steyaert reported that the conidia of the variety *major* are larger and the setulae longer than those of the species. However, the descriptions of the two forms do not disclose significant specific differences and the illustrations of the conidia of both are identical. Both are similar to *Pestalotia menezesiana* Bres. & Torr.

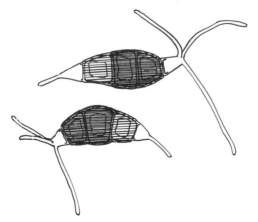

FIG. 75 [226]. *Pestalotia menezesiana* Bres. & Torr.

227. **Pestalotia clavispora** Atk., Bull. Cornell Univ. 3(1):37,1897; Syll. Fung. 14:1028,1899.

P. burchelliae Laughton, Bothalia 4:821,1948.

P. encephalartos Laughton, Bothalia 4:823,1948.

Pestalotiopsis clavispora (Atk.) Stey., Bull. Jard. Bot. État Bruxelles 19: 335,1949.

Pustules largely epiphyllous, numerous, punctiform, 150–275 μ in diam, scattered or loosely gregarious, immersed, then erumpent, the conidia exuding in black coils, blackening the matrix. Conidia 5-celled, erect or sometimes unequilateral, rather clavate-fusiform, 18–26 × 6.5–8.5 μ, rarely narrower, slightly constricted at septa; apical cells broad-conic, short, turbinate, often somewhat hidden, basal cells acute or long-conoid; intermediate colored cells 14–16 μ, the upper 2 of them umber or fuliginous; setulae 3 or rarely 4, rarely branched, 17–31 μ, widely divergent; pedicels 4–7 μ long.

On fallen, somewhat green, leaves of *Quercus* sp., Auburn, Ala., Oct. 3, 1891, in herb. G. F. Atkinson No. 2288, Dept. Plant Path. Cornell University [Fig. 76a]. According to Atkinson, the pustules are irregularly scattered, 150–200 μ in diam, the conidia exude in black coils which later dissolve, forming black effuse areas. The conidia are clavate, basal cells long conoid, apical cells short conoid; setulae 3, rarely 4, 25–35 μ long.

Leaves of *Quercus* (black oak), Elizabethtown, Ill., Oct. 7, 1937, J. C. Carter. On leaves of *Q. minima* Small, Miami, Fla., Feb. 11, 1917, G. R. Lyman [Fig. 76b]. On leaves of *Quercus velutina* Lam., Polk County, Tenn., Geo. G. Hedgcock, April 18, 1914 in Nat. Fungus Coll., Forest Path., U.S.D.A. No. 17116. On spots in fruit husks and leaves of *Aleurites fordii* Hemsl. Albany, Ga., J. B. Demaree; Plant Introduction Garden, U.S.D.A., Savannah, Ga., Nov., 1933, David Bisset.

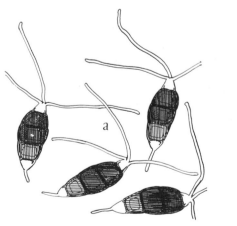
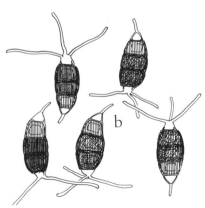

FIG. 76 [227]. *Pestalotia clavispora* Atk.

On spots in living leaves of *Burchellia bubalina* (L.) Sims [=*B. capensis* (L. f.) R. Br.], Knysna, South Africa, May 6, 1945, Laughton, No. 34912, associated with leaf minor injury sub *Pestalotia burchelliae* Laughton. Steyaert (Bothalia 6:381,1954) reported this species a synonym of *Pestalotiopsis glandicola* (Cast.) Stey. [=*Pestalotia glandicola* (Cast.) Guba].

On dead areas in leaves of *Encephalartos villosus* (Gaertn.) Lem. Malvern, No. 861, Durban, No. 2131, South Africa, I. B. Pole Evans, sub *P. encephalartos* Laughton. In dead areas in leaves of *Stangeria eriopus* Nash, Pietermaritzburg, South Africa, Doidge, No. 864, sub *P. encephalartos* Laughton. Steyaert (Bothalia 6:381,1954) reported this species a synonym of *Pestalotiopsis glandicola* (Cast.) Stey. [=*Pestalotia glandicola* (Cast.) Guba].

228. **Pestalotia photiniae** Thuem. Boll. Soc. Adriatica Sci. Nat. Trieste 6: No. 1, 134,1881; Syll. Fung. 3:787,1884.

P. foliorum Ell. & Ev., Fung. Col. No. 1551, Dec., 1901, nom. nud.

P. photiniae Servazzi Boll. Lab. Sper. R. Osserv. Fitopat. Torino 14, 35–37,1937, tab. I, II.

Pustules epiphyllous, gregarious, hemispherical-lenticular, at first covered by the epidermis, then free, black, on dry dirty brown spots with dark brown borders. Conidia elongate-ellipsoid, 5-celled, pedicellate, strongly constricted at septa, $20–24 \times 7–8 \mu$; 3 intermediate cells dark, the apical cells hyaline; setulae 3, long, curved, filiform.

On living leaves of *Photinia serrulata* Lindl. Pola, Istria, Austria.

On dead leaves of *Diospyros virginiana* L. Tuskegee, Ala., Sept. 15, 1900, G. W. Carver, as *P. foliorum* Ell. & Ev. Conidia similar to the type, measuring $19–23 \times 7–8 \mu$, the colored cells $13–15 \mu$, the setulae 3, $17–34 \mu$ long [Fig. 77].

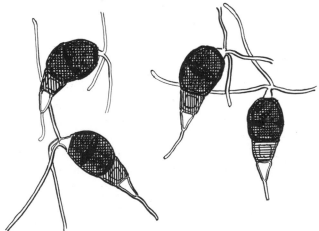

Fig. 77 [228]. *Pestalotia photiniae* Thuem.

Pestalotia photiniae Servazzi was described on leaves of *Photinia arbutifolia* Lindl. [= *Heteromeles arbutifolia* (Ait.) M. Roem.], San Remo, Italy. It appears to be identical with the original species according to its type description. Pustules 200–300 μ, globose-lenticular, seated in dead round, brown spots, 2–5 mm diam, circumscribed by dark margins. Conidia 5-celled, 23–26 × 6.5–9 μ, usually 8.5 μ wide, fusoid, often gibbous, intermediate colored cells 16–18 μ long, the upper 2 fuliginous, central cells obscure or opaque; apical hyaline cells conic, cylindric, short, basal cells long conic; setulae 2–3, flexuous, 16–33 μ, usually about 26 μ long; pedicels up to 7 μ long. Servazzi recognized the indefinite description of *P. photiniae* Thuem. It is difficult to understand why he used the same name for his species.

On dead leaves of *Zephyranthes* sp., Cinchona, Jamaica, British West Indies, Aug., 1919. D. S. Johnson, Nat. Fungus Coll., U.S.D.A.

229. Pestalotia laricicola Sawada, Bull. Govt. For. Exp. Sta. Japan 46:128, 1950.

Pustules black, punctiform, sparse, hypodermal, at length erumpent, 280 μ diam. Conidia fusiform or ovoid-fusiform, 5-celled, 23–27 × 6–7 μ; 3 intermediate colored cells dark, obscure, upper 2 of them more saturated than lowest colored cells, 14.5–18 μ long; hyaline apical cells conoid, 4–6 × 4.5 μ; setulae 3, rarely 4, 28–39 μ long, basal hyaline cells obconic, 3–5 × 4.5 μ; pedicel slender, 5–7 μ long.

In leaves and young stems of *Larix kaempferi* Sarg. [= *Pseudolarix amabilis* (Nels.) Rehd.], Japan. Foliage, stems and young plants are reported to be killed by the fungus. The disease causes a withering of the terminals.

230. Pestalotia longisetula Guba sp. nov.

Pustulae densae, punctiformes, globoso-lenticulares, 140–280 μ in diam, in cortice insidentes, erumpentes et fragmentis laceratis epidermidis cinctae, massa sporarum effusa, matricem inquinante; conidia 5-cellularia, longe fusiformes, erectae, ad septa vix constricta, 20–28 × 6–8 μ, plerumque 21–26 μ longae, ad basim attenuata; cellulae mediae coloratae 15–19 μ longae, duae superiores vulgo fuligineae, ad tunicas et septas atrae, cellulae infima olivacea; cellula apicalis hyalina, longe conica usque cylindrica, prominens; cellula basalis hyalina, longe acuta, prominens; setulae 3, interdum 2, rare 4, 22–44 μ longae, late divergentes; pedicellus 9–12 μ, rare furcatus.

Pustules dense, punctiform, globose-lenticular, 140–280 μ diam, seated in the bark, erumpent and surrounded by torn shreds of epidermis, contents effuse, blackening the matrix. Conidia 5-celled, long fusiform, erect, hardly constricted at septa, 20–28 × 6–8 μ, usually 21–26 μ long, tapering to the base; intermediate colored cells 15–19 μ long, the upper 2 usually fuliginous, black at septa and walls, lowest cell olivaceous; apical hyaline cells long conic to cylindric, prominent; basal hyaline cells long acute, prominent; setulae 3,

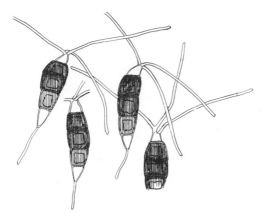

Fig. 78 [230]. *Pestalotia longisetula* Guba

sometimes 2, rarely 4, 22–44 μ long, flexuous, widely divergent; pedicels 9–12 μ, rarely forked.

On canes of *Rosa* sp., var. White Kilarney, Bell, Md., Feb. 25, 1924, G. E. Yerkes, Nat. Fungus Coll., U.S.D.A. [Fig. 78].

231. **Pestalotia glandicola** (Cast.) Guba, Phytopathology 19:206,1929.
    Robillarda glandicola Cast., Cat. Plantes Marseille 205, 1845, pl. IV.
    P. castagnei Desm., Ann. Sci. Nat. Bot. III, 6:64,1846; Desm. Plantes
        Crypt. de France 30:1490,1846; Syll. Fung. 3:793,1884.
    P. versicolor Speg. var. *cupaniae* Sacc. & Berl., Atti R. Ist. Ven. Sci. Arti
        Venezia 6:721,1885; Syll. Fung. 10:489,1892.
    P. versicolor Speg. var. *vagans* Speg. Revista Mus. La Plata, Argentina 15:
        42,1908; Syll. Fung. 22:1226,1913.
    Pestalotiopsis glandicola (Cast.) Stey. Bull. Jard. Bot. État Bruxelles 19:
        330–334,1949.

Pustules subepidermal, erumpent on maturity, coalescing freely, forming dense black cushions, subglobose to lenticular, 160–480 × 160–320 μ or larger, tearing the cover irregularly. Conidia 5-celled, erect, clavate-fusiform, sometimes curved, sometimes elliptic-fusoid, 20–26 × 7–9.5 μ, tapering to the base, strongly constricted at septa dividing the two lower colored cells; exterior cells large, prominent, the apical ones conic-cylindric, the basal ones conic, tapering; intermediate colored cells 14–18 × 4 μ long, the upper two umber or fuliginous, lowest olivaceous or lighter; setulae 2–4, usually 3, of unequal length, divergent, 9–20 μ; pedicels 3–8 μ.

On fallen acorns of *Quercus ilex* L., France, in Desm. Plantes Crypt. de France 30:1490,1846, and herb. Curtis in herb. Farlow and herb. Dr. Roussel in Mus. d'Hist. Nat., Paris, sub *P. castagnei* Desm. [Fig. 79a]. On acorns of *Quercus*, France, E. Requien, 1846, in Mus. d'Hist. Nat., Paris, sub *Robillarda*

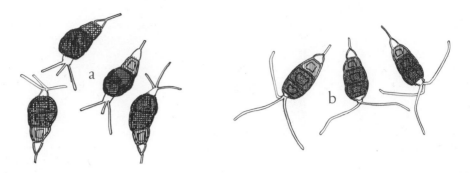

FIG. 79 [231].   *Pestalotia glandicola* (Cast.) Guba

glandicola Cast. (*P. castagnei* Desm.); herb. Durieu de Maisonneuve, sub *Robillarda glandicola* Cast. (*P. castagnei* Desm.), L. Motelay, 1878. On dead leaves and acorns of *Quercus coccifera* L., Desmazières, 1863, No. 8, in Mus. d'Hist. Nat., Paris, sub *P. castagnei* Desm.

The black contents of the confluent pustules issue in thick, coarse threads out around the perforations.   Three hyaline filiform setulae shorter than the conidia surmount the apical cells.   The species was originally described by Castagne with 3-celled conidia, a central colored cell and hyaline exterior cells.   Setulae were not mentioned.   Steyaert (Bull. Jard. Bot. État Bruxelles 19:179–180,1948:330–334,1949) asserted that *P. congensis* P. Henn., *P. aucoumeae* Cl. & M. Moreau (Rev. Mycol. Fr. 13:14,1948), and *P. scirrofaciens* N. A. Brown are synonyms.   Steyaert's study of type material showed conidia 21–28 × 8–11 μ, colored cells 16–20 μ, setulae 2 to 4, usually 3, 10–37 μ.

On brown dead areas on leaves of *Clivia miniata* Regel, Pref. Matsudo, Chiba-Ken, Japan, Feb. 11, 1935, S. Murato.

On leaves of *Cupania anacardioides* A. Rich, Australia (South Queensland), 1885, B. Scortechini sub *P. versicolor* Speg. var. *cupaniae* Sacc. & Berlese in herb. P. A. Saccardo, Padua.   The original description reported conidia 30–32 × 10–12 μ, setulae 30–33 μ long, and pedicels 15–16 μ long. Author's study found conidia 22–25 × 9.5 μ, 3 setulae 6–19 μ long, pedicels short.

On acorns of *Lithocarpus brevicaudatus* Hayata, Korea, Feb. 13, 1919, Nat. Fungus Coll., U.S.D.A., E. H. Wilson.   On dead areas in leaves of *Pandanus odoratissimus* Blume [=*P. tectorius* Sol.], Taiwan, Formosa, Feb. 20, 1920, K. Sawada, in Nat. Fungus Coll., U.S.D.A., sub *P. pandani* Sawada; *Pandanus* sp., Tonkin, Indo-China, 1887, Balansa, in herb. P. A. Saccardo, sub *P. funerea* Desm. var. *brevior* Sacc.

On leaves of *Persea carolinensis* Nees [=*P. borbonia* (L.) Spreng.] in Langlois, Flora Ludoviciana No. 1552 sub *P. maura* Ell. & Ev., St. Martinsville, La., Nov. 1, 1888, A. B. Langlois [Fig. 79b]; on *Persea pubescens* (Pursh) Sarg. (leaves), in Plants of Florida, No. 1923, Eustis, Lake County, Fla., May, June 1895, J. B. Ellis. *Pestalotia maura* Ell. & Ev. is a 4-celled conidial form originally described on *Psychotria rufescens* H.B.K. and would not apply here. One Langlois specimen No. 1552 bears the designation *Pestalotia laurina* Mont., another *P. maura* Ell. & Ev. Both specimens are deposited in the National Fungus Collections, U.S.D.A. The specimen with the inscription *P. maura* Ell. & Ev. (Jour. Mycol. 4:123,1888) appears in the Ellis collection in the Farlow herbarium. One of the forms has olivaceous concolorous colored cells, 17–22 × 5–7 μ, 3 setulae, 5–13 μ and is *P. breviseta* Sacc. This form appeared again as *P. maura* on dejected leaves of *Persea*, St. Martinsville, La., Apr. 4, 1896, A. B. Langlois, and Langlois reported this collection supplementary to his specimen No. 1552 on *Persea*, Nov. 1, 1888. The versicolorous, fuliginous-olivaceous conidial form is *P. glandicola* (Cast.) Guba. On insect eaten leaves of *Raphiolepsis umbellata* (Thunb.) Makino, Plant Introd. Gard., Savannah, Ga., Nov. 4, 1943, Carter, Mayer & Blizzard, No. 605, sub *P. sphaerelloides* Ell. & Langl.

On wilting leaves of a shrub-like tree, Ipiranga, São Paulo, Brazil, Jan. 1905, A. Usteri, sub *Pestalotia versicolor* Speg. var. *vagans* Speg. According to the author's study of type material, the fungus agrees with *P. glandicola* (Cast.) Guba. Spegazzini's measurements of the fungus are very different. In addition to the type specimen with fuliginous versicolorous conidia, there is another form with fusiform, olivaceous, concolorous conidia 19–22 × 6–8 μ, and 3 setulae, 6–16 μ long which is *P. microspora* Speg.

232. Pestalotia flagisetula Guba sp. nov.

Acervuli depressi, globoso-lenticulares, plerumque 75–150 μ in diam, atri, carbonacei, dispersi vel aggregati, coalescentes, subepidermicales, tegumentum elevantes et in lineis vel irregulariter fissentes, massa atra sporarum globosa vel conica supra superficiem emergenti et fragmentis laceratis cincta, dein collabente et matricem inquinante; conidia 5-cellularia, clavato-fusiformia, 20–24 × 8–9.5 μ; cellulae mediae versicolores, duae superiores fuligineae, inflatae, dolabriformes; cellula infima flavo-brunnea vel olivacea, ad septa paulo constricta, 14–16 μ longa; cellula apicalis hyalina breviter et late conica, setulis duis tenuissimis, flagellatis, flexuosis, late divergentibus, 12–25 μ longis cristata; cellula basalis hyalina conica; pedicellus brevis.

Acervuli depressed, globose-lenticular, usually 75–150 μ in diam, black, carbonaceous, scattered or gregarious, coalescing, generally distributed, borne under the epidermis, raising and tearing the covering in linear or irregular manner; the black contents issuing in a cone or globose mass above the surface, surrounded by the torn shreds, collapsing and blackening the matrix. Conidia 5-celled, clavate fusiform, $20–24 \times 8–9.5 \mu$; intermediate cells versicolorous, the upper two fuliginous, swollen, cask-shaped, the lowest colored cells yellow brown, olivaceous, somewhat constricted at the dividing septa, $14–16 \mu$ long; apical hyaline cells short and broad conic, crested with 3 very frail, flagellate, flexuous, widely divergent setulae $12–25 \mu$ long; basal hyaline cells conic, pedicels short.

On rind of dry arils of *Garcinia mangostana* L., Indonesia, April 8, 1953, T. Hino, in herb. Moji Animal and Plant Quarantine Station, Japan.

233. **Pestalotia clusiae** Griffon & Maubl., Bull. Soc. Mycol. Fr. 25:239,1909, tab. 27, figs. 1–3; Syll. Fung. 22:1219,1913.

Spots large, of variable shape, amphigenous, with white raised lines, yellow margined; pustules numerous, epiphyllous, punctiform, subcutaneous, erumpent, $200–300 \mu$ in diam, oblong-round, black at maturity, opening by a pore. Conidia ovate-oblong, often curved and unequilateral, 5-celled, $20–25 \times 8–10 \mu$; 3 intermediate colored cells, the central ones very dark, upper one less so, the lowest one olivaceous; exterior cells hyaline; setulae 3, rarely 4, divergent, flexuous, $20–30 \mu$; pedicels filiform, hyaline, 5μ.

On living leaves of *Clusia* sp., Paris, France. The conidia are rather large, corpulent, and deformed with flexuous, long setulae. Ciferri (Riv. Patol. Veg. 17:244–247,1927) obtained negative results in his attempt to infect leaves of *Clusia rosea* Jacq. with *P. clusiae*.

234. **Pestalotia paeoniicola** Tsukamota & Hino, Ann. Phytopath. Soc. Japan 21:4,181–184,1956.

Pustules under the epidermis, crowded, punctiform, black, globose or subglobose, at length rupturing the epidermis. Conidia 5-celled, fusiform, $17–33 \times 6–9 \mu$, 3 intermediate colored cells brown, the upper two of them saturated, fuliginous, the lowest one of them pallid; exterior cells hyaline, the apical cells conoid, $2–5 \times 2.5–3.1 \mu$, crowned with 3–4 setulae, $15–27 \mu$ long, the basal cells obtuse $3–6 \times 2.8–4 \mu$; pedicels hyaline $3.5–7 \times 1 \mu$.

On twigs of *Paeonia suffruticosa* Andr. in cultivation. Akita, Pref. Akita, Mar. 15, 1952, E. Tsukamota, in herb. Akita Univ., Japan.

The fungus causes an important twig blight of the tree peony about Akita City, Japan. The disease is first indicated by numerous minute black spots in the bark of living branches. The infected bark turns gray and the branches dry out and die. A full description is given of this severe twig blight and the relation of temperature and hydrogen ion concentration to the growth of the fungus. There is no reference to the occurrence of the fungus on the foliage. Author has specimens of a Pestalotia on dead concentric areas in leaves of the tree peony collected at Matsudo, Chiba-Ken, Japan, by C. Kurada. The fungus is different in many respects and has been grouped under *P. langloisii* Guba.

235. **Pestalotia sphaerelloides** Ell. & Langl., Ellis & Everhart, N. Am. Fungi No. 2387, nom. nud.; Syll. Fung. 13:268,1898; Phytopathology 19: 206–207,1929, fig. 2.

Pustules punctiform, pycnidia-like, subglobose, 75–150 μ in diam, scattered or densely gregarious in places, amphigenous, subepidermal, erumpent at maturity and surrounded by the torn epidermis. Conidia 5-celled, clavate fusiform, equilateral, 19–26 × 8–9.5 μ, slightly constricted at septa especially at septum dividing the two lowest colored cells; intermediate cells dark colored, the upper 2 umber or fuliginous, the lowest olivaceous, 14–17 μ long; exterior hyaline cells elongate, the basal broad conic, the apical conic-cylindric bearing 2 or usually 3, filiform, widely divergent setulae, 15–30 μ; pedicels 4–7 μ.

On dead decaying leaves of *Carya aquatica* (Michx. f.) Nutt., Bayou Chêne, La., Oct. 1888, A. B. Langlois in Ellis & Everhart, N. Am. Fungi No. 2387 [Fig. 80]; Flora Ludoviciana No. 1526, St. Martinsville, La., Oct. 25, 1888, A. B. Langlois. The pustules have the appearance of pycnidia.

236. **Pestalotia diospyri** Syd. Ann. Mycol. 11:117,1913; Syll. Fung. 25:601, 1931.

P. euonymi Hori. Shokubutsu byôgai Kôwa (Lectures on Plant Diseases) 2:173–174,1916, Tokyo (in Japanese); K. Hara, List of Japanese Fungi, 3rd ed., p. 252, nom. nud.

P. kaki Ell. & Ev., Byochugai Zasshi 15:2,1928 (Preliminary report in Japanese). National Agr. Japan 9: (10), 1915. Bull. Kagosima Imp. Col. Agr. For. 7,34,1929 (Japanese); abstract in Jour. Bot. Japan 5: (16)–(17),1930.

Spots amphigenous, irregular in outline, brown or dark, 0.5–2 cm in diam, with elevated dark or dark purple concentric lines. Acervuli subglobose,

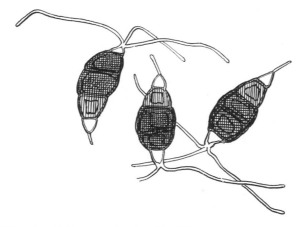

FIG. 80 [235]. *Pestalotia sphaerelloides* Ellis & Langl.

punctiform, 75–250 μ in diam, epiphyllous, gregarious, erumpent, the contents expelled and blackening the matrix. Conidia broad, ovate-oblong, or pyriform, 5-celled, 19–23 × 8–10 μ, frequently inequilateral, the 3 intermediate colored cells 13–16 μ long, the upper 2 opaque, fuliginous, globose, the lowest umber or olivaceous; apical hyaline cells short and broad conic, basal hyaline cells short, obtuse; apical setulae 3, coarse, 16–24 μ or longer, usually 18–22 μ long; usually with lumen; pedicels 2.5–6 μ long.

On living leaves of *Diospyros kaki* L., Ishie, Pref. Mutsu, Japan., Oct. 16, 1911, in herb. Mus. Bot., Stockholm, and Berlin Bot. Museum [Fig. 81]. According to Sydow the pustules are epiphyllous, punctiform, seated in spots marked with concentric lines; conidia pyriform, 19–23 × 8–10 μ, the setulae 18–22 μ long.

Other specimens; Nonodakemura, Pref. Miyagi, Japan, Aug. 1924, T. Abe; Kasuda, Pref. Saitama, Japan, Oct. 29, 1950, Y. Urasawa; Kyoto, Japan, Sept. 30, 1926, T. Nojima; Toyoda, Pref. Kanagawa, Japan, Aug. 24, 1950, T. Kigawa; Ebina, Pref. Kanagawa, Japan, Aug. 24, 1950, M. Tsuyuki; Ninomiya, Pref. Kanagawa, Japan, Aug. 24, 1950, Y. Usami.

The appellation *P. kaki* Ell. & Ev. has been carried along in the Japanese literature with *Cercospora kaki* Ell. & Ev., dating from a thesis by Murata "The Damaging Disease of the Persimmon," Part I, in National Agr. Japan 9 (10) 1915, but the name is a Japanese invention and has been discredited by Nojima (Pestalozzia parasitic on Diospyros kaki L., Rev. Appl. Mycol. 9: 536,1930). H. & P. Sydow named the persimmon fungus *P. diospyri* based on specimens collected near Aomori, Pref. Mutsu, Japan, by Michiya Miura. *Cercospora kaki, Pestalotia diospyri* and *P. theae* are reported to be damaging diseases of persimmon leaves in Japan and may be differentiated by shape, size, and details of the leaf lesions. The same fungus is associated with the fruit rot and gray leaf spot of loquat in Japan described by Konishi (Inst.

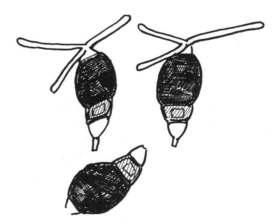

Fɪɢ. 81 [236]. *Pestalotia diospyri* Sydow.

Pflanzenkr. K. Univ. Kyoto 3:137–146,1937, figs. 1–4). A second distinct form associated with the disease is *P. adusta* Ell. & Ev.

On leaves of *Euonymus alatus* Rupr., Kinugasa, Kyoto, Japan, Nov. 9, 1924, T. Nojima. On spots in leaves of *Euonymus japonicus* L., Camden, S. C., Feb. 23, 1913, R. K. Beattie, Nat. Fungus, Coll., U.S.D.A. No. 8260; Iwatsukii, Pref. Saitama, Japan, Jan. 20, 1950, Y. Urasawa (conidia 20–25 × 8–9.5 μ, fuliginous, versicolorous, setulae 3, coarse, 12–25 μ long); Tokyo, Japan, in herb. Imp. Central Exp. St., Nishigahara, Tokyo, sub *P. euonymi* Hori (type). The gray leaf spot and shot-hole disease of *Euonymus* is caused by the fungus *Fusicladium euomymi-japonici* Hori. It is often associated with *Alternaria euonymi* Hori and *Macrophoma euonymi-japonici* Nishikado *et al.* in addition to *Pestalotia*. The disease is also the subject of a paper by Nishikado, Kimura, and Miyawaki in Nogaku Kenkyu (Ohara Inst. Agr. Research), 31:349–367,1939 (p. 365). Specimens from Tokyo, Pref. Osaka, and Matsudo, Pref. Chiba, bear the name *P. gracilis* Kleb. According to Nishikado *et al.*, the pustules measure 200–400 μ diam, 88–144 μ depth, conidia broad fusiform, 5-celled, 21–27 × 7–8.5 μ, upper 2 colored cells fuliginous; setulae 3, 14–25 μ, pedicels 3–5 μ.

On *Podocarpus macrophylla* Lamb., Sashi-cho, Higashimatsura-gun, Saga-ken, Japan, Sept. 10, 1951, T. Hino.

On leaves of *Rhus javanica* L., Toyotsu-mura, Miyako-gun, Fukuoka-ken, Japan, Oct. 14, 1951. T. Hino.

On leaves of *Smilax china* L., Toyotu-Mura, Miyako-gun, Fukuoka-ken, Japan, Oct. 14, 1951, T. Hino.

237. **Pestalotia versicolor** Speg., Michelia 1:479,1879; Syll. Fung. 3:790,1884.

> *P. aucoumeae* Cl. & M. Moreau, Rev. Mycol. Fr. 13: Suppl. Colon. No. 1:14–24, Fig. 1–2, pl. IV, V, June 1948; Steyaert, Bull. Jard. Bot. État Bruxelles 19:333–334,1949, fig. 26.
>
> *P. byrsonimae* Hoehn. Ergeb. Bot. Ex. süd. Brazil, 1901, Denk. Math-Nat. Kl. K. Akad. Wiss. Wien, 83:36,1907; Syll. Fung. 22:1221,1913.
>
> *P. cliftoniae* Tracy & Earle, Bull. Torrey Bot. Club 22:178,1895; Syll. Fung. 14:1027,1899.
>
> *P. coccolobae* Ell. & Ev., Field Columb. Mus. (Bot.) 1:286,1896; Syll. Fung. 14:1028,1899.
>
> *P. laurophylli* Laughton, Bothalia 4:824,1948.
>
> *P. pelargonii* Laughton, Bothalia 4:827,1948.
>
> *P. podocarpi* Laughton, Bothalia 4:827,1948.
>
> *P. rapaneae* Laughton, Bothalia 4:829,1948.
>
> *P. sapotae* P. Henn., Hedwigia 48:17,1908; Syll. Fung. 25:606,1931.
>
> *Pestalotiopsis versicolor* (Speg.) Stey., Bull. Jard. Bot. État Bruxelles 19: 336,1949.

Pustules largely epiphyllous, sparse, distributed without order, globose-lenticular, at first covered then erumpent, raised, surrounded by shreds of the torn epidermis, 80–215 μ wide, the black contents discoloring the surrounding matrix. Conidia 5-celled, clavate-fusiform, erect or somewhat curved, 22–27 × 7.5–9.5 μ; intermediate cells colored, guttulate, the two uppermost ones cask-shaped, fuliginous, usually opaque, the lowest one olivaceous, 14–19 μ long, constricted at the septa between the versicolored cells,, exterior cells hyaline, prominent, the apical cells usually short, cylindric, bearing 3, rarely 4, coarse or stout, flexuous, widely divergent setulae, 17–27 μ long; hyaline basal cells long and broad conic, descending into short straight pedicels, 4–7 μ long.

On fallen decaying leaves of *Nerium oleander* L., Conegliano, Italy, 1876, C. Spegazzini [Fig. 82a], in herb. P. A. Saccardo, Padua, Italy, and herb. C. Spegazzini, La Plata, Argentina.

Spegazzini reported conidia 30 × 10 μ, the two upper colored cells dark, the lowest colored cells bright; setulae 3 to 4, 25–30 μ long, pedicels 5–8 μ long. Klebahn's understanding of this species (Myc. Centralbl. 4:12–13, 1914), not based on type study, is conidia 22–29 × 7–9 μ, upper 2 colored cells cask-shaped, dark brown, the lowest colored cells brighter; setulae as long as conidia. Klebahn regarded all 5-celled spore forms with intermediate cells of contrasted color as *P. versicolor*. He included many forms from different hosts within the species *P. versicolor*, based on Saccardo's compilation of this species and his study of certain exsiccati. Type specimens were not considered. According to Klebahn, the following specimens belong to *P. versicolor*; (1) D. Saccardo, Myc. Ital. No. 978, named *P. versicolor* Speg. var. *rhododendri* D. Sacc. (on leaves of *Rhododendron hybridum* Ker. and *R. ponticum* L.), (2) Bartholomew, Fungi Col. No. 2441, named *P. guepini* Desm. (on *Ribes rubrum* L.), (3) Rick, Fungi Austro-Americani No. 255 named *P. versicolor* Speg. var. *guarantica* Speg. (on *Myrtacea*, São Leopoldo, Brazil, 1908), and (4) Cavara, Fung. longobard No. 193 named *P. palmarum* Cooke (on spathes of *Chamaerops humilis* L. in Hort. Bot. Pavia). Klebahn successfully infected a wide range of plants under bell jars with a form from *Darlingtonia* (conidia 26–31 μ long) which he determined to be *P. versicolor* (conidia 22–26.5 μ). Infection in the open greenhouse was generally unsuccessful. Thus he assumed that the fungus was of world-wide distribution and that it was essentially a saprophyte capable of existing under moist conditions on different substrata but not causing infection of living or freshly wounded tissue.

Specimens examined: On living leaves of *Achras zapota* L., São Paulo, Brazil, March 1905, A. Puttemans, No. 1253 in herb. Berlin Bot. Mus., sub *P. sapotae* P. Henn. Hennings reported conidia 10–14 × 5–6 μ, intermediate cells black, setulae 3, 10–15 μ long. Properly, the conidia are clavate-fusiform, 19–26 × 7.5–9 μ, upper two colored cells cask-shaped, fuliginous, the lowest umber, setulae 3, coarse, 15–28 μ, hence agreeing with *P. versicolor* Speg.

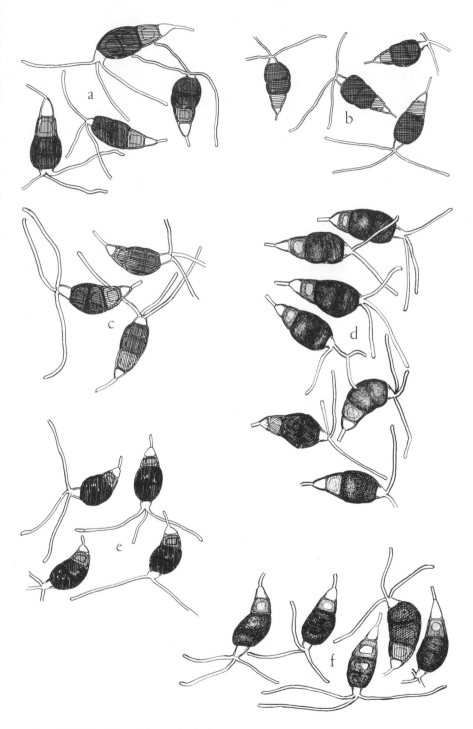

FIG. 82 [237].   *Pestalotia versicolor* Speg.

On leaves of *Areca rubra* Bory, São Paulo, Brazil, Feb. 1903, A. Puttemans, No. 619, Feb. 1902 in herb. Berlin Bot. Mus., sub *P. palmarum* Cooke.

On living leaves of *Artocarpus integrifolia* L. [= A. integra (Thunb.) Merr.], Est. do Rio, Brazil, Aug. 15, 1910, A. Puttemans.

In tumors and cankers in leaves, twigs and branches of *Aucoumea klaineana* Pierre, (Okoumé), Roger Heim, Gabon, French Congo, Africa, 1947, associated with other fungi, notably *Hypomyces ipomoeae* (Hals.) Wr. *Pestalotia aucoumeae* Cl. & M. Moreau was reported to cause tumors in leaves and cankers in branches and young trunks of *Aucoumea klaineana* Pierre in Gabon, French Congo, Africa, killing twigs, branches and trees. The pathogencity of *Pestalotia* was not established by infection studies. Claude and Mireille Moreau described both normal and abnormal conidial forms, but Steyaert (Bull. Jard. Bot. État Bruxelles 19:333–334,1949, fig. 26) who studied the original cultures expressed disagreement and reported only normal conidia. He placed the species *P. aucoumeae* in synonymy under *P. glandicola* (Cast.) Guba. To these circumstances the Moreaus replied (Rev. Mycol. Fr. 14: Suppl. Col. 2:99–101,1949): "Placés de telles affirmations nous nous sommes étonnés d'un si grave aveuglement de notre part." The Moreaus confirmed their original characterization of the species.

According to Claude and Mireille Moreau, the fungus is characterized as follows: conidia 25×8–9 μ, the intermediate colored cells 18 μ long, upper two of them fuliginous; setulae 2–4, usually 3, 25–35 μ long; pedicels 3–6 μ long, sometimes up to 10 μ. Steyaert (Bull. Jard. Bot. État Bruxelles 19: 1949) described conidia as 21–28×7–10 μ, claviform, intermediate colored cells 15–18 μ, the upper two fuliginous and opaque, lowest colored cells tawny brown; setulae 3, 14–29 μ long, usually 17–26 μ long; pedicels 2–6 μ. No aberrant forms were observed. *P. glandicola* (Cast.) Guba and *P. versicolor* Speg. are similar except that the latter species has longer setulae. Thus *P. aucoumeae* Cl. & M. Moreau is placed in synonymy under *P. versicolor* Speg.

On leaves of *Byrsonima verbascifolia* Rich., São Paulo, Brazil, sub *P. byrsonimae* Hoehn. No fungus is present in the type specimen at Farlow Herbarium but Hoehnel's drawing of the conidium and the original description would place the fungus with *P. versicolor* Speg.

On leaves of *Camellia japonica* L. (culture) Alice J. Watson, Nat. Fungus Coll., U.S.D.A.

On discolored spots in leaves of *Cliftonia ligustrina* Spreng. [= C. monophylla (Lam.) Sarg.], Ocean Springs, Miss., Nov. 1893, herb. F. S. Earle, Nat. Fungus Coll., U.S.D.A., designated *P. cliftoniae* Tracy & Earle. The fungus is typical of *P. versicolor* Speg.

On leaves of *Coccoloba uvifera* L., Yucatan, Mexico, 1895, Millspaugh, No. 3, in herb. Farlow and N. Y. Bot. Gard., sub *P. coccolobae* Ell. & Ev. (type). The original description of *P. coccolobae* reported 3-septate conidia but error is due apparently to the invisibility of the septa dividing the 2 upper opaque cells. The conidia have 3, rarely 2 or 4 setulae. The conidia are broadclavate, $18–25 \times 7–10\ \mu$, upper 2 colored cells fuliginous, opaque, swollen, setulae thick, $15–29\ \mu$ long. Stevens, Puerto Rican Fungi No. 399b, Boqueron, Puerto Rico, Feb. 15, 1913, F. L. Stevens in herb., Dept. Bot., University of Illinois [Fig. 82b]; Mayaguez, Puerto Rico, March 3, 1916, C. E. Chardon, No. 484, and Whetzel and Olive, No. 655 in herb. Dept. Plant Path., Cornell University [Fig. 82c]; Miami Beach, Fla., April 7, 1924, L. W. Nuttall, in herb. Bartholomew (N. Am. Fungi No. 34).

On *Coccothrinax argentea* Bailey, Miami, Fla., J. A. Stevenson, Nat. Fungus. Coll., U.S.D.A.

On leaves of *Cocos nucifera* L., Rio Piedras, Puerto Rico, Aug. 25, 1914, J. A. Stevenson, sub *P. palmarum* Cooke; herb. N. Y. Agr. Exp. Sta., Geneva, N. Y., Oct. 11, 1899, F. C. Stewart and F. H. Blodgett; Biol. Reichsanstalt, Berlin, culture No. 2414a from material from Java, Sept. 1926, O. A. Reinking, sub *P. cycadis* Allescher.

In irregular discolored areas in dead leaves of *Colocasia antiquorum* Schott., Pasadena, Cal., Apr. 3, 1931, O. A. Plunkett [Fig. 82d].

In twigs of *Cornus florida* L., originally from South Carolina, Starkington, N. Y., March, 1934, G. Graves.

On leaves of *Eriobotrya japonica* Lindl., Brooksville, Fla., Aug. 5, 1913, P. Spaulding, Nat. Fungus Coll., U.S.D.A.; on fruits, Agr. Sta., Paget, Bermuda, Feb. 1922, H. H. Whetzel.

In spots in living leaves of *Eugenia malaccensis* L., British Guiana, herb. F. L. Stevens, No. 128–280; on *E. uniflora* L., A. S. Müller, Fung. Minas Geraes No. 95; on *Eugenia* sp., Est. do Rio, Brazil, A. Puttemans, Oct. 5, 1910, sub *P. eugeniae* Thuemen in herb. Secc. Fit. Inst. Biol. Veg., Rio de Janeiro, Brazil Nos. 13 and 14.

On insect-eaten leaves of *Feijoia sellowiana* Berg., Miami, Fla., Feb. 6, 1917, G. R. Lyman, No. 3427 in Nat. Fungus Coll. U.S.D.A.

On living leaves of *Gossypium herbaceum* L., Central Univ. Agr. Col., Nanking, S. C. Teng, No. 684, Sept. 15, 1930, sub *P. gossypii* Hori.

On dried brown pods of *Hippocratea volubilis* L., Rio Piedras, Puerto Rico, Apr. 29, 1911, J. A. Stevenson, No. 5313 [Fig. 82e].

On leaves of *Ilex* sp., Alabama, herb. Berk. No. 4871, and herb. Beaumont No. 371 in herb. Farlow, sub *P. annulata* Berk. & Curt.

On leaves of *Klainedoxa gabonensis* Pierre, Wombali, Banningville-Kwango, District of Kasai, Belgian Congo, H. Vanderyst. This collection bears three distinct species of *Pestalotia*, according to Steyaert, namely:

1. *P. theae* Sawada var. *minor* Stey. (Bull. Jard. Bot. État Bruxelles 19: 184,1948, pl. 6, fig. A), and later *Pestalotiopsis theae* (Sawada) Stey. var. *minor* Stey. (Bull. Jard. Bot. État Bruxelles 19:327–328,1949, pl. 14, fig. E, fig. 24A). Conidia $21–28 \times 6–7\ \mu$; colored part $14–19\ \mu$, olivaceous and

concolorous; setulae 18–29 μ, spatulate (Steyaert).   In spite of careful search, this conidial form was not found.   Steyaert has embraced within his concept of this species the following material on leaves of *Camellia thea* (L.) Kuntze.

(a) Sydow, Fungi exot. Exs. No. 146.   This fungus is *P. theae* Sawada.

(b) Culture of *Pestalotia*, Buitenzorg, Java, C. M. Doyer, which in my judgment is *P. theae* Sawada.   Both (a) and (b) have spatulate setulae characteristic of *P. theae* Sawada and *P. elasticae* Koord.   The latter has the smaller measurements of the two species.   Therefore, the name *Pestalotiopsis theae* Sawada var. *minor* Stey. is unacceptable.   If the name must be preserved on the basis of something observed by Steyaert on *Klainedoxa*, the designation *Pestalotia elasticae* Koord. is preferred.

2. *P. clavispora* Atk. (most frequent).   Conidia 20–25 × 7–9 μ; colored part versicolorous, 13–17 μ, upper two colored cells fuliginous; setulae 11–32 μ (Steyaert).

3. *P. mangiferae* P. Henn.   Conidia 18–22 × 5–7 μ; colored part 12–14 μ; setulae 8–16 μ (Steyaert).

These two conidial forms on *Klainedoxa* embrace a common, typical form, *P. clavispora* Atk., and an atypical form, *P. mangiferae* P. Henn., according to Steyaert.   But both conidial forms appear in the same microscopic mounts and both occur in the same acervulus; yet they are different in the light of my study as follows:

Typical form, *P. clavispora*.   Conidia broad, clavate, 19–24 × 6.5–9 μ; colored cells 12–15 μ long, olivaceous or umber, concolorous; upper two colored cells fuliginous, cask-shaped; setulae 3, rarely 4, 15–36 μ long, coarse.

Atypical form, *P. mangiferae*.   Conidia 15–19 × 5–6.5 μ, elliptic fusoid, olivaceous and concolorous, 9.5–13 μ long; setulae 3, 9–14 μ long.

Conidia are present in all stages intermediate between the (a) and (b) types.   It is concluded that the form is plastic, and that it fits *P. versicolor* Speg.   The classification of distinct species of *Pestalotia* on the basis of form, color, and biometric measurements of typical conidia can be difficult.   If a species in the same matrix must be subdivided further, with designations for aberrant forms, then taxonomy can be futile.

In spots in living leaves of *Laurophyllus capensis* Thunb., Knysna, South Africa, May 6, 1945, E. M. Laughton, sub *Pestalotia laurophylli* Laughton. Steyaert (Bothalia 6:381,1954) regarded this species as a synonym of *Pestalotiopsis glandicola* (Cast.) Stey. [= *Pestalotia glandicola* (Cast.) Guba].

On leaves of *Lysimachia clethroides* Duby, Toyotsu-mura, Myako-gun, Fukuoka-ken, Japan, July 28, 1951, T. Hino in herb. Moji Animal and Plant Quar. Station.

In dead weathered leaves of *Marica gracilis* Herb. [= *Neomarica gracilis* (Herb.) Sprague], greenhouse, Cincinnati, Ohio, April 8, 1936, W. B. Cooke.

In leaves of *Martinezia caryotaefolia* H.B.K., Rio de Janeiro, Brazil, June 28, 1910, A. Puttemans.

On leaves of *Myrtaceae*, São Leopoldo, Brazil, 1908 in Rick, Fungi Austro-Americani No. 255, sub *P. versicolor* Speg. var. *guaranitica* Speg. The specimen shows conidia 18–25 × 7.5–9.5 μ; setulae 3, coarse, 13–25 μ. Klebahn (Myc. Centralbl. 4:12–13,1914) considered this fungus typical of *P. versicolor* Speg. However, the type of *P. versicolor* Speg. var. *guaranitica* Speg. collected in 1882 in Paraguay and the description published in 1886 differ. The salient characters of the latter are: conidia 20–25 × 12–16 μ, 2 upper colored cells fuliginous, swollen; setulae 2, up to 20 μ long; pedicels 8–10 μ. Even though the width of the conidia appears to be in error, *P. versicolor* Speg. var. *guaranitica* Speg. is retained as a distinct species with the combination *P. guaranitica* (Speg.) Guba.

On spots in leaves of *Pelargonium cordatum* L'Herit, sub *Pestalotia pelargonii* Laughton, Knysna, South Africa, May 14, 1945, E. M. Laughton, No. 34918. Steyaert (Bothalia 6:381,1954) considered this species a synonym of *Pestalotiopsis glandicola* (Cast.) Stey.

On *Persea carolinensis* Nees [*P. borbonia* (L.) Spreng.], Darien, Ga., Nov. 1881, H. W. Ravenel in herb. Ellis No. 4025, Nat. Fungus Coll., U.S.D.A.; on *P. gratissima* Gaertn. [=*P. americana* Mill.] (leaves), Miami, Fla., Hickson Bros., sub *P. funerea* Desm. in Nat. Fungus Coll., U.S.D.A.; Brooksville, Fla., Feb. 1920 and Feb. 1922, J. A. Stevenson in Nat. Fungus Coll., U.S.D.A., sub *P. guepini* Desm.; Lemon City, Fla., Feb. 28, 1917, J. T. Rogers, No. 2922 in Nat. Fungus Coll., U.S.D.A.

On living leaves of *Podocarpus latifolia* R. Br., Garden of Eden Nature Reserve, Knysna, South Africa, E. M. Laughton, No. 34917.

On fruits of *Psidium guajava* L., from Mexico, intercepted at Hidalgo, Texas, Sept. 2, 1934, I. W. Berryhill, Nat. Fungus Coll., U.S.D.A.

On spots in living leaves of *Rapanea melanophleos* (R. Br.) Mez., Humansdorp District, South Africa, Doidge; Knysna, South Africa, E. M. Laughton, sub *Pestalotia rapaneae* Laughton. Steyaert (Bothalia 6:829,1954) placed this species in synonymy under *Pestalotiopsis glandicola* (Cast.) Stey.

On *Rhizophora mangle* L. (leaves), Brown, Britton, and Seaver, Harrington House, Bermuda, No. 1355, Nov. 29, Dec. 14, 1912, sub *P. guepini* Desm. in herb. N. Y. Bot. Gard.; Walsingham, Bermuda, Nov. 30, 1938, Dec. 4, 1940, F. J. Seaver and J. M. Waterston, Bermuda Fungi Nos. 50 and 393.

On *Saccharum officinarum* L. (leaves), Central Isabel, Manzanillo (Oriente), Cuba, Dec. 15, 1924, J. R. Weir, sub *P. fuscescens* Sor. var. *sacchari* Wakk. Also other collections from Cuba. The fungus appears in abundance on yellow brown dead areas with reddish margins on living leaves.

On *Syzygium aromaticum* Merr. & Perry [=*Eugenia caryophyllata* Thunb.] Est. do Rio, May 24, 1910, herb. Secc. Fit. Inst. Biol. Veg., Brazil.

Water culture EHC 256, Lytle Creek, Clinton County, Ohio, Feb. 24, 1953, W. B. Cooke.

On brown weathered leaves of *Zamia* sp., Coconut Grove, Fla., 1897 and 1898, R. Thaxter, herb. Farlow [Fig. 82f].

Boneh-Borut (Bull. Research Coun. Israel, Sec. D, 5:1,109–110,1955) reported that *P. versicolor* Speg. produced disease after wounding among five of 14 common garden plants and that oleander was not susceptible.   They were *Acacia cyanophylla*, the most sensitive, *Dodonea viscosa*, *Euonymus japonicus*, *Populus nigra*, and *Schinus molle*.

238. **Pestalotia scirpina** Ell. & G. Martin, Am. Naturalist 19:76,1885.

> *P. versicolor* Speg. var. *americana* Speg., Anal. Soc. Ci. Argent. 13:21, 1882; Syll. Fung. 3:791,1884.
> *P. linearis* Sacc., Nuovo Gior. Bot. Ital. (n. s.) 22:67–78,1915; Syll. Fung. 25:601,1931.

Pustules lenticular to long hysteriform, scattered and distinct, subcuticular, rupturing the cuticle longitudinally, contents at length oozing out and staining the matrix, 140–1,000 × 100–300 μ.   Conidia clavate-fusiform, obconic, 5-celled, 20–25 × 7–9 μ, usually curved and unequilateral, constricted at septa dividing the two lower colored cells; colored cells 15–18 μ, the upper two fuliginous, opaque, cask-shaped, the lowest olivaceous; apical hyaline cells conic-cylindric, elongate and tapered, basal hyaline cells broad, conic or obtuse; setulae 3, sometimes 2, curved, coarse, flexuous, divergent, 18–30 μ; pedicels 3–10 μ.

On culms of *Scirpus maritimus* L., Chesapeake Bay, Md., July 1884, J. T. Rothrock in Ellis & Everhart, N. Am. Fungi No. 1626 [Fig. 83a].   On dead culms of *Scirpus olneyi* Gray, Point a la Hache, La., March 1887, A. B. Langlois in Ellis & Everhart, N. Am. Fungi, 2nd Ser. No. 2181 [Fig. 83b]. On fallen decaying culms of *Scirpus palustris* L. [= *Eleocharis palustris* (L.) R. & S.], Rio de la Placta, near Palermo, Argentina, May 15, 1881, Spegazzini, sub *P. versicolor* Speg. var. *americana* Speg. [Fig. 83c].   On dead stems of *Scirpus holoschaenus* L., Vied-il-Kleigha, Malta, No. 1913 in herb. P. A. Saccardo No. 598, sub *P. linearis* Sacc.

Saccardo (Syll. Fung. 15:241,1901) listed *P. americana* Speg. as a synonym of *P. versicolor* Speg. var. *americana* Speg., but the writer could not find any reference to *P. americana* Speg. in Spegazzini's publications.   *P. americana* Montagne in Gay, Historia de Chile (Bot.) 7:481,1850 is *Monochaetia americana* (Mont.) Sacc. (Syll. Fung. 18:485,1906).   *P. linearis* Sacc. has hysteroid acervuli arranged in parallel lines 1–2 mm long × 200–300 μ wide, conidia pyriform, 21–26 × 7.5–9.5 μ, setulae 3, 15–28 μ long.   Saccardo described conidia 20–22 × 7.5–8 μ and setulae 15–22 μ long.   This fungus is like *P. scirpina* Ell. & G. Martin.

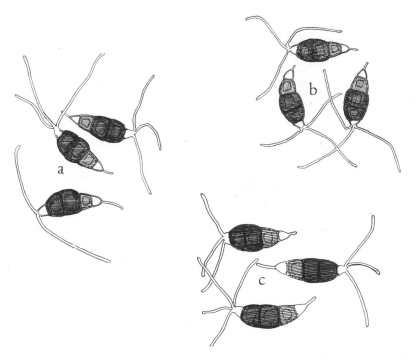

FIG. 83 [238]. *Pestalotia scirpina* Ellis & G. Martin.

239. **Pestalotia filisetula** Guba sp. nov.

Pustulae amphigenae, dense distributae, confluentes, globosae usque globoso-lenticulares, subepidermicales, massis atris epidermidem fissentibus et in cono protrusis, plerumque 75–225 μ in diametro; conidia 5-cellularia, longe fusiformia, ad basim attenuata, subinaequilateralia, 19–26 × 7.5–10 μ; cellulae mediae coloratae 14–19 μ longae, duae superiores atro-fuligineae, opacae, infima umbrina; cellulae apicales hyalinae, late conicae, breves saepe occultae; cellulae basales hyalinae longe acutae; setulae 2, interdum 2 vel 4, late divergentes, 15–45 μ longae, ex apice oriundae; pedicellus 6–10 μ longus, rectus.

Pustules amphigenous, densely distributed, confluent, globose to globose-lenticular, borne under the epidermis, the black masses pushing away the epidermis and protruding like a cone, sooty and staining the matrix, usually 75–225 μ diam. Conidia 5-celled, long fusiform, tapering to the base, rather inequilateral, 19–26 × 7.5–10 μ; intermediate colored cells 14–19 μ long, upper two of them black, fuliginous, opaque, the lowest umber; apical hyaline cells broad conic, short, often hidden; basal hyaline cells long, acute; setulae 3, sometimes 2 and 4, widely divergent, 15–45 μ long, arising from the apex; pedicels 6–10 μ, erect.

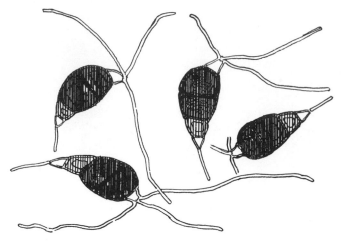

Fig. 84 [239].   *Pestalotia filisetula* Guba.

On dead leaves of palm (Palmaceae), Florida, Roland Thaxter, herb. Roland Thaxter, No. 960 in herb. Farlow (type).

On dead blades of *Vincentia angustifolia* Gaudich, Hawaii, F. L. Stevens, No. 459–824, in herb. Dept. Bot., University of Illinois [Fig. 84].

240. **Pestalotia magoscyi** Bubak, Beiblatt Novenytani Kozlemenyek 6, pt. 4, 52, 1907; Ann. Mycol. 5:440,1907; Syll. Fung. 22:1222,1913.

Pustules at first subepidermal, later exposed, round to elongate, 200–300 μ diam, black, sooty.   Conidia 5-celled, elliptic-fusoid or clavate, sometimes curved, strongly narrowed at the base, 20–26 × 8–9 μ, the two colored superior cells brown, the lowest colored cells yellowish or yellow brown and often much narrower than the others; exterior cells small, conic, hyaline; setulae 4 and 5, strongly divergent, up to 40 μ, rarely up to 50 μ long, curved; pedicels short, cylindrical, 10–15 μ long.

On dead stems of *Seseli glaucum* L., Dunakeszi-Alag, near Budapest, Hungary.   The species is dedicated to Dr. S. Magocsy.

241. **Pestalotia guaranitica** (Speg.) Guba comb. nov., Anal. Soc. Ci. Argent. 22 (2); 205,1886; Syll. Fung. 10:486,1892.

P. coffeicola Averna-Saccá, Para Estud. Molesti Crypt. Caffeeiro, Sao Paulo, Brazil 2:21–23,1925, fig. 7.

Spots irregular, determinate, 3–5 mm in diam, dirty grayish-black, with age deciduous.   Acervuli epiphyllous, densely scattered, lenticular, 90–100 μ in diam.   Conidia 5-celled, fusoid-elliptic, somewhat swollen at the middle, both ends acute, 20–25 × 12–16 μ; setulae 2, simple, opposite, rather coarse, up to 20 μ long, end cells hyaline, the upper two colored cells or middle ones the darkest, the lowest yellowish; pedicels slender, 8–10 × 5 μ, hyaline.

On living leaves of *Myrtaceae*, forests of Caa-Guazu, Paraguay, Jan. 1882, No. 11863, C. Spegazzini.

P. coffeicola Averna-Saccá was published without formal description and no specimens were preserved. The report described hemispherical, conical pustules, 5-celled conidia, $16-27 \times 7-10 \mu$, setulae 2, $24-29 \mu$ long. There are dubious aspects to the illustration and description of the fungus which render its identification difficult but, in the above respects and in host relations and geographic area there is agreement with *P. guaranitica*. The fungus was associated with dead areas in the tips and margins of coffee leaves, *Coffea arabica* L., Sao Paulo Province, Brazil, in Oct. 1923. Infection followed a chlorotic condition of the foliage. Eventually the dry, dead areas and the fungus covered all of the affected leaves.

242. **Pestalotia rapaneae** Viégas, Bragantia 6:21–22,1946, fig. 2.

Spots numerous, amphigenous, circular or subcircular, distinct or confluent, 2–8 mm in diam, slightly depressed with definite margins. Pustules amphigenous, sparse, bullate or swollen, $200-300 \mu$ diam, subepidermal. Conidiophores short, hyaline, obscure. Conidia napiform, $20-24 \times 9-12 \mu$, 5-celled, not constricted at septa; 3 intermediate colored cells broad, swollen, dark brown, fuliginous, dividing septum indistinct, $12-14 \mu$ long, lowest colored cell dilute brown, tending to collapse; setulae 3, filiform, $12-16 \mu$ long; apical cells obtuse or attenuated.

On living leaves of *Rapanea gardneriana* (DC.) Mez., Faz. Baleia, Bello Horizonte, Minarum Province, State of Minas Gerais, Brazil, Jan. 19, 1943. A. P. Viégas and H. Melo Barreto.

243. **Pestalotia congensis** P. Henn., Ann. Mus. du Congo, Bot., Ser. 5, 2, fasc. 3:229,1908; Syll. Fung. 22:1221,1913.

Spots gray, effuse, dark or brown, large, more or less limited to the margins of matrix. Pustules globose, globose-lenticular, or discoid, epiphyllous, somewhat gregarious in places, $75-225 \mu$ diam, subepidermal, erumpent, tearing epidermis in stellate or sometimes in linear manner, lifting it completely away, exposing the black contents, surrounded by the torn epidermis. Conidia 5-celled, clavate-fusiform, tapering to the base, equilateral, $22-26 \times 8-11 \mu$; upper two colored cells dark brown, opaque, the lowest olivaceous, together usually $15-19 \mu$ long; basal hyaline cells usually acute, long, tapering; apical hyaline cells small, papilliform, hidden, bearing 3, sometimes 4 setulae, $6-22 \mu$ long, rarely branched; pedicels up to 6μ long.

On leaves of *Parinarium* sp., Kisantu, Belgian Congo, Africa, Aug. 1906, Vanderyst, No. B114, in herb. Berlin Bot. Mus. Hennings reported conidia $15-22 \times 6-10 \mu$, colored cells $15-18 \mu$ and setulae $6-10 \mu$. Steyaert (Bull. Jard. Bot. État Bruxelles 19:179–182,1948) described conidia measuring $21-29 \times 8-11 \mu$, average $25.1 \times 9.2 \mu$, upper 2 colored cells dark brown, opaque, lowest colored cells brown, clear, together 16–20 μ long; 3, sometimes 2, setulae, 7–20 μ long. He reported *P. congensis* a synonym of *P. glandicola* (Cast.) Guba.

244. **Pestalotia mangiferae** P. Henn., Ann. Mus. Congo, Bot., Ser. 5, 2: fasc. 2:102,1907–1908; Syll. Fung. 22:1223,1913; Steyaert, Bull. Jard. Bot. État Bruxelles 19:173–174, 1948 pl. 3, fig. A.

    Pestalotiopsis mangiferae (P. Henn.) Stey., Bull. Jard. Bot. État Bruxelles 19:320,1949, pl. 14, fig. B.

Spots brown, round or angular, definitely margined, gregarious, coalescing. Pustules hypophyllous, rarely epiphyllous, conic-globose to lenticular, 75–175 μ diam, numerous and distinct, subepidermal then erumpent, protruding above the epidermis, the naked spreading mass surrounded by whitish torn shreds of epidermis, sooty contents staining the matrix. Conidia 5-celled, oblong-clavate or clavate-fusiform, 22–26 × 8–11 μ; colored cells 15–16 μ long, upper two of them umber to fuliginous or slightly darker than the lowest olivaceous colored cell, subglobose, the septa and walls sometimes black, indistinct; setulae 3, coarse, widely divergent, 19–26 μ long; pedicels short.

On leaves of *Mangifera indica* L. Kisantu, Belgian Congo, July 1906, Vanderyst, No. 1386. The type description by Hennings is indefinite. He described 5-celled clavate-oblong conidia, 20–24 × 4–6 μ, 3 black intermediate colored cells 14–18 μ long, conoid exterior cells 4–5 μ long, 3 filiform setulae, 15–18 μ long.

Steyaert found an admixture of three distinct conidial forms in the type matrix of *Mangifera indica* (Vanderyst, No. 1386) which he reported as follows:

	P. congensis P. Henn.	P. mangiferae P. Henn.	P. annulata Berk. & Curt.
Conidia.	20–30 × 8–11 μ	18–24 × 5–7 μ	24–30 × 6–8 μ
Colored cells	14–20 μ	12–15 μ	17–20 μ
Setulae	3, 9–20 μ	2–4 (3); 5–15 μ	2–4 (3); 15–28 μ

P. congensis was described with versicolorous intermediate cells, the upper two of them fuliginous, the lowest ones pallid. The other two forms have olivaceous concolorous colored cells. My study of the type material revealed only two distinct conidial forms. One is *P. mangiferae* P. Henn. (*P. congensis* P. Henn. sense of Steyaert). The other form with long fusiform conidia, 22–29 × 6.9–8.5 μ, olivaceous, concolorous intermediate cells, 15–19 μ, 3 or often 4 setulae, 15–26 μ, long, hyaline exterior cells is *P. mangifolia* Guba (*P. mangiferae* P. Henn. and *P. annulata* Berk. & Curt., sense of Steyaert). *P. annulata* Berk. & Curt. has knobbed setulae and other differences and cannot apply here. Steyaert (Trans. Brit. Mycol. Soc. 36:239,1953) described *P. mangiferae* much differently from the type, as follows: conidia 16–22 × 5–7 μ, colored cells cinnamon brown, 10–14 μ long, setulae 2–3, 5–18 μ long, sometimes spatulate. The species was reported on *Mangifera indica* L., *Elaeis guineensis* Jacq. and *Hyphaene thebaica* Mart.

Mundkur and Kheswalla (Mycologia 34:309,1942) considered *P. funerea* Desm. var. *mangiferae* Sacc., *P. virgatula* Kleb., and *P. pauciseta* Sacc. synonyms of *P. mangiferae* P. Henn.

Tandon *et al.* (Proc. Indian Acad. Sci., Sec. B, 42,5,219–225,1955) described the pathogenicity of *P. mangiferae* on fruits and leaves of mango at Allahabad, India. Inoculation experiments showed that the fungus is a weak parasite capable of infecting injured leaves and fruits and healthy fruits in contact with diseased ones. Sechet (Fruits d'outre mer 8; 6,270–272,1953 and 10:7,276–277,1955) described a leaf spot of mango leaves associated with Pestalotia and the ascus fungus *Calonectria mangiferae* Sechet in Madagascar. Another *Calonectria* appeared on guava leaves (*Psidium guajava* L.) bearing a different Pestalotia. The connection of the ascus fungus with these Pestalotias was not established.

245. **Pestalotia laughtonae** Doidge, Bothalia 4:824,1948.

Leaf spots irregular in outline, 1–2 cm diam, or larger, often spreading from the leaf margin, yellow brown on upper surface with raised dark brown margins, on the under side wood-brown, usually without darker margins. Acervuli epiphyllous closely and evenly distributed over the whole spot, lenticular, usually 300–350 μ diam, occasionally 400–450 μ, about 100 μ or up to 150 μ high in the centre, discrete, not coalescent, black, punctiform, subepidermal, erumpent by means of a central pore, which may be more or less round, or stellate through the formation of three or more crevices running out from the central pore. Conidia ovoid, straight or unequilateral and gibbous, 4-septate, not constricted at the septa, 22.5–25 μ long; three central colored cells 15–17.5 × 9–11 μ, mostly 5 × 10 μ, the two upper clove-brown, later opaque and almost black, the lowest drab in color; apical cells hyaline, cylindrical, bearing 3, rarely 2, rigid, widely divergent setulae, 20–25 μ long, most commonly horizontal and almost at right angles to the axis of the conidia, basal cells subhyaline, turbinate; pedicels hyaline, slender, 4–6 μ long.

On *Cassine sphaerophylla* O. Ktze. [= *Elaedendron sphaerophyllum* Presl.], Brenton, Knysna, in coastal scrub forest, E. M. Laughton, No. 35145, often associated with *Pestalotia cassinis* Laughton. On *Pterocelastrus tricuspidatus* (Lam.) Walp., Knysna, E. M. Laughton, No. 35146.

Steyaert (Bothalia 6:381,1954) placed this species in synonymy under *Pestalotiopsis glandicola* (Cast.) Stey. [= *Pestalotia glandicola* (Cast.) Guba].

246. **Pestalotia curta** Sacc., Bull. Soc. Bot. Ital. 1904:209,1904, fig. 5; Syll. Fung. 18:480,1906.

Pustules usually concentrically disposed, largely epiphyllous, prominent, breaking through the epidermis in elongate fissures, 160–320 × 80–230 μ, exposing black contents, irregularly scattered and sometimes confluent, seated on subcircular, dark brown spots or areas of different shape, usually marked by concentric zones above and lacking them below. Conidia broad-clavate, 5-celled, usually curved and unequilateral, 20–24 μ long; intermediate cells 14–16 × 8.5–10.5 μ, colored, the two upper umber or fuliginous, the lowest olivaceous, constricted at the septum dividing the two lowest colored cells; basal hyaline cells broad conic and small, superior cells narrow conoid or tapering, sometimes hidden, bearing 3 or rarely 2 or 4 setulae, sometimes branched, 16–34 μ; pedicels erect, 2–5 μ.

On wilting leaves of *Ceratonia siliqua* L. in D. Saccardo, Myc. Ital. No. 1570, Bot. Gard., Padua, Italy, April 1904 [Fig. 85]. According to Saccardo, the pustules are ovate-oblong and concentrically disposed, conidia ovoid-oblong, gibbous, 21–24 × 10–11 μ, intermediate cells fuliginous; exterior cells minute and hyaline; setulae 12–18 μ and pedicels 4–6 μ long. *P. sonsensis* P. Henn. appears to be the same fungus.

247. **Pestalotia dianellae** Alm. & Camara, Rev. Agron. Portugal 2:192,1904, tab. 1, figs. 1–2; Bol. Soc. Broteriana 24:206,1909; Syll. Fung. 18:483, 1906.

Pustules epiphyllous, covered at first by epidermis, later erumpent, puncti-form, scattered, 80–150 μ wide. Conidia clavate-fusiform, 5-celled, not or only slightly constricted at septa, 25–30 × 7.5–9 μ; exterior cells hyaline,

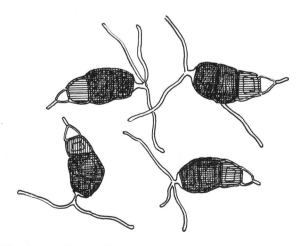

Fig. 85 [246]. *Pestalotia curta* Sacc.

intermediate colored cells brown, the center one the darkest; pedicels 10–15 μ; setulae 3, sometimes curved downward, 13–16 μ long.

On leaves of *Dianella tasmanica* Hook. f., Bot. Gard., Coimbra, Portugal, A. Moller, Dec. 1903.

248. **Pestalotia elasticola** P. Henn., Hedwigia 48:16,1908; Syll. Fung. 25:603, 1931.

Spots angular, at length effuse, pale, papery, dried out with definite brown margins. Pustules amphigenous, globose-lenticular, 175–300 μ in diam, subepidermal, erumpent through linear crevices in the white, gray papery epidermis, exposing the black contents, scattered or gregarious, coalescing to form chains of fruiting pustules, the contents blackening the matrix. Conidia 5-celled, long-fusiform, tapering to base, only slightly constricted at the septa, 22–29 × 7.5–9.5 μ; intermediate colored cells usually 15–18 μ long, the upper two umber, sometimes fuliginous, the lowest ones olivaceous; apical hyaline cells long conic; basal hyaline cells acute, tapering into short pedicels 3–6 μ long; setulae 3, rarely 2 or 4, divergent, slender, 12–22 μ long.

On leaves of *Ficus elastica* Roxb., Sao Paulo, Brazil, June 1904, A. Puttemans, No. 1169, in herb. Berlin Bot. Mus. Hennings reported conidia 14–20 × 7–10 μ; setulae 10–18 μ, and pedicels 5–10 μ.

On *Clivia miniata* Regel (leaves), Matsudo, Chiba-ken, Japan, Feb. 11, 1935, S. Murata.

249. **Pestalotia scirrofaciens** N. A. Brown, Phytopathology 10:383–393,1920; Syll. Fung. 25:605,1931.

Pustules immersed, later erumpent, covered with an irregular layer of thickened bark. Conidia ovate-oblong to spindle shape, 5-celled, slightly curved, 22–29 × 7–10 μ; lowest colored cells olivaceous, the two above umber or fuliginous, 14–19 μ, with slight or no constriction at the septa; setulae 3, rarely 4, bent at right angles to the conidia, slender, 9–23 μ; end cells conic, the basal cells sometimes tapering; pedicels short, erect, 3–6 μ.

On bark of *Sapota achras* Mill. [= *Achras zapota* L.], associated with hard woody galls or tumors partly covered with lichens, algae, and other fungi, Buena Vista, Fla., P. H. Rolfs.

Study was confined to a culture received from Brown. Host tissue bearing the fungus was not available, but Brown (Phytopathology 10:383–393,1930) supplied the spore measurements on different media as follows:

On Sapota Achras Mill. . . . . 16–24 × 6–10 μ
On potato pieces . . . . 20–26 × 5–6 μ
On corn meal agar . . . . 16–30 × 6–8 μ

Brown regarded this species as the cause of tumors on stems of the sapodilla tree and her contention is supported by artificial production of the disease. Older tissue was especially susceptible. Leaves of sapodilla inoculated with the sapodilla-tumor *Pestalotia* produced reddish, well-defined spots and the conidia recovered from these spots maintained the typical characteristics of those produced in the tumor. She also produced by artificial methods of inoculation, tumors on mango (*Mangifera indica* L.), olive (*Olea europaea* L.), and balsam [*Abies balsamea* (L.) Mill.], and the fungus was again recovered from these tumors. On larch (*Larix occidentalis* Nutt.) blue spruce (*Picea pungens* Engelm.), and hemlock (*Tsuga canadensis* (L.) Carr.), the fungus produced a blight instead of outgrowths. Wounding was unnecessary for infection but helped to increase it.

Doyer (Med. Phytopath. Lab. "Willie Comm. Scholt." 9:1–72,1925), using Brown's original culture of *P. scirrofaciens*, was unable to produce galls or blight after a long series of attempts and consequently denied the infectious nature of this species. Further biologic studies are desirable in view of the fact that investigations dealing with the biology of species of *Pestalotia* generally show the innocuous nature of the species to healthy tissue.

Doyer believed that *P. scirrofaciens* N. A. Brown is the same as *P. versicolor* Speg. The writer's study of both forms indicates a close relationship.

250. **Pestalotia rhododendri** Guba, Phytopathology 19:215–216,1929, [non (D. Sacc.) Guba, non Westendorp in schedulis]. Steyaert, Bull. Jard. Bot. État Bruxelles 19:65,1948.

> *P. versicolor* Speg. var. *rhododendri* D. Sacc., Myc. Ital. 978, 1902 (nom. nud.)

Pustules black, epiphyllous, densely gregarious or scattered without order, often confluent, erumpent on maturity, tearing epidermis irregularly, the sooty contents spreading over matrix, 140–400 μ diam. Conidia 5-celled, 20–29 × 7.5–10 μ, broad fusiform, erect or unequilateral; intermediate colored cells 14–19 μ long, the upper two fuliginous, often swollen and more or less opaque, the lowest colored cells light brown, constricted at the septa dividing the two groups of cells; apical hyaline cells broad conic-cylindric, basal hyaline cells long conic; setulae typically 3, sometimes or rarely 2 and 4, rarely branched, widely divergent, 15–34 μ long; pedicels 4–13 μ long.

On blighted leaves, decayed discolored stems and branches of *Azalea* and *Rhododendron*. On leaves of *Rhododendron hybridum* Ker. and *R. ponticum* L., D. Saccardo, Myc. Ital. No. 978, 1902, Padua, Italy, Nov. 1901, sub *P. versicolor* Speg. var. *rhododendri* D. Sacc. (type) [Fig. 86a]. On leaves of *R. arboreum* Smith, Rosslyn, Va., Dec. 17, 1914, from Holland, G. A. Comley, U.S.D.A.; Washington, D. C. Dec. 8, 1914, from Holland, R. G. Pierce, No. 2867, both in Nat. Fungus Coll., U.S.D.A. On leaves of *R. maximum* L., Andrews, N. C., July 21, 1925, G. G. Hedgcock, herb. Dearness No. 8798. On blighted leaves of *R. obtusum* Planch. var. *amoenum* Rehd., Jamaica, Long Island, N. Y., Sept. 1924, P. E. Case [Fig. 86b]. On stems of *Rhododen-*

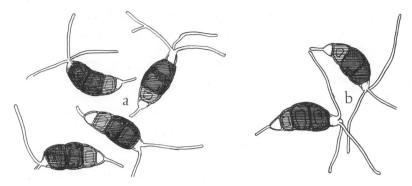

Fig. 86 [250].   *Pestalotia* rhododendri Guba.

dron sp., Boxford, Mass., Jan. 16, 1955, from Holland, in decayed areas about union of stock and scion with other fungi causing death of plants.

The species was regarded by Klebahn (Myc. Centralbl. 4:12–13,1914) as *P. versicolor* Speg.; conidia 25–29 × 7–9 μ, pustules 1–2 mm diam, seated on large leaf spots.   The disease was reported by White (Jour. Econ. Ent. 26: 631–640,1933) and White and Hamilton (N.J. Agr. Exp. Sta. Circ. 350, 1935). The species differs from *P. macrotricha* Kleb. [= *P. sydowiana* Bres.] by broader and darker conidia.   The colored cells are strongly contrasted, the two upper ones fuliginous, and the setulae are rather coarse in contrast and not so long.

251. **Pestalotia paraguariensis** Maubl., Sao Paulo Bol. Agr., Ser. 16A, No. 4: 321,1915, tab. VII, fig. 6; Bull. Soc. Mycol. Fr. 36:40,1920, pl. IV, fig. 1; Syll. Fung. 25:599,1931.

Pustules epiphyllous, scattered, depressed, perforating the epidermis near center of elevation, 250 μ in diam.   Conidia 5-celled, fusoid or pyriform, often somewhat curved, inequilateral, 23–28 × 8–10 μ, the 2 upper colored cells dark or black, the lowest ones pale, middle colored cells the largest; apical hyaline cells conoid; setulae 3, rarely 4, separated at the apex of the cells, divergent, 25–35 μ; basal hyaline cells conic, attenuated; pedicels filiform, 6–7 μ long.

In spots in living leaves of *Ilex paraguariensis* A. St. Hil., with *Phyllosticta yerbae* Speg., Parana, Brazil, July 1912.

252. **Pestalotia longi-aristata** Maubl., Bull. Soc. Mycol. Fr. 21:92,1905, pl. 6, fig. 10; Syll. Fung. 18:478,1906.

P. versicolor Speg. var. *darlingtoniae* Trav., Syll. Fung. 25:607,1931; Klebahn, Myc. Centralbl. 3:109–115,1913, fig. 35, 12e.

Spots amphigenous, orbicular, pale yellow, becoming more or less white, bordered with dark raised narrow lines 1 cm wide.   Pustules epiphyllous, black, pulvinate, erumpent, 250–333 μ in diam.   Conidia fusoid-clavate, inequilateral, 5-celled, 25–30 × 8–10 μ; intermediate colored cells fuliginous, the two uppermost ones broad, opaque, the basal cells hyaline, conic, tapering into short filiform pedicels, 4–6 μ long; apical hyaline cells with 2, usually 3, rarely 4, long divergent flexuous setulae, often up to 40 μ long.

On living leaves of *Eriobotrya japonica* Lindl., Bot. Gard., Sao Paulo, Brazil, A. Puttemans; Bermuda Fungi, H. H. Whetzel, No. AA2 in herb. Dept. Plant Path., Cornell University.

On dead leaves of *Darlingtonia californica* Torr., Bot. Gard., Hamburg, Germany, sub *P. versicolor* Speg. var. *darlingtoniae* Trav. According to Klebahn, the fungus occurs on leaves previously attacked by *Gloeosporium*. The sporogenous cavity is surrounded by a narrow-walled irregular pseudoparenchymatic conceptacle. Klebahn reported that the fungus is a saprophyte, gaining entrance into dead parts and growing very slowly into the healthy parts and under excessively moist conditions. In culture, the fruiting structure reminds one of the *Excipulaceae* by the development of true pycnidia with pseudoparenchymatic cover. On the basis of Klebahn's study, Traverso recognized the fungus as a variety of *P. versicolor* Speg. The variety was described as follows: acervuli lenticular, 130–200 × 90–120 μ; conidia 26–31 × 7–9 μ; setulae usually 3, filiform, 26–33 μ long.

On *Diospyros kaki* Thunb. (leaves), Goutazaka, Yokohama, Japan, Sept. 20, 1950, K. Togashi.

On leaves of *Photinia serrulata* Lindl. Shiloh, N. J., Nov. 17, 1927, R. P. White.

On leaves of *Rhizophora mangle* L., Coconut Grove, Dade County, Fla., Feb. 29, 1944, Arthur S. Rhoads.

253. Pestalotia triseta (M. & Mme. F. Moreau) Guba comb. nov.

Pestalotia funerea Desm. var. *macrochaeta* Speg. forma *triseta* M. & Mme. F. Moreau, Rev. Mycol. Fr. 6:49,1941.

Pestalotiopsis triseta (M. & Mme. F. Moreau) Stey. Bull. Jard. Bot. État Bruxelles 19:337–338,1949, pl. 16, fig. C.

Conidia 5-celled, long clavate, erect, 24–30 × 8–10 μ (22–30 × 6–8 μ fide Cl. F. Moreau): 3 intermediate colored cells 16–21 μ, versicolorous, the inferior colored cells pallid, the two colored superior cells dark fuliginous, principally in zone adjoining septa; exterior cells hyaline, apical cells cylindric or conoid; 2–4, usually 3 thick setulae, with lumen definitely visible, 12–25 μ and sometimes up to 42 μ long, spreading [30–40 μ long, 2–5, usually 3 setulae (Moreau)]; basal cells long conoid tapering; pedicels usually 4–7 μ long.

Culture from bush of *Hippophae rhamnoides* L., France, Pointe du Calvados. Setulae spread out, thick, coarse, with a very visible lumen. The fungus is totally different from *P. funerea* Desm. A negligible portion of conidia of *P. triseta* show some abnormalities, supernumerary septa, deformed apical cells and branched setulae, a consequence of artificial culture.

254. **Pestalotia brassicae** Guba n. sp.

Conidia 5-cellularia, ellipticalia usque cylindrica, fusiformia, 25–32 ×
8.5–9.5 μ, ad septa tantum vix constricta; setulae 3–5, rare 6, plerumque 4–5,
longae, filiformes, flexuosae, eminentes vel recurvatae, 20–35 μ, plerumque
25–32 μ longae; cellulae mediae coloratae 17–21 μ longae, duae superiores
vel centrales fuligineae, opacae vel umbrinae et translucidae; cellula infima
brunnea, interdum cellulae tres omnes brunneae et concolores; cellula basalis
hyalina, longe acuta usque late conica, granulas sparsas continens; cellula
apicalis hyalina conico-cylindrica, lata, appendice breve obliqua superflua
seape e basi cellulae inferioris hyalinae emergente; pedicelli erecti, 6–50 μ
longi, paulo crassi vel robusti.

Conidia 5-celled, elliptic to cylindric, fusiform, 25–32 × 8.5–9.5 μ, only
slightly constricted at septa; setulae 3 to 5, rarely 6, usually 4 or 5, long, filiform, flexuous, projecting forward or recurved, 20–35 μ, usually 25–32 μ
long; intermediate colored cells 17–21 μ long, the upper 2 colored cells or
central ones fuliginous, opaque or umber and translucent, lowest colored cells
brown, sometimes all 3 cells brown, concolorous; basal hyaline cells long
acute or broad conic containing sparse granules, apical hyaline cells conic-
cylindric, broad; short oblique superfluous appendage often projecting from
base of inferior hyaline cell; pedicels erect, 6–30 μ long, somewhat coarse or
stout.

Culture from Swedish rape, *Brassica* sp. G. H. Cunningham, New Zealand,
deposited in British Mycol. Inst. and Centr.-Bur. Schimm.-Cult., Baarn,
Netherlands [Fig. 87], sub *Pestalotiopsis funerea* (Desm.) Stey., Bull. Jard.
Bot. État Bruxelles 19:341,1949, pl. 17, fig. D, tab. IV.

Steyaert and Cunningham placed the fungus in the species "*funerea*" but
the author believes that it is different. Steyaert described 5-celled, elliptic-
fusiform conidia 26–31 × 8–13 μ; colored cells with large irregular guttules,
18–23 μ; setulae 4–5, sometimes 3 or 6, 13–27 μ, apical; pedicels 5–11 μ long,
sometimes with an axillary superfluous pedicel.

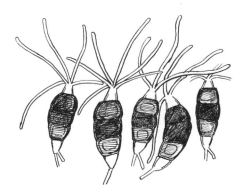

FIG. 87 [254]. *Pestalotia* brassicae Guba.

255. **Pestalotia sonsensis** P. Henn., Ann. Mus. du Congo, Bot., Ser. V: 2: fasc. 3:229,1908; Syll. Fung. 22:1221,1913.   Steyaert, Bull. Jard. Bot. État Bruxelles 19:182–183,1948, pl. 5, fig. C.

Pestalotiopsis sonsensis (P. Henn.) Stey., Bull. Jard. Bot. État Bruxelles 19:336,1949.

Spots definitely limited, 1–1.5 cm diam.   Pustules hysteriform, 250–300 μ diam, rupturing epidermis longitudinally.   Conidia cylindrical to obclavate, 5-celled, long fusiform, 21–31 × 9–11 μ, intermediate colored cells 16–21 μ long, upper 2 fuliginous, the lowest olivaceous, apical hyaline cells conic-cylindric, appendages 3, sometimes 4, variable in length, 16–33 μ, basal hyaline cells short, conoid; pedicels 3–10 μ.

On leaves of *Ceratonia siliqua* L. Sonso, near Kisantu, Belgian Congo, June 1906, Vanderyst (B 42) (type).

Hennings described fusoid conidia, 18–22 × 6–7 μ, dark concolorous intermediate cells 15–18 μ; 3 setulae 18–22 μ, pedicels 18 μ long.   According to Steyaert, the conidia are large and massive, the setulae are longer.   The description by Hennings hardly corresponds to the type material in the opinion of Steyaert.   On the basis of Hennings dimensions, Wollenweber and Hochapfel (Z. Pflanzenkr. XLVI, 408,1936) considered *P. sonsensis* a synonym of *P. cruenta* Syd., but according to Steyaert this synonymy is incorrect.   A drawing of the conidia of *P. cruenta* Syd. by K. Röder (Berlin-Dahlem, July 28, 1936) shows that the fungus is distinct from *P. sonsensis* P. Henn.

256. **Pestalotia calophylli** P. Henn., Hedwigia 48:17,1908; Syll. Fung. 25: 599,1931.

Pustules amphigenous, largely hypophyllous, 120–300 × 105–150 μ, lenticulate, longer than wide, scattered or gregarious, sooty at maturity, erumpent by a linear fissure, the dark contents staining the surrounding matrix. Conidia 5-celled, 25–29 × 8.5–11 μ, pyriform, tapering to the base; colored part 17–19 μ long, upper 2 colored cells fuliginous, the lowest one olivaceous, not or slightly constricted at the septa; basal hyaline cells long acute, the apical hyaline cells short obtuse, usually hidden; setulae 3, divergent, 19–29 μ; pedicels 3–5 μ.

On dry leaves of *Calophyllum* sp., Morro Pellada, Sao Paulo, Brazil, A. Puttemans, July 1904, No. 1133, in herb. Berlin Bot. Mus. Hennings reported conidia 13–18 × 6–8 μ, setulae up to 20 μ, pedicels up to 10 μ long.

257. **Pestalotia tiliae** Guba, Mycologia 24:383–384,1932.

Pustules amphigenous, scattered or gregarious, subepidermal, erumpent on maturity, surrounded by the torn shreds of the epidermis, black, effuse, 75–200 μ in diam, seated on large definite brown areas.   Conidia 5-celled, broad fusoid or pyriform, usually inequilateral, 24–29 × 9.5–11.5 μ; intermediate colored cells 16–19 μ long, the upper two fuliginous, opaque, subglobose, the lowest umber, strongly constricted at the dividing septum; apical hyaline cells short, conic, basal hyaline cells usually long and tapering; setulae 3, coarse, 18–27 μ, widely divergent; pedicels 4–7 μ.

On leaves of *Tilia* sp., Santee River, Ala., Curtis, No. 4608 (Beaumont, No. 266) in herb. Farlow and herb. Roy. Bot. Gard., Kew, sub *P. stictica* Berk. & Curt. The type of *P. stictica* Berk. & Curt. (Grevillea 2:155,1874) was described on leaves of *Platanus occidentalis* L. and *Tilia* sp. The specimens are distinct and since the form on *Platanus* agrees with the type description of *P. stictica*, the new name *P. tiliae* Guba was given to the form on *Tilia*.

258. **Pestalotia conspicua** Servazzi, Boll. Lab. Sper. R. Osserv. Fitopat. Torino 1,11–13,1934.

Acervuli resembling pycnidia, gregarious, innate then erumpent, black, globose-conic or globose, 250–450 × 200–250 μ, seated in definite wide whitish spots with dark brown borders. Conidia broad fusoid, or subclavate, erect or sometimes slightly swollen, 5-celled, 25–32 × 8.5–11.5 μ usually 26–29 × 9–10 μ; three intermediate colored cells guttulate, 17–20 μ, upper two colored cells fuliginous, opaque, subglobose, lowest ones olivaceous; exterior cells hyaline, prominent, up to 6 μ long; the inferior cells long conic, the apical cells truncate-conic or cylindric; setulae 3, rarely 2 or 4, stout or coarse, 20–60 μ, usually 45–50 μ long, divergent or reflexed; pedicels up to 10 μ or longer.

On living leaves of *Stanhopea tigrina* Batem, Bot. Gard., Turin, Italy, associated with *Gloeosporium* sp.

On brown dead stems of *Bixa orellana* L., Savannah, Ga., Feb. 24, 1924, J. A. Stevenson, in Nat. Fungus Coll., U.S.D.A. On *Oncidium bicallosum* Lindl., San Francisco, Cal., Apr. 23, 1938, W. H. Wheeler, No. 14676, in Nat. Fungus Coll., U.S.D.A.; on *Oncidium* sp., Costa Rica, intercepted at Hoboken Plant Quar. Sta., May 1, 1945, No. 4232 in Nat. Fungus Coll., U.S.D.A.

Section *Sexloculatae*
Species Nos. 259–262

259. **Pestalotia valdiviana** Speg., Revista Facult. Agron. Vet. de La Plata, 6:178–179,1910; Syll. Fung. 22,1219,1913.

Spots suborbicular, amphigenous, determinate, 3–15 mm in diam, tobacco-colored below, dark ash-colored above, prominently limited by narrow rough line. Pustules small, subepidermal, epiphyllous, surrounded by circular margin, 120–150 μ in diam. Conidia somewhat clavate, 6-celled, not or slightly constricted at septa, 20 × 8 μ; the 4 intermediate colored cells olivaceous, the uppermost ones broad, more deeply colored; exterior cells cone-shaped, small, hyaline; apical cells rather long, bearing 3 setulae, 10 μ long; the basal cells short, pedicels 5 μ long.

On living leaves of *Drimys winteri* Forst., in region of Ciudad de Valdivia, Chile, C. Spegazzini.

260. **Pestalotia corni** Allescher, Ber. Bot. Ver., Landshut (Bavaria) 12:83–84 (1890–1891),1892.   Bot. Centralbl. 42:106,1890; Syll. Fung. 10:488, 1892.

Conidia fusiform, 6-celled, 24–30 × 8–10 μ, the two central interior cells shorter than two adjacent cells and, like them, brownish, guttulate; exterior cells hyaline, acute, small, coniform, the basal cells with hyaline pedicels; the apical cells with a 2–3 parted or dichotomously branched setulae.

On dry twigs of *Cornus alba* L., Isaranlagen, near Flaucher, Munich, Germany, May 1882.

The author states that both hyaline exterior cells fall away, and the conidia then appear truncate at both ends with 4 colored cells.   The accounts of the fungus in the two references cited differ in some details.   The author reported that the fungus differs from *Coryneum corni-albae* (Roum.) Sacc. (Syll. Fung. 3:774,1884) in the hyaline exterior cells and setulae; from *Hendersonia decipiens* Thuem. in the interior colored cells of unequal size. In *Hendersonia corni* Fckl. only the lower cell is hyaline and the setulae are lacking.   Allescher reported that it approaches *Pestalotia veneta* Sacc. [= *Monochaetia veneta* (Sacc.) Allescher] on *Cornus sanguinea* L.

261. **Pestalotia pezizoides** de Not., Mem. R. Accad. Sci. Torino II 3:80–81, 1839; Syll. Fung. 3:789,1883.

   P. compacta Berk. & Curt., Grevillea 2:155,1874; Syll. Fung. 3:795,1884.

   P. ramosa Alm., Rev. Agr. Soc. Sci. Agron. Portugal 1:23–26,1903; Syll. Fung. 18:481,1906.

   P. tremelloides Ell. & Ev., Zabriskie, Jour. N. Y. Microscop. Soc. 7:102, 1891.

   P. ampelogena Bres., Studi Trentini, Sci. Nat. Econ. Trento, classe II, 7, fasc. 1:73,1926.

   Hendersonia longipes Berk. & Curt., Grevillea 3:4,1875; Syll. Fung. 3: 423,1884.

   Sporocadus longipes (Berk. & Curt.) Kuntze, Rev. Genera Plant. 3: Pt. II, 532, 1898.

Pustules definite, scattered or gregarious, often confluent, erumpent, borne on a thick gelatinous stroma, discoid, pezizoid, apothecioid, 225–600 × 100–300 μ, protruding well above the epidermis.   Conidia long fusiform, equilateral or slightly curved, tapering at the ends, 6-celled, 27–36 × 6–9 μ; intermediate colored cells 4, olivaceous, each comprising a refractive globule separated by pseudo-septa, slightly constricted at the septa, 19–26 μ long;

exterior cells hyaline, the lowest often dilutely colored; setulae short, 2 to 5, branched or simple, 6–18 μ, recurved, rarely one and branched and 12–31 μ; pedicels simple or forked, 2–10 μ, sometimes 5–22 μ and slender.

On canes of *Vitis vinifera* L., *V. riparia* Michx., and related species.

Specimens examined: On canes of *Vitis*, Milan, Italy, de Notaris, 1845, in herb. Mus. d'Hist. Nat., Paris; in herb. Durieu de Maisonneuve, L. Motelay (1878) in Mus. d'Hist. Nat., Paris; Herb. Curtis No. 1653, Pennsylvania 1853, E. Michener in herb. Farlow; in herb. Curtis No. 861, Hillsborough, N. C., March 1846, sub *Hendersonia longipes* Berk. & Curt.; Ellis N. Am. Fungi No. 35 [Fig. 88a]; Ravenel, Fungi Am. Exs. 256, Aiken, S. C., 1877; Marshall Hall, Md., V. K. Charles, July 6, 1906 in Nat. Fungus, Coll., U.S.D.A., sub *P. ramosa* Alm. [Fig. 88b,c]; Roumeguere, Fungi Galliae Exs. No. 2886, Carcassonne, (Aude), France, 1883; Bartholemew, Fung. Col. No. 1631, on *Vitis riparia*, Rooks County, Kan., March 1897 and Nov. 15, 1901; Michener Fungi 19:82, No. 2790, New Garden, Chester County, Penn., sub *P. compacta* Berk. & Curt. in Nat. Fungus Coll., U.S.D.A., and similar specimens in herb. Curtis No. 6030 in herb. Farlow and herb. Berkeley, Kew, England, wrongly reported on stems of *Humulus lupulus* L. [Fig. 88d,e].

The acervulus is supported by a dense thick stroma which arises above the epidermis and in habit resembles the apothecium of a *Peziza*. Steyaert (Bull. Jard. Bot. État Bruxelles 19:3,285–354,1949) believes that this species belongs with the *Discellaceae* not to the *Melanconiaceae*. The conidia are exposed on flat or concave stromatic cushions [Fig. 88f].

Most students consider the conidia to be comprised of 6 cells, but Steyaert asserted that the exterior cells are hyaline and that the colored part does not have well characterized cells, rather four strongly delimited zones or refractive globular locules separated by pseudo-septa or rings. Pirotta (Arch. Trienn. Lab. Bot. Critt. Pavia 2:196–198,1878) and Thuemen (Pilze des Weinstockes, Wien. 142–144, 1878, tab. V, fig. 1) published very good descriptions of the fungus.

Cooke (Nuovo Gior. Bot. Ital. 10:27,1878) regarded *Hendersonia longipes* Berk. & Curt. synonymous with *P. pezizoides*. According to the type description of *H. longipes* Berk. & Curt., this form has 3-septate spores and no setulae but my study of type material from North Carolina (Curtis No. 861) reveals that the fungus is *P. pezizoides*.

Pestalotia tremelloides Ell. & Ev., found on canes of cultivated grape, Skaneateles Lake, N. Y. July 1872, is a synonym. In the original report by Zabriskie (Journ. N. Y. Microscop. Soc. 7:102,1891), Ellis and Everhart were credited with the name. Reference to such characters as setulae 3–6, the tremellaceous character of the moistened fruiting body, the size and elegance of the compound spore, and the number and branching of the setulae are suggestive of *P. pezizoides*.

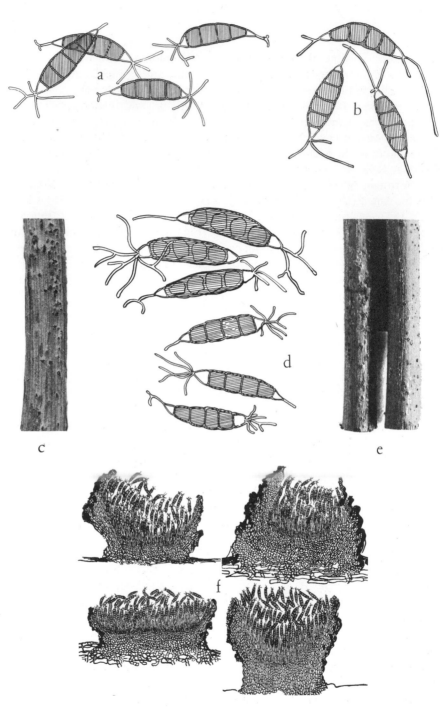

Fig. 88 [261]. *Pestalotia pezizoides* de Not. (*c*, *e*) fruiting pustules in grape canes; (*f*) vertical sections of fruiting pustules.

In 1903, d'Almeida described the species *P. ramosa* on canes of *Vitis vinifera*, Chamusca, Portugal. The figures accompanying the description show that the fungus is identical with *P. pezizoides*. Duplication of names for this species was due apparently to confusion in the literature regarding the number of septa in the spores. De Notaris specified and figured 5-septate conidia, although he allowed for an exception when he stated "sporidia . . . plerumque 5-septata." Saccardo (Syll. Fung. 3:789, 1883) and Allescher (Rabh., Krypt. Flora 1: Abt. 7:693,1902) stated that *P. pezizoides* has 5-celled conidia. Voglino (Atti Soc. Ven.-Trent. Sci. Nat. Padova 9:209–243,1885) regarded it as a 4- to 5-septate form. Desmazières (Ann. Sci. Nat. Bot. II, 19:336,1843) mentioned 5 septa. Klebahn (Myc. Centralbl. 4:1–19,1914) observed 6-celled conidia in specimens of *P. pezizoides* in Bartholomew, Fung. Col. No. 1631. My study of many exsiccati specimens confirms the 6–celled character of the conidia of this species.

The name *P. compacta* Berk. & Curt. was apparently intended for another species, for the type description by Berkeley mentioned 3-septate brown conidia and the source of the material as South Carolina. The original material on *Humulus* (No. 6030) was acquired by Michener in Pennsylvania. Michener gave specimens to Curtis, and Curtis shared his material with Berkeley. The pencil drawing of the fungus accompanying the type material from Kew, presumably by Berkeley, shows 5-celled conidia, 3 colored cells and exterior hyaline cells. Either an error was committed in the designation of the host by the collector or Michener confused this material with something else. Dr. E. C. Jeffrey of Harvard University, to whom material was submitted, reported that the host is a species of *Vitis*, not *Humulus lupulus*. The fungus is identical with *P. pezizoides* on canes of *Vitis* collected in 1853 (herb. Curtis No. 1653) in Dr. Michener's garden.

Pestalotia ampelogena Bres. was described in 1926 and is the same as *P. pezizoides* de Not.

262. Pestalotia cornu-cervae (Brenckle) Guba comb. nov.

Labridella cornu-cervae Brenckle, Fungi Dakotenses, No. 663, Oct. 1929; Mycologia 22:160–161,1930.

Pestalotia pezizoides de Not. var. *longiseta* Dearn. in Bisby *et al.*, Fungi of Manitoba 1929, p. 135, and Bisby *et al.*, Fungi of Manitoba and Saskatchewan 1938, p. 131.

Pustules black, linear, lanceolate and rimose-gaping, the wall of two layers, inner of yellowish indistinct cells, outer of dark septate branching hyphae, 0.5–2 × 0.2–5 mm, dehiscent by cracking and spreading of the dome, edges of pycnidial membrane falling away and finally widely open. Conidia fusiform, straight or slightly curved, of 5 brown or dark colored cells, equally colored, tapering into the pedicel, upper end superimposed by a long cell or attenuated beak, 3–4 μ wide at the base with 2–5 setulae projecting from the axis, mostly from the base, often curved and arranged like a deer-horn; basal colored cells conic; pedicels deciduous, 8–12 × 2 μ, coarse, the conidial body 30–35 × 8–11 μ, apical attenuated beaks of the same length.

On branches and twigs of *Symphoricarpus occidentalis* Hook., Northville, S. D., J. F. Brenckle; Brenckle, Fungi Dakotenses, No. 663, Northville, S. D., Oct. 1929, sub *Labridella cornu-cervae* Brenckle; Brenckle, Fungi Dakotenses No. 100, Kulm, N. D., March 1909, designated *Zignoella morthieri* (Fckl.) Sacc. [= *Griphosphaerioma symphoricarpi* (Rehm) Hoehn], which is the name of the perfect stage [Fig. 89a]; herb. Guba as *Curreyella symphoricarpi* (Rehm) Petr., Northville, S. D., Apr. 1930, J. F. Brenckle; herb. E. F. Guba as *Pestalotia cornu-cervae* (Brenckle) Guba, S. D., March 1929, J. F. Brenckle. The perfect stage *Griphosphaeronema* and the imperfect stage *Pestalotia* appear together in the foregoing specimens; herb. Dearness No. 5973, Winnipeg, Canada, sub *P. pezizoides* de N. var. *longiseta* Dearn. The variety is described as follows: Conidia 28–36 × 9–10 μ, setulae 3 or 4 up to 60 μ long or nearly twice the length of conidial body.

On dead stems of *Lonicera tatarica* L., Ottawa, Canada, Sept. and Oct. 1935 [Fig. 89b]. Conidia 23–28 × 7–9.5 μ, rostrum attenuated, branched or setulae numerous, simple, 9–30 μ long; 5 colored cells 23–28 × 7–9.5 μ, hyaline beak or rostrum below branches 6–8 μ long.

The perfect stage of the fungus was named *Plowrightia symphoricarpi* Ell. & Ev. (Proc. Acad. Nat. Sci., Philadelphia, Oct. 14, 1890, p. 249; Syll. Fung. 9:1042,1891). The name appeared first in Jour. Mycol. 5:84,1889, as a nomen nudum by Ellis and Galloway. The type specimen was issued by Ellis & Everhart, N. Am. Fungi No. 2374. The fungus also appears in Rehm, Ascomycetes No. 1974, 1912 as *Plowrightia symphoricarpi* Rehm (Ann. Mycol. 10:58,1912). The former specimen was collected at Sand Coulee, Cascade County, Mont., Dec. 1888, the latter at Kulm, N. D., March 1911, by

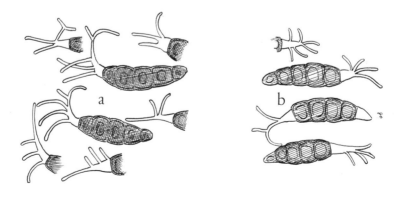

Fig. 89 [262].   *Pestalotia cornu-cervae* (Brenckle) Guba.

J. F. Brenckle. Both are the same species (Ann. Mycol. 11:169,1913). Brenckle cited the fungus in Mycologia 9:289,1917. Theissen and Sydow changed the name of the Ellis fungus to *Valsaria symphoricarpi* (Ell. & Ev.) Theiss. & Syd. (Ann. Mycol. 13:327,1915). Hoehnel studied the Rehm specimen (Fragm. z. Myk. No. 1177, Sitzb. Akad. K. Wiss. Wien, Math.-Nat. Kl. Abt. 1:128:7–8, p. 61, 1919) and placed the fungus in his new genus, designating and treating it as follows: *Griphosphaerioma symphoricarpi* (Rehm.) Hoehn.

Syn.　*Plowrightia symphoricarpi* Ell. & Ev.
　　　Plowrightia symphoricarpi Rehm.
　　　Valsaria symphoricarpi (Ell. & Ev.) Theiss. & Syd.

Ellis & Everhart (N. Am. Pyrenomycetes p. 249, 1892) proposed the new name *Otthia symphoricarpi* (Ell. & Ev.) Ell. & Ev., with *Plowrightia symphoricarpi* Ell. & Ev. a synonym, based on specimens from Sand Coulee, Cascade County, Mont. (Anderson, No. 210) designated *Plowrightia symphoricarpi* Ell. & Ev. Brenckle [Fungi Dakotenses No. 98 (1910), Kulm, N. D., March 1909, Brenckle; Mycologia 9:289,1917 and Rehm, Ascomycetes No. 2040, Kulm, N. D. Feb. 1913, Brenckle 1913; Ann. Mycol. 11:169,1913], designated their specimens *Otthia symphoricarpi* Ell. & Ev. and *Pseudotthia symphoricarpi* (Ell. & Ev.) Rehm, respectively.

Pseudotthia symphoricarpi (Ell. & Ev.) Rehm also appears in Sydow, Fungi exot. Exs. No. 391 on *Symphoricarpus*, Kulm, N. D., Oct. 5, 1914, J. F. Brenckle, and it also appears as a synonym of *Valsa symphoricarpi* Rehm (Ann. Mycol. 9:365,1911 and Sydow, Fungi exot. Exs. No. 389, Kulm, N. D., March 4, 1914, Brenckle). Rehm considered *Otthia symphoricarpi* Ell. & Ev. a synonym. Hoehnel (Fragm. z. Myk. No. 1177; Sitz. Akad. K. Wiss. Wien, Math.-Nat. Kl. Abt. 1:128,58–60. 1919) made both names synonyms of *Dothidotthia symphoricarpi* (Rehm) Hoehn., but Petrak (Ann. Mycol. 25: 301,1927) preferred to name the fungus *Dibotryon symphoricarpi* (Rehm) Petr.

Still another specimen on stems of *Symphoricarpus* in Brenckle, Fungi Dakotenses No. 100, Kulm, N. D., March 1909, was distributed under the name of *Zignoella morthieri* (Fckl.) Sacc., but this too, according to Hoehnel, (p. 62) is the same as Rehm, Ascomycetes No. 1974 and Ellis & Everhart, N. Am. Fungi No. 2374 and thus is *Griphosphaerioma symphoricarpi* (Rehm) Hoehn., a species with ovate, 2-celled, hyaline ascospores. Petrak (Ann. Mycol. 19:193–194,1921) disagreed with Hoehnel's treatment and asserted that *Griphosphaerioma symphoricarpi* (Rehm) Hoehn. belongs to the genus *Curreyella* (Sacc.) Lindau and thus Rehm's Ascomycetes No. 1974 is more properly *Curryella symphoricarpi* (Rehm) Petr.

Thus the fungus in Petrak, Mycotheca generalis No. 69, and Brenckle, Fung. Dakotenses No. 533, Kulm, N. D., Dec. 27, 1922, J. F. Brenckle,

appears as *Curreyella symphoricarpi* (Rehm) Petr.   Another collection by
Brenckle at Northville, S. D., Apr. 1930, is similarly designated.   However,
Curreyella is a genus with hyaline dictyospores which could not apply.
Clements and Shear (Genera of Fungi, 1931), unaware of the error, placed
the genera *Griphosphaerioma* and *Curreyella* in synonymy under *Thyridella*
Sacc.

INDEFINITE SPECIES OF PESTALOTIA

Species Nos. 263–286

The species in this section were published either without description or without sufficient definition to be understood. The specimens on which the names or descriptions are based are presumably nonexistent or have not been available or obtainable for study. Some of them, at least, may exist, and in recognition of this presumption they are recognized provisionally as indefinite species, and, as such, are included here in the manner originally published. Their correct determination is possible only from study, and since this remains a possibility, they cannot be classed as dubious or excluded species (Table 1).

263. **Pestalotia aucubae** Gutner, Acta Inst. Bot. Acad. Sci. U.S.S.R.   Ser. II. fasc. 1:291,1933, tab. 1, fig. 12.

Spots diffuse, gray, often torn.   Acervuli epiphyllous, black.   Conidia 4-septate, dark olivaceous, erect or unequilateral, $18–29 \times 4.5–6 \, \mu$, exterior cells conic, setulae 2–3, hyaline $10.5–15 \, \mu$.

On leaves of *Aucuba japonica* Thunb., in greenhouse, Leningrad and Detskojesslo, Russia.

264. **Pestalotia austro-caledonica** Crié, "Recherches sur les Pyrenomycetes inférieurs du groupe des Depazéés," L'Acad. de Médicine Libr., Paris, 1878, p. 55, pl. 8, fig. 27.   Also, Rev. Sci. de la France et de l'étranger II:22,514–516,1878, and Compt. Rend. Acad. Sci. 89:994–95,1879, nom. nud. Syll. Fung. 10:491,1892.
P. novae caledoniae Crié, *Ibid.*, L'Acad. de Médicine Libr., Paris, 1878, p. 42, nom. nud.

Conidia with 3 colored cells, guttulate, elliptic or elongate-ovoid, $40 \times 14 \, \mu$; exterior cells hyaline, setulae $17–20 \, \mu$, sometimes 1 and branched, otherwise 3 or 4 and simple.

On leaves of *Ionidium latifolium* Vieill., *I. linarifolium* Ging., *I. ilicifolium* Vieill. [all 3 species = *Hybanthus linearifolius* (Vahl.) Urban], *Bignonia* sp., and *Melodinus scandens* Forst., Gatope, Wagap, and Balade, New Caledonia. The fungus, according to Crié, is destructive to the foliage in that region.

This species, in the opinion of Voglino (Atti Soc. Ven.-Trent Sci. Nat. Padova 9:209–243,1885), is not understood.   The lack of good illustration and description of the fungus and the fact that the conidia are considered

Table 1

Indefinite Species of Pestalotia

No.	Species	Conidia		Setulae	
		No. of cells	Dimensions (μ)	No.	Length
263.	*P. aucubae* Gutner	5	18–19 × 4–6	2–3	10–15
264.	*P. austro-caledonica* Crié	5	40 × 14	3–4	17–20
265.	*P. brevipes* Cooke	4		3–4	
266.	*P. capimonti* Sartory & Bainier	3–6 (5)	26–28; 15–19 (col. cells)	3	7–14
267.	*P. cinnamomi* B. de Haan		12 × 14	2 or more	
268.	*P. conglomerata* Bres. var. *folicola* Cif. & Gonz.-Frag.		18 × 7		22
269.	*P. cornifolia* Ell. and Ev.	5		3	8–15
270.	*P. cycadis* Allescher	5	18–24 × 5–8	2–3	
271.	*P. duportii* Pat.	5	10–15 × 5 (col. cells)	2	6–8
272.	*P. funerea* Desm., var. *coumarounae* Cif. & Gonz.-Frag.	5	18–22 × 8–9	3	
273.	*P. funerea* Desm., var. *discolor* Speg.	5	25–30 × 7–8	4–5	15–20
274.	*P. funerea* Desm., var. *sarcomphali* Cif. & Gonz.-Frag.	5			
275.	*P. genistae* Cocc. & Mor.	5		1, forked	10–18
276.	*P. gongrogena* Temme	4	24 × 4	1	
277.	*P. herbicola* Sacc.	5	25 × 6	3	15
278.	*P. landolphiae* P. Henn.				
279.	*P. liliorum* Rich.				
280.	*P. mangalorica* Thuem.	6	15 × 7 (col. cells)	3	
281.	*P. medinillae* Rangel	5	12–16 × 6–8 (col. cells)	2–3	up to 20
282.	*P. mori* Mont.	5		2	
283.	*P. ornithogali* Bacc.	4–5	14–15 × 8–9	3	
284.	*P. pipericola* Mund. & Kheswalla	5	16–26 × 5–11	3	
285.	*P. richardiae* Halst.				
286.	*P. tubericola* Pass.	5		3–4	

from Crié's figures to be totally colored and 2-septate would exclude the fungus from the genus *Pestalotia*. However, there is some suggestion in these drawings of hyaline exterior cells. Plate 8, fig. 27, shows a conidium with 4 setulae but the legend states: "est couronné par 3 cils apiculaires très longs." Saccardo's conception of the fungus is built around Crié's illustrations and the spore measurements are from the scale of the plate drawings.

Another contribution by Crié (Compt. Rend. Acad. Sci. 86:769–770,1878) only added to the dubious character of the species. Among conidia of *P. austro-caledonica* with symmetrical superimposed cells, Crié found conidia with three to several irregularly shaped agglomerated cells for which he proposed the new genus *Desmazierella* Crié.

"Pycnidia subspherical, black; conidia dark to somewhat black, irregularly spherical, 0.003–0.006 mm wide, loculate, 3 setulae, cells close, each with a single guttule."

He added that the *Desmazierella* species constituted a remarkable form of *Pestalotia* and that the typical character of *Pestalotia* was lacking. No type species was named. There is no further record of this genus in the literature. *Desmazierella* Crié is a homonym. This name was first introduced by Libert (Ann. Sci. Nat. 1829, p. 82) for a genus of the *Pezizaceae* and for the type species *Desmazierella acicola* Lib.

265. **Pestalotia brevipes** Cooke, Grevillea 6:135,1877–78; Syll. Fung. 3:788, 1884.

Pustules small, covered, the apex perforated. Conidia somewhat sessile, elliptic, 2-septate, pale brown, $18 \times 7.5 \mu$; setulae 3 to 4.

On petioles of *Aralia spinosa* L., Gainesville, Fla. Another *P. brevipes* Prill. & de Lacr. (Bull. Soc. Mycol. Fr. 10:84–85,1894) [=*P. palmarum* Cooke], on palm leaves, is not to be confused with this species.

The illustration by Cooke (Grevillea 6:1877–78, pl. 101, fig. 3) represented the conidia with 4 septa. The fungus was supposedly distributed in Ravenel, Fungi Am. No. 255, but it is lacking in every Ravenel set examined.

266. **Pestalotia capimonti** A. Sartory & Bainier, Soc. Biol. (Fr.), June 30, 1911; Ann. Mycol. 10:433–436,1912, nom. nud.; Syll. Fung. 25:609,1931.

Conidia fusoid, 3 6-celled, usually 5-celled, for the most part constricted at the septa, $26.3–28.1 \mu$ long (Syll. Fung., $30–55 \mu$); intermediate colored cells 1 to several, dark, $15.7–19.3 \mu$ long; apical hyaline cells bearing 3, rarely 4, divergent setulae, $7–14 \mu$ long (Syll. Fung., $10–12 \mu$); pedicels long.

On moist grass (Gramineae) in laboratory, France. The same text was published twice with different titles and with the author's names reversed. The order of names of the authors in the earliest publication of the article is accepted. The diagnostic characters of the type are based on the original drawings and authors' text, there being no formal description.

267. **Pestalotia cinnamoni** B. de Haan, Bull. Inst. Bot. Buitenzorg 6:12,1900.

Pustules sub-epidermal. Conidia dark brown, $12 \times 14 \mu$, hyaline exterior cells and 1 to 3 central cells; setulae 2 or more.

On young twigs and leaves of *Cinnamomum zeylanicum* Blume. Breyn, Java.

268. **Pestalotia conglomerata** Bres. var. **foliicola** Cif. & Gonz.-Frag., Estac.
  Agron., Moca, Rep. Dominicana, Ser. Bot. No. 11:45,1928.

Conidia somewhat small, up to $18 \times 7 \mu$, setulae longer, up to 22μ long.

On dried spots on living leaves of *Anona muricata* L., near Moca, Dominican Republic, leg. R. Ciferri, existing as a saprophyte, usually or sometimes associated with *Zignoella anonicola* Speg. and *Placosphaeria anonicola* Cif. & Gonz.-Frag.

269. **Pestalotia cornifolia** Ell. & Ev., Jour. Mycol. 4:51,1888; Syll. Fung. 10:
  488,1892.

Spots circular, brown, 3–4 mm in diameter, with a narrow, slightly raised dark border surrounded by a tinge of purple. Pustules punctiform, black, partly prominent, epiphyllous. Conidia oblong-elliptical, 5-celled, acute below but less distinctly so above, surmounted by a crest of 3 hyaline divergent setulae, $8–15 \mu$ long; exterior cells hyaline, intermediate colored cells brown, sometimes almost opaque.

On living leaves of *Cornus sericea* L. [= *C. amomum* Mill.], St. Gabriel, La., Sept. 1886, A. B. Langlois, in herb. A. B. Langlois 2, IX, 1886, in Nat. Fungus Coll., U.S.D.A. This and two other collections of No. 506, on the same host, St. Gabriel, La., IX, 1886, by Langlois, Nat. Fungus Coll., U.S.D.A. are empty.

270. **Pestalotia cycadis** Allescher, Hedwigia 34:219,1895; Syll. Fung. 14:
  1029,1889.

Acervuli scattered, black. Conidia 5-celled, fusiform, rarely clavate-fusiform, $18–24 \times 5–8 \mu$, considerably pointed at both ends; 3 intermediate colored cells olivaceous-brown; exterior cells coniform, hyaline; apical cells with 2–3 setulae; pedicels $5–8 \mu$.

On wilting leaves of *Cycas revoluta* Thunb., Bot. Gard., Munich, Germany.

271. **Pestalotia duportii** Pat., Bull. Soc. Mycol. Fr. 28:36,1912, fig. 5; Syll.
  Fung. 25:602,1931.

Spots superficial, dirty white, orbicular, 3–6 mm diam. Pustules black, grouped in the center of dead spots, subepidermal, later exposed, round, $200–300 \mu$. Conidia 5-celled, cylindric, prominently constricted at septa; 3 intermediate reddish-brown colored cells, $10–15 \times 4–5 \mu$; apical hyaline cells long, conic-truncate, crowned with 2 setulae, $6–8 \mu$ long; basal hyaline cell cylindric, tapering into short pedicels.

On upper surface of an old pileus of *Boletus* sp. growing on trunk of a palm, Conacry, French Guinea.

272. **Pestalotia funerea** Desm. var. **coumarounae** Cif. & Gonz.-Frag., Estac.
  Agron., Moca, Rep. Dominicana, Ser. Bot. No. 11:45,1928.

Pustules innate, indistinct, up to 180μ diam. Conidia ovate-oblong, $18–22 \times 8–9 \mu$, 5-celled, the intermediate cells dark, exterior cells hyaline, setulae 3.

On living leaves of *Coumarouna punctata* Blake, Moca, Dominican Republic, R. Ciferri.   On spots caused by *Leptosphaeria coumarounae* Gonz.-Frag. & Cif.

273. **Pestalotia funerea** Desm. var. **discolor** Speg., Michelia I; no. 5,479,1879; Syll. Fung. 3,792,1884.

Conidia oblong-fusoid, 5-celled, $25-30 \times 7-8 \mu$, the 3 intermediate cells olivaceous, central cells intensely colored; setulae 4–5, 15–20 μ; pedicels 8–10 μ.

On dead leaves of *Buxus sempervirens* L. and *Scrophularia canina* L. Tarzo, near Conegliano, Italy, 1872, C. Spegazzini. A specimen on *Erica* sp., Belluno, Italy, 1879, C. Spegazzini bearing the above epithet in herb. Spegazzini No. 11,880 is distinct and is more like *P. sydowiana* Bresadola.

274. **Pestalotia funerea** Desm. var. **sarcomphali** Cif. & Gonz.-Frag., Estac. Agron., Moca, Rep. Dominicana, Ser. Bot. No. 8:57,1927 (as No. 11 in error).

Acervuli at first covered, then open, erumpent.   Conidia 5-celled, intermediate cells dark, broader.

On leaves of *Sarcomphalus domingensis* (Spreng.) Krug. & Urb., near Haina, Dominican Republic, R. Ciferri, Feb. 15, 1926.

275. **Pestalotia genistae** Cocc. & Mor., Mem. R. Acad. Sci. Ist. Bologna, Ser. IV. 5:293,1883, fig. 3; Syll. Fung. 3:785,1884.

Pustules scattered, covered, later erumpent, round to oblong, black, rupturing the epidermis longitudinally. Conidia 5-celled, fusoid, intermediate colored cells dark, the exterior cells hyaline; pedicels 16–20 μ long; setulae 2, divergent, unequal in length, one 10–12 μ, the other 15–18 μ long.

On twigs of *Genista germanica* L. Pontecchio, Italy (Giugno).   According to fig. 3 (see above), the hyaline exterior cells of the conidia are small, the 3 intermediate cells dark and concolorous; apical hyaline cell crowned with 1 erect setula with 2 divergent branches, one longer than the other.

276. **Pestalotia gongrogena** Temme, in Thiel, Landw. Jährb. 16:437–445, 1887: Ber. Deut. Bot. Ges. 8:218,1890; Syll. Fung. 10:489,1892.

The fungus was reported to cause hypertrophies and tumors in branches of *Salix viminalis* L. and *S. undulata* Ehrh.   It was also mentioned that malformations often lack the fungus.

The fungus was characterized by thin-walled globose superficial pycnidia without ostiole; pycnidial membrane thin, carbonaceous, the base thick and pseudo-parenchymatic.   Conidia clavate, curved, hyaline, 4-celled, $24 \times 4 \mu$, rounded at apex and surmounted by a filiform setula which is sometimes absent or deciduous.   The conoid base of the conidium rests on a filiform, erect pedicel which might also suggest or represent a setula. The fungus was considered the cause of a widespread "Holzkropfe" of birch, aspen and willow. Frank (Pilzp. Krankh. Pflanz. 2:422,1896) considered it the type of a new genus rather than a species of *Pestalotia*.

Recently the same disease was reported by Bittman (Wiener Allg. Forstw. u. Jagdz. 52: Mar. 9, 50, 1931 and Abst. Neuheiten Gebiet des Pflanzsch. 27: 6,146,1934). Numerous species of willows in Austria were reported to be infected by *P. gongrogena* Temme causing hypertrophies in the bark often encircling the branches.

The writer has examined numerous specimens from abroad but none shows the fungus. Diedicke (Krypt. Flora Mark Brandenb. 9:5,887,1915) correctly asserted that the gall-like formations on willow are entirely independent of *Pestalotia* and he suggested dropping the name from the literature. There have been no further collections of the fungus to afford a correct identification of the species.

277. **Pestalotia herbicola** Sacc., Atti Soc. Ven.-Trent. Sci. Nat. Padova 2:247, fig. 27, 1873; Voglino, Atti Soc. Ven.-Trent. Sci. Nat. Padova 9: tab. 9, fig. 14, 1885; Syll. Fung. 3:795,1884.

Acervuli convex-flattened, erumpent. Conidia fusoid, attenuated downwards, 5-celled, 25×6 μ, the intermediate cells dark, guttulate, constricted at the septa, exterior cells hyaline; pedicels hyaline, 10 μ long; setulae 3, spreading, 15 μ long.

On dry leaves of *Galium sylvaticum* L. and *Stellaria holostea* L. in forest, Montello, near Treviso, Italy, Saccardo.

278. **Pestalotia landolphiae** P. Henn., Beeli, Bull. Jard. Bot. État Bruxelles 8:97,1923, and Hendrickx, Syll. Fung. Congensium p. 171, 1948.

This binomial is a nomen nudum. Hennings did not describe such a species. There is a specimen in Jard. Bot. État Bruxelles, Belgium, which was studied by Hennings, who wrote on the herbarium sheet "*Pestalotia . . . Landolphia . . .* zu alt." Steyaert (Bull. Jard. Bot. État Bruxelles 19:347, 1949) examined the specimen and saw only remnants of spores unworthy of study.

279. **Pestalotia liliorum** Richon, Soc. Sci. & Arts, Vitry-le-François 15:409 (1887–1888) publ. 1889, nom. nud.; Syll. Fung. 10:492,1892.

On stems of *Lilium candidum* L.

280. **Pestalotia mangalorica** Thuem., Rev. Mycol. Fr. 2:37,1880; Syll. Fung. 3:790,1884.

Pustules in dense groups, epiphyllous, punctiform, applanate, scattered, immersed, very small, black, seated in dry, whitish, irregular orbicular spots, rust-colored below. Conidia 5-septate, orculiform, with hyaline, acute exterior cells, not constricted at septa; colored part $15 \times 7\,\mu$; setulae 3; pedicels long.

On weak living leaves of *Bridelia scandens* Willd. [= *B. stipularis* (L.) Blume], Mangalore, Terre Canarie, India, leg. Keck.

281. **Pestalotia medinillae** Rangel, São Paulo Bol. Agr. 15: no. 4, 1915, tab. 7, fig. 7; Syll. Fung. 25:604,1931.

Pustules amphigenous, small, in dense groups, erumpent, black. Conidia fusoid or clavate-oblong, 5-celled, according to figure 7 cited above, but 4-celled according to description; constricted at septa; intermediate cells dark, the upper 2 the darkest, $12-16 \times 6-8\,\mu$, exterior cells hyaline, superior cell conic or hemispherical, bearing 2-3 divergent setulae up to 20 μ long, inferior cell conoid, descending into a short, filiform pedicel, 5 μ long.

On spots associated with *Laestadia medinillae* on leaves of *Medinilla magnifica* Lindl., Icarahy, near Nictheroy, Brazil, Nov. 1913.

282. **Pestalotia mori** Mont., Ann. Sci. Nat. Bot. III, 11:44,1849; Syll. Fung. 3:793,1884.

Pustules gregarious, conic-hemispherical, sub-dimidiate, innate-erumpent, black, at first covered, then tearing the epidermis. Conidia fusiform, 5-celled, 20 μ long, the intermediate cells brown, exterior cells hyaline; setulae 2, the basal cell supported by a pedicel.

On dead bark of *Morus* sp. According to Montagne (Ann. Sci. Nat. Bot. III, 11:44,1849 and Syll. Gen. Sp. Crypt., 1856, p. 262), this fungus was originally named and described as *Sphaeria mori* Cast. (Cat. Plantes Marseille, 1845, p. 175). There is nothing in the description furnished by Castagne to suggest analogy with the genus *Pestalotia*.

283. **Pestalotia ornithogali** Bacc., Nuov. Gior. Bot. Ital. 1904; 422,1904; Syll. Fung. 18:483,1906.

Acervuli small, covered by the epidermis, later erumpent, 300 μ wide. Conidia 4- or 5-celled, clavate-fusiform, $14-15 \times 8-9\,\mu$; intermediate cells fuliginous, exterior cells hyaline; apex crested with 3 setulae, 23-28 μ long, base pedicellate.

On leaves of *Ornithogalum umbellatum* L., Bot. Gard., Pisa, Italy, Beccari, April 1862.

284. **Pestalotia pipericola** Mund. and Kheswalla, Mycologia 34:314,1942.

Pseudopycnidia, 40-137 μ in diam, subglobose, numerous, epiphyllous, scattered, at first subepidermal, later bursting through the epidermis, seated on ashen gray dead areas without definite margins. Conidia 5-celled, straight or slightly curved, bulged in the middle, 16.6-25.9 μ; intermediate cells 3, dark brown, 11–18.5 × 5.5–11 μ, the central cell 3.7–7.5 × 3.5–11.5 μ; pedicels filiform; setulae 3 rarely 2, at subobtuse angle to each other.

On leaves of *Piper nigrum* L., Wynaad, Malabar, 1909, W. McRae, No. 2244, herb. Crypt. Ind. Orient., New Delhi. The species is apparently the same as *P. piperis* Petch collected in Ceylon and described in 1925 on the same host. The latter species has been placed in synonymy under *P. calabae* West.

285. **Pestalotia richardiae** Halst., New Jersey Agr. Exp. Sta. Ann. Rep. 14: 401,1893,1894, nom. nud.

On *Richardia africana* Kunth. [= *Zantedeschia aethiopica* (L.) Kunth].

286. **Pestalotia tubericola** Pass., Nuov. Gior. Bot. Ital. 7:191,1875; Syll. Fung. 10:492,1892.

Pustules small, punctiform, innate, scattered, black. Conidia fusiform, dilute yellowish, 4- to 5-celled; setulae 3 to 4, not as long as conidia, spreading, deciduous.

On dried-out tuber stalk (pseudo-bulb), probably of the *Orchidaceae*, Keren, Abyssinia, Beccari, 1870.

EXCLUDED SPECIES

Species Nos. 287–331

The species in this section are excluded from the genera *Monochaetia* and *Pestalotia* according to description or to my study of the type specimens. They do not conform to these genera. Many of them have been referred to other genera by earlier investigators, and all of the circumstances relating to each, and familiar to the author, have been compiled. In other instances new combinations have been proposed by the author on the basis of the original descriptions or the study of type material.

Excluded Species and Synonyms

	Species No.
Amphichaeta compta (Sacc.) Hoehn. = *Cryptostictis cynosbati* (Fckl.) Sacc.	298
A. europaea Grove = *Cryptostictis hysterioides* Fckl.	320
A. physocarpi (Vest.) Hoehn. = *Cryptostictis lonicerae* (Thuem.) Sacc.	319
Clasterosporium uncinatum G. W. Clint. & Peck = *Ceratophorum uncinatum* (G. W. Clint. & Peck) Sacc.	315
Coryneum rhododendri Cooke = *Cryptostictis mariae* (G. W. Clint.) Sacc.	316
Cryptostictis physocarpi Vest. = *Cryptostictis lonicerae* (Thuem.) Sacc.	319
Dochmolopha clintonii Cooke = *Cryptostictis mariae* (G. W. Clint.) Sacc.	316
Hendersonia cynosbati Fckl. = *Cryptostictis cynosbati* (Fckl.) Sacc.	298
H. hysterioides Fckl. = *Cryptostictis hysterioides* Fckl.	320
H. lonicerae Thuem. = *Cryptostictis lonicerae* (Thuem.) Sacc.	319
H. ribis-alpini Fautr. = *Cryptostictis ribis-alpini* (Fautrey) Guba	307
Hyaloceras comptum (Sacc.) Died. = *Cryptostictis cynosbati* (Fckl.) Sacc.	298
H. comptum (Sacc.) Died. var. *ramicola* Berl. & Bres. = *Cryptostictis cynosbati* (Fckl.) Sacc.	298
H. depazeoides (Otth) Died. = *Cryptostictis cynosbati* (Fckl.) Sacc.	298
H. hypericinum (Ces.) Sacc. = *Diploceras hypericinum* (Ces.) Died.	309
H. kriegerianum (Bres.) Died. = *Monoceras kriegerianum* (Bres.) Guba	312
H. spiraeicola (P. Henn.) Died. = *Cryptostictis lonicerae* (Thuem.) Sacc.	319
H. viticola (Cav.) Died. = *Cryptostictis hysterioides* Fckl.	320
Monochaetia americana (Mont.) Sacc. = *Mastigonetron fuscum* Kleb.	290
M. ampelophila Speg. = *Cryptostictis ampelophila* (Speg.) Guba	287
M. brachypoda (Sacc.) Sorok. & Busch = *Cryptostictis brachypoda* (Sacc.) Guba	294
M. camptosperma (Peck) Sacc. = *Coryneum bicorne* Rostr.	296
M. compta (Sacc.) Allescher = *Cryptostictis cynosbati* (Fckl.) Sacc.	298
M. compta (Sacc.) Allescher var. *ramicola* Berl. & Bres. = *Cryptostictis cynosbati* (Fckl.) Sacc.	298
M. depazeoides (Otth) Allescher = *Cryptostictis cynosbati* (Fckl.) Sacc.	298

Species
No.

P. flagellifera Ell. & Ev.=*Mastigosporella hyalina* (Ell. & Ev.) Hoehn.=
imperfect stage. *Cryptodiaporthe auberti* (West.) Wehm. var. *comptoniae*
(Schw.) Wehm.=perfect stage   305
P. funerea Desm. var. *heterospora* Desm.=*Coryneum juniperinum* Ell. and
Pestalotia funerea Desm.   306
P. hendersonioides Fautrey=*Cryptostictis ribis-alpini* (Fautr.) Guba   307
P. heteromorpha Thuem.=*Bartalinia*   308
P. heterospora Desm. var. *cupressi* Ces.=*Coryneum juniperinum Ellis* and
Pestalotia funerea Desm.   306
P. hypericina Ces.=*Diploceras hypericinum* (Ces.) Died.   309
P. hypericina Ces. var. *hyperici-humifusi* Allescher=*Diploceras hypericinum*
(Ces.) Died.   309
P. insidens Zabr.=*Cryptostictis insidens* (Zabr.) Guba   310
P. intermedia Sacc.=*Cryptostictis cynosbati* (Fckl.) Sacc.   298
P. juniperi Allescher=*Coryneum juniperinum* Ell.   311
P. kriegeriana Bres.=*Monoceras kriegerianum* (Bres.) Guba   312
P. lateripes Ell. & Ev.=*Hyalotia lateripes* (Ell. & Ev.) Guba   313
P. laurina Mont.=*Hyalotia laurina* (Mont.) Guba.   314
P. libertiana Sacc.=*Cryptostictis libertiana* (Roum. & Sacc.) Guba 318
P. lupini Sor.=*Pleiochaeta setosa* (Kirch.) Hughes   315
P. mariae G. W. Clint.=*Cryptostictis mariae* (G. W. Clint.) Sacc.   316
P. microsora Sacc.=*Cryptostictis microsora* (Sacc.) Guba   317
P. monochaeta Desm. var. *libertiana* Roum. & Sacc.=Cryptostictis *libertiana*
(Roum. & Sacc.) Guba   318
P. monochaeta Desm. var. *rosae* Roum.=*Cryptostictis cynosbati* (Fckl.) Sacc. 298
P. monochaeta Desm. var. *rubi*. Sacc. & Roum.=*Cryptostictis cynosbati*
(Fckl.) Sacc.   298
P. monochaetoidea Sacc. & Ell.=*Cryptostictis lonicerae* (Thuem.) Sacc. 319
P. monochaetoidea Sacc. & Ell. var. *affinis* Sacc. & Briard=*Cryptostictis*
hysterioides Fckl.   320
P. monochaetoidea Sacc. & Ell. var. *parasitica* Dearn. & House=*Cryptostictis*
parasitica (Dearn. & House) Guba   321
P. monochaetoidea Sacc. & Ell. var. *rubi* Ell. & Ev.=*Cryptostictis cynosbati*
(Fckl.) Sacc.   298
P. monochroa Tassi=*Pestalozzina thuemenii* (Speg.) Guba   328
P. mycophaga Vuill.=*Coryneum*   322
P. myrticola Bubak=*Pestalozzina unicolor* (Berk. & Curt.) Sacc.   330
P. oenotherae Ell. & Barth.=*Cryptostictis oenotherae* (Ell. & Barth.) Guba 323
P. persea-drymifolia Calvino=*Pestalozzina thuemenii* (Speg.) Guba   328
P. phacidioides Ces.=*Heteropatella lacera* Fckl.   324
P. primaria Ell. & Ev.=*Neobarclaya primaria* (Ell. & Ev.) Kuntze   325
P. saccardiana Vogl. var. *libertiana* Sacc.=*Cryptostictis libertiana* (Roum. &
Sacc.) Guba   318
P. salicis Hollós=Bartalinia or Hyalotia   326
P. sarmenti Pass.=*Cryptostictis hysterioides* Fckl.   320
P. sessilis Sacc.=*Robillarda sessilis* Sacc.   327
P. thuemenii Speg.=*Pestalozzina thuemenii* (Speg.) Guba   328
P. thujae Hollós=*Hyalotia thujae* (Hollós) Guba   329
P. unicolor Berk. & Curt.=*Pestalozzina unicolor* (Berk. & Curt.) Sacc. 330

Species
No.

P. viridis Torr. = *Hyalotia viridis* (Torr.) Guba — 331
P. viticola Cav. = *Cryptostictis hysterioides* Fckl. — 320
Pestalozziella geranii-pusilli Massal. = *Pestalozziella subsessilis* Sacc. & Ell. — 327
Pestalozzina laurina (Mont.) Sacc. = *Hyalotia laurina* (Mont.) Guba — 314
Scolecosporium camptosperma (Peck) Hoehn. = *Coryneum bicorne* Rostr. — 296
Seiridina rubi Hoehn. = *Cryptostictis cynosbati* (Fckl.) Sacc. — 298
Seiridium inarticulatum Berk. & Curt. = *Mastigonetron fuscum* Kleb. — 290
S. liquidambaris Berk. & Curt. = *Mastigonetron fuscum* Kleb. — 290
Toxosporium abietinum Vuill. = *Coryneum bicorne* Rostr. — 296
T. camptospermum (Peck) Maubl. = *Coryneum bicorne* Rostr. — 296

Species Descriptions

287. **Monochaetia ampelophila** Speg., Anal. Mus. Nac. Buenos Aires 20:410, 1910; Syll. Fung. 22:1228,1913.

Pustules gregarious, erumpent, hemispherical, depressed, 150–250 μ diam. Conidia 5-celled, somewhat large, suboblanceolate, fusiform, somewhat inequilateral, slightly constricted at septa, 24–30 × 6–8 μ; 3 intermediate cells subhyaline, greenish, iridescent, or pale yellow-brown, with contents; exterior cells empty, hyaline; 1 apical setula, horizontal or projecting at right angles to axis of conidia, straight or curved, 5–10 × 1 μ and 1 oblique setula affixed at base and of the same length; pedicels rather short, hyaline, 5–10 × 1–3 μ, thickened, drawn out from basal, conoid cells.

On living canes of *Vitis vinifera* L., Villa Hojo del Agua, Santiago del Estero, Argentina, Oct. 1909. According to Spegazzini, the species closely approaches *P. thuemeniana* Speg. (*P. thuemenii* Speg.) = *Pestalozzina thuemenii* (Speg.) Guba. The latter species has multi-setulate colored conidia and thus is distinct. *M. ampelophila* Speg. is more properly *Cryptostictis ampelophila* (Speg.) Guba comb. nov.

288. **Monochaetia muscicola** Nicot-Toulouse, Rev. Mycol., Fr. (n.s.) XII: 130–134,1947.

Plectenchyma compact, brilliant black, supporting a salty white mycelium, generally in tufts. Acervuli erumpent, small. Conidia cylindric, slightly curved, 3 to 4, usually 3-septate, 9–18 × 2.5–3 μ; exterior cells hyaline, prolonged; one setula at each extremity affixed eccentrically or laterally; intermediate cells slightly colored, dissymmetric, very clear; pedicels broad, when deciduous the base of conidia truncate.

On *Cephalozia bicuspidata* (L.) Dumort., Paris, France, Mme. J. Nicot-Toulouse.

The illustration of the conidia (Rev. Mycol. XII, 1947, fig. 3) and the type description clearly indicate that the fungus does not belong to the genus *Monochaetia*. Determination is not possible without a study of the material. The genera *Cryptostictis* or *Discosia* are suggested.

289. **Monochaetia pinicola** Dearn., Mycologia 20:244,1928.

On blighted needles of *Pinus palustris* Mill. (G. G. Hedgcock, Nos. 25, 156) and *P. echinata* Mill. (G. G. Hedgcock, Nos. 24, 395, Dearness, No. 5863), Hogan, Fla., March 1918. There is also a specimen from Brooksville, Fla., by Hedgcock on *P. palustris* Mill., March 25, 1918 in Nat. Fungus Coll., U.S.D.A., No. 3105 [Fig. 90a]. For a report on the distribution of the pathogen, see Hedgcock, Plant Disease Reporter, U.S.D.A. 16:28–42,1932. Recent studies on the distribution and pathology of the fungus were reported by Boyce (Phytopathology 48:516–17, fig. 1, 1958).

The conidia are 5-celled, fusiform, 21–26 × 8–9.5 μ (without apical beak), short pedicellate, lowest hyaline cell conic to obtuse, 4 cells above colored, guttulate, 17–21 μ long, 2 intermediate or central colored cells fuliginous or dark brown; exterior colored cells pale brown; apex with a hyaline attenuated beak 25–33 μ long; pedicels 7–12 μ long.

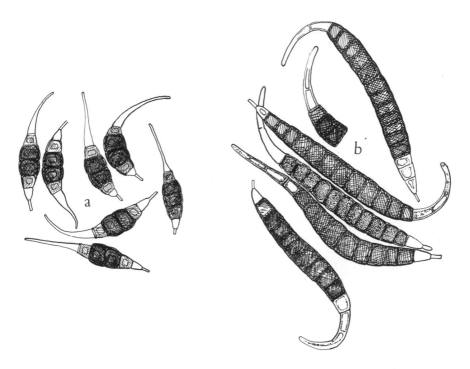

FIG. 90 [289]. (*a*) *Monochaetia pinicola* Dearn. [= *Coryneum pinicola* (Dearn.) Guba]. (*b*) *Scolescosporium fagi* Lib.

Dearness (see above) described the fungus incorrectly as with 4-celled conidia 14–19 × 5.5–8.5 μ (without beak), 2 dark brown colored intermediate cells, exterior cells pale brown, truncate-conic, ciliate-pedicellate, similarly ciliate at apex and 7–14 × 0.75 μ.

The attenuated hyaline beak at the apex of the spore and the lack of a hyaline apical cell would exclude the fungus from the genus of *Monochaetia*. *Scolecosporium*, judging from the type species *S. fagi* Lib. (Michelia II, 355, 1882; Fungi Ital., tab. 1091, 1881; Syll. Fung. 3:782,1884), is hardly the proper genus for this fungus. The conidia of *Scolecosporium fagi* are 7–12-septate, with chocolate-brown intermediate cells; the basal cell is sub-hyaline or pale brown, the first and second cells above are sometimes slightly darker, the beak at the apex is attenuated, septate, subhyaline or pale brown, and the cell on which the beak rests is sometimes subhyaline or slightly darker [Fig. 90b]. Also, the pycnidia are large, depressed, and pulvinate. Study is based on specimen in Kabat & Bubak, Fungi Imp. Exs. No. 531 on *Fagus sylvatica* L, Türnau, Bohemia, Apr. 16, 1908.

The fungus belongs in the genus *Coryneum* and is given the new designation *Coryneum pinicola* (Dearn.) Guba, comb. nov. *Pestalotia mycophaga* Vuill. is similar.

290. **Pestalotia americana** Mont., Gay, Historia de Chille (Bot.) 7:481,1850 and Syll. Gen. Spec. Crypt., No. 931, Paris 1856; Syll. Fung. 3: 798, 1884.

   Seiridium inarticulatum Berk. & Curt., Curtis, Bot. North Carolina 120, 1867, nom. nud.

   Seiridium liquidambaris Berk. & Curt., Grevillea 2:154 (84), No. 483, 1874; Syll. Fung. 3:783,1884.

   Monochaetia liquidambaris (Berk. & Curt.) Died., Ann. Mycol. 11:544, 1913.

   Monochaetia americana (Mont.) Sacc., Syll. Fung. 18:485,1906.

The fungus was originally described with 3-celled ellipsoid conidia, but Montagne's drawing of the fungus and my study show dark colored 1-celled ellipsoid conidia, one attenuated apical setula and rather broad pedicels. Montagne showed fruiting pustules resembling pycnidia but they are more properly acervuli.

In fallen leaves, Chile, South America (Gay), [Fig. 91a]. *Pestalotia americana* Mont. is more properly *Mastigonetron fuscum* Kleb. (Myc. Centralbl. 4:17–18,1914).

The same fungus appears in leaves of *Myrtaceae* in Rick, Fungi Austro-Americana No. 255, Sao Leopoldo, Brazil, 1908, associated with *Pestalotia versicolor* Speg. var. *guaranitica* Speg., which was studied by Klebahn (Myc. Centralbl. 4:17–18,1914) and Hoehnel (Sitzb. K. Akad. Wiss. Wien, Math-Nat. Kl. 123, Abt. 1, 86–87, 1914, Fragm. z. Myk. 864). The fungus differs

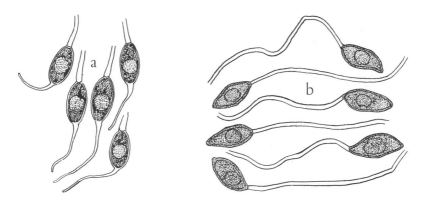

Fig. 91 [290]. (a) *Pestalotia americana* Mont. [= *Mastigonetron fuscum* Kleb.]. (b) *Harknessia uromycoides* Speg.

from *Harknessia* by the presence of long hyaline apical appendages [Fig. 91b]. The conidia of *Harknessia* sometimes have a hyaline papilla at the apices.

Harknessia caudata Ell. & Ev., N. Am. Fungi No. 1573 on white oak leaves and twigs is, according to Hoehnel, *Mastigonetron caudata* (Ell. & Ev.) Hoehn.

Seiridium inarticulatum Berk. & Curt., *S. liquidambaris* Berk. & Curt., and *Monochaetia liquidambaris* (Berk. & Curt.) Died., on twigs of *Liquidambar*, are similar and more properly *Mastigonetron fuscum* Kleb. Specimens examined: herb. Curtis No. 143 in herb. Farlow, Texas, 1869 (Billings); herb. Curtis No. 3718, Society Hill, S. C., 1857; herb. Curtis, Alabama (Beaumont, No. 11), all designated *Seiridium inarticulatum* Berk. & Curt.

291. **Pestalotia anomala** Harkn., Bull. Cal. Acad. Sci. 1884, p. 13; Syll. Fung. 3:800,1884; Voglino, Atti Soc. Ven.-Trent. Sci. Nat. Padova 9: fasc. 2, 1885, tab. VIII, fig. 2.

This fungus was described on stems of *Eriogonum virgatum* Benth. collected at Mt. Diablo, Cal. Specimens on *E. tomentosum* Mich. were distributed in Rabenhorst, Fungi, europ. No. 3399 and Ellis & Everhart, N. Am. Fungi, 2nd ser., No. 1625, collected at Antioch, Cal. [Fig. 92].

The conidia are 4-celled, 14–18 × 5–6 μ, slightly curved, rounded at apex, intermediate cells pale brown, exterior cells hyaline, basal cells truncate; pedicels broad and deciduous, 14–20 μ long; one flexuous appendage at apex, simple or branched; one simple flexuous appendage at base, oblique, persisting and lateral to the deciduous pedicels.

Voglino (see above, tab. VIII, fig. 2) illustrated 4-celled conidia, the exterior cells hyaline with 2–3 divided appendages, deciduous pedicels, both

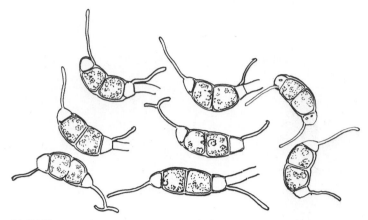

FIG. 92 [291]. *Pestalotia anomala* Harkn. [= *Cryptostictis anomala* (Harkn.) Guba].

borne laterally. He placed the fungus in the section *Eupestalotia*. Grove (Jour. Bot. 55:134,1917; British Stem and Leaf Fungi II, 354,1937) asserted that *P. anomala* Harkn. is an *Amphichaeta* with trimorphic spores like *A. europaea* Grove and *A. hakeae* Grove, and that *Amphichaeta* has hitherto been known only from California as this species. Hoehnel (Sitzb. K. Akad. Wiss. Wien., Math. Nat. Kl. Abt. I: 125,1–2,1916), on the basis of a specimen in Rabenhorst, Fungi europ. Exs. No. 3399, asserted that *P. anomala* Harkn. is related to *Pestalotia hypericina* Ces. (Bot. Z. 13; 599,1855). Based on comparison with the type specimen in Klotzsch, Rabenhorst Herb. Myc. II, No. 64, 1855, Saccardo (Syll. Fung. 10:485,1892) believed that *P. hypericina* Ces. (Syll. Fung. 3:795) is more properly *Hyaloceras hypericinum* (Ces.) Sacc. in the subgenus *Diploceras* Sacc., characterized by hyaline fusiform conidia and 2 flexuous filiform appendages at each extremity. Hoehnel believed that *P. anomala* Harkn. represented a new form genus related to *P. hypericina*. The author disagrees since the two forms are totally distinct. Hoehnel named the fungus *Diploceras anomalum* (Harkn.) Hoehn. and proposed modification of the genus *Diploceras* to embrace it.

The fungus is placed in the genus *Cryptostictis* Fckl., which is the same as *Amphichaeta* McAlp., a later genus agreeing with the conidial type of *C. hysterioides* Fckl. except that the apical setulae are sometimes branched at their extremities. The fungus is named *Cryptostictis anomala* (Harkn.) Guba, comb. nov., and on the basis of the fruiting structure would belong with the *Melanconiaceae*.

292. **Pestalotia artemisiae** Pass., Atti R. Accad. Lincei, Sci. fisiche. mat. nat., Ser. 4:7, fasc. 2,51,1891.

On dry stems of *Artemisia camphorata* Vill., Vigheffio, Parma prov., Italy (Jour. Mycol. 7:183,1894).

Passerini assigned the fungus to his new subgenus *Pestalozziana* but Saccardo (Syll. Fung. 10:508,1892; 15:242,1901) placed the species in synonymy under *Morinia pestalozzioides* Berl. & Bres. (Microm. Trident. 14: 82–83,1887–1888, publ. 1889) collected on the same host plant by Bresadola in April, 1888.

The acervuli are globose-conic, bearing elliptic fusoid, muriform conidia with 5, sometimes 4, transverse septa and numerous vertical septa, 16–22 × 5–7 μ; exterior cells olivaceous or subhyaline with contents, the intermediate cells umber, 12–15 μ long or umber and concolorous throughout, septa and walls darker. The apex of the conidium is crowned with 3, sometimes 4, rarely 2 setulae, 12–19 μ long, arising from scattered points about the periphery of the hemispherical apical cells. The basal cell is conic or hemispherical and supported by a filiform flexuous pedicel.

Specimen examined: dead stems of *Artemisia camphorata* Vill., Vigheffio, Italy, Apr. 1888, Bresadola, in herb. Naturhis. Riksmus. Bot. Avdel., Stockholm [Fig. 93].

293. **Pestalotia bicornis** Dur. & Mont., Flor d. Algerie Crypt I: 586,1846; Syll. Fung. 3:797,1884.

The fungus was described on leaves of *Phillyrea media* L. Stora, Algeria [Fig. 94]. The fusiform 5-celled conidia have 3 intermediate colored cells and hyaline exterior cells, a thick deciduous pedicel, one setula at apex, and an oblique setula projecting from base of inferior hyaline cell. The genera

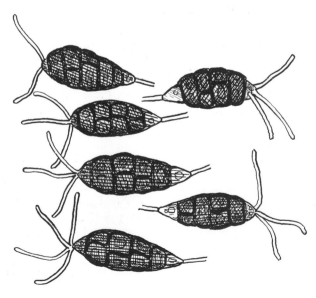

FIG. 93 [292]. Pestalotia artemisiae Pass.[= *Morina pestalozzioides* Berl. & Bres.]

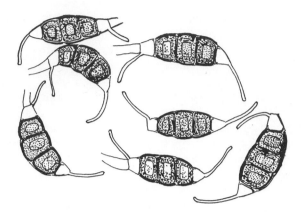

FIG. 94 [293].   *Pestalotia bicornis* Dur. & Mont. [= *Cryptostictis bisetulata* Guba].

Amphichaeta (Syll. Fung. 18:486), *Cryptostictis* (Syll. Fung. 3:443) and *Seiridina* (Mitt. Bot. Inst. Techn. Hochsch. Wien 7:29–32,1920) are alike. Morphologically, the species under consideration agrees with the type of the genus *Cryptostictis* except that the conidia are 5-celled.   The fungus is more properly *Cryptostictis bisetulata* Guba nom. nov.   The name *Monochaetia bicornis* (Dur. & Mont.) Sacc. is applied to the elected type fungus on leaves of *Quercus coccifera* L.   In this manner the two specimens bearing the epithet *Pestalotia bicornis* Dur. & Mont. are preserved as types of distinct species.

294. **Pestalotia brachypoda** Sacc., Grevillea 21:68,1892, pl. 184, fig. 12; Syll. Fung. 11:579,1895.

> *Monochaetia brachypoda* (Sacc.) Sorokin & Busch (Trudy Obs. sches. Jest. pri. Imp. Kasan. Univ. 24:13,1892; Z. Pflanzenkr. 3:162,1893).

Conidia 4-celled, elliptic to narrow fusiform, $18 \times 5\,\mu$, pointed at apex; 1 short setula at each end; lowest cells conic-truncate; 2 intermediate colored cells olivaceous or faintly brown; pedicels coarse, deciduous.   The fungus belongs to the genus *Cryptostictis* and is named *C. brachypoda* (Sacc.) Guba, comb. nov.

On living leaves of *Viburnum opulus* L., herb. P. A. Saccardo, Padua, Italy [Fig. 95].

295. **Pestalotia callunae** Ces., Rabenhorst, Fungi europ. Exs. No. 161, 1860; Bot. Ztg. 18:174,1860; Syll. Fung. 3:801,1884.

On dead stems of *Calluna vulgaris* (L.) Hull., Oropa (Piedemont), Italy, (Cesati), in Rabenhorst, Fungi europ. Exs. No. 161 (Fig. 96].

Conidia $18–22 \times 2\,\mu$, curved or arched, narrow cylindric, hyaline, usually obscurely 3-septate, slightly attenuated toward the ends, but muticate and never pointed; appendages absent: conidiophores $25 \times 1\,\mu$.

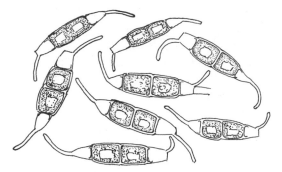

FIG. 95 [294]. *Pestalotia brachypoda* Sacc. [=*Cryptostictis brachypoda* (Sacc.) Guba].

Niessl (Verh. Nat. Ver. Brunn 10:1871, p. 62d, Sep. A) and Tubeuf (Beitr. Kennt. Baumkrankh., 1888) noted that the conidia are 4-celled, hyaline, and without appendages and that the species does not belong to *Pestalotia*. Saccardo placed the fungus in the subgenus *Pestalozzina* but made no new combination when the subgenus was made a genus. Hoehnel (Sitzb. K. Akad. Wiss. Wien. Math. Nat. Kl. I: 125,7–8,1916 and Mitt. Bot. Lab. Techn. Hochsch. Wien 2:26–29,1925) placed the fungus with *Sphaerocista schizo-thecioides* Preuss (Linnaea 25 (9):734,1852), under which it was published originally as the type. The genus *Sphaerocista* Preuss, as originally des-cribed by Hoehnel, is untenable. Hoehnel emended the genus and des-cribed the fungus in detail, assigning it to the *Pachystromaceae* (*Sphaeropsi-dales*) with a stroma having a single spore cavity without ostiole. Other synonyms given by Hoehnel are *Stagonospora lambottiana* Sacc., 1884, *Aposphaeria schizothecioides* (Preuss) Sacc., 1884, and *Collonaema schizo-thecioides* (Preuss) Grove, 1892. Clements and Shear (Genera of Fungi, 1931, p. 373) placed the genus *Sphaerocista* Preuss among the uncertain genera of the *Leptostromaceae*.

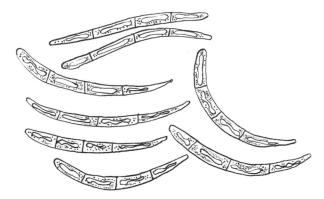

FIG. 96 [295]. *Pestalotia callunae* Ces. [=*Sphaerocista schizothecioides* Preuss].

296. **Pestalotia camptosperma** Peck; N. Y. State Mus. Rep. 39:48,1886; pl. I, figs. 10–11; Syll. Fung. 10:495,1892.

The fungus was described on dead needles of *Abies balsamea* (L.) Mill., Adirondack Mts., N. Y. [Fig. 97]. The name was changed to *Monochaetia camptosperma* (Peck) Sacc. (Syll. Fung. 18:485,1906). Subsequently, Maublanc (Bull. Soc. Mycol. Fr. 23; 172,1907; Syll. Fung. 22:1219,1913) designated the fungus *Toxosporium camptospermum* (Peck) Maubl. Vuillemin (Bull. Soc. Mycol. Fr. 12:33,1896; Syll. Fung. 14:1030; Allescher in Rabh. Krypt. Flora 1: Abt. 7:708,1902) described the fungus on *Abies pectinata* DC. as new, giving it the name *Toxosporium abietinum* Vuill. It is the type of the genus *Toxosporium* and the only species. Rostrup (Bot. Tidsskr. 22:271, 1898) described the fungus on the same host as *Coryneum bicorne* Rostr. (Syll. Fung. 16:1013,1902; Allescher in Rabh. Krypt. Flora 1: Abt. 7:638, 1902). Wilson and Waldie (Trans. Brit. Mycol. Soc. 13:154,1928) and Grove (British Stem and Leaf Fungi II, 339,1937) recognized the name *Toxosporium camptospermum* (Peck) Maubl.

Oudemans (Nederl. Kr. Arch., Ser. III, 2:4, Suppl., Flore Mycol. Pays-Bas 20, tab. 12, fig. 5) considered the fungus a *Scolecosporium* and Hoehnel (Fragm. z. Myk. Nos. 561 and 663, 1910) designated it *Scolecosporium camptosperma* (Peck) Hoehn.

The genera *Toxosporium* and *Scolecosporium* are quite distinct. Both belong to the *Melanconiaceae-Phaeophragmiae*. Neither has appendaged conidia. *Scolecosporium* conidia have a long hyaline attenuated beak, the cells below are totally or in part dark, the lowest cell pale brown or sub-hyaline, conoid, resting on a short narrow pedicel. The type is *S. fagi* Lib. In the genus *Toxosporium* the conidia are fusoid, curved, 4-celled, 2 inter-mediate colored cells guttulate, umber or fuliginous, exterior cells hyaline, somewhat attenuated, the apical cell conic, mucronate, muticate; pedicels short, coarse, deciduous. In the light of studies on the mucronate conidial forms of *Coryneum*, notably by Servazzi (Boll. Lab. Sper. R. Osserv. Fitopat.

Fɪɢ. 97 [296]. *Pestalotia camptosperma* Peck [= *Coryneum bicorne* Rostr.].

12:4,1934, reprint, pp. 1–16), the present author prefers the name *Coryneum bicorne* Rostr. Thus the genus *Toxosporium* Vuill. is superfluous. Hoehnel (Sitz. K. Akad. Wiss. Wien, Math-Nat. Kl. I: 127,617–618,1918) assumed that the perfect stage is *Asterina nuda* Peck.

297. **Pestalotia celastri** Tassi, Boll. Lab. Ort. Bot. Univ. Siena 3:131,1900; Syll. Fung. 16:1014,1902.

The fungus is characterized by 5-celled, hyaline, narrow-fusiform conidia crowned with 2 divergent appendages. It appears to be more properly *Hyalotia celastri* (Tassi) Guba, comb. nov. See No. 314, *Pestalotia laurina* Mont. for a formal description of the new genus *Hyalotia*.

On leaves of *Celastrus buxifolius* L., Siena, Italy, Aug. 1900.

298. **Pestalotia compta** Sacc., Michelia 2:542,1882; Fungi Ital. 1881, tab. 1116; Syll. Fung. 3:798,1884.

This fungus is *Cryptostictis cynosbati* (Fckl.) Sacc., Syll. Fung. 3:443,1884. It has an extensive synonymy as follows:

Hendersonia cynosbati Fckl. Symb. Mycol. 1869 p. 392, tab. IV, fig. 23.

Monochaetia compta (Sacc.) Allescher, Rabh. Krypt. Flora 1: Abt. 7:672–673,1902.

Hyaloceras comptum (Sacc.) Died. Krypt. Flora Mark Brandenb. 9: VII, 879,1915.

Amphichaeta compta (Sacc.) Hoehn., Mitt. Bot. Inst. Techn. Hochsch. Wien 7:29–32,1930.

Pestalotia monochaetoidea Sacc. & Ell. var. *rubi* Ell. & Ev. N. Am. Fungi No. 3070, 2nd ser. 1894.

Monochaetia monochaetoidea (Sacc. & Ell.) Allescher var. *rubi* Ell. & Ev., Rabh. Krypt. Flora 1: Abt. 7:675,1902.

Pestalotia monochaeta Desm. var. *rubi* Sacc. & Roum., Roumeguère. Fungi Galliae Exs. No. 3285, 1885.

Pestalotia monochaeta Desm. var. *rosae* Roum., Fungi Galliae Exs, No. 6162, 1892.

Seiridina rubi Hoehn., Mitt. Bot. Inst. Techn. Hochsch. Wien 7:29–32, 1930.

Pestalotia compta Sacc. var. *ramicola* Berl. & Bres., Ann. Soc. Alpinisti Tridentini 14:81,1889, pl. 6, fig. 9.

Monochaetia compta (Sacc.) Allescher var. *ramicola* Berl. & Bres., Rabh. Krypt. Flora 1: Abt. 7:673,1902.

Hyaloceras comptum (Sacc.) Died. var. *ramicola* Berl. & Bres., Diedicke, Krypt. Flora Mark Brandenb. 9:879,1915.

Pestalotia depazeoides Otth, Mitt. Naturf. Ges. Bern, 1868, 58–59; Syll. Fung. 11:579,1895.

Monochaetia depazeoides (Otth) Allescher, Rabh. Krypt. Flora 1: Abt. 7:674,1902.

Hyaloceras depazeoides (Otth) Died., Krypt. Flora Mark Brandenb. 9:
879,1915.

Pestalotia intermedia Sacc., Bommer & Rousseau, Bull. Soc. Roy. Belg.
26:231,1887; Syll. Fung. 10:486,1892.

Pestalotia discosioides Ell. & Ev., Jour. Mycol. 4:51,1888; Syll. Fung. 10:
493,1892.

Monochaetia discosioides (Ell. & Ev.) Sacc., Syll. Fung. 18:485,1906.

Cryptostictis cynosbati (Fckl.) Sacc. was described on fruits of *Rosa
pimpinellifolia* L. [= *R. spinosissima* L.], based on material collected in the
Rhineland and Bavaria.   The conidia are structurally similar to *Cryptostictis hysterioides* Fckl. found widely on berries and canes of grape [Fig.
98a,b].   Originally *Hendersonia cynosbati* Fckl., the species has been overlooked and misunderstood and in consequence numerous synonyms have
appeared in the literature.   Many of the synonymous species have appeared
in the genera *Monochaetia* and *Pestalotia*.

Hoehnel (Fragm. z. Myk. XVI, no. 871, 1914) studied *Cryptostictis
cynosbati* (Fckl.) Sacc. in Fungi Rhenani No. 455 and Thuemen, Fungi
Austriaci No. 1061 and, finding no appendaged conidia, insisted that the
fungus is *Coryneum microstictum* Berk. & Br. (Ann. Mag. Nat. Hist., Ser. 5:
II:458,1850).   Fuckel reported setulae at both ends of the conidia.   The
present author agrees that both types of conidia appear together.   The fungus
produces both pycnidia and acervuli.

Coryneum microstictum is the imperfect stage of *Griphosphaeria corticola*

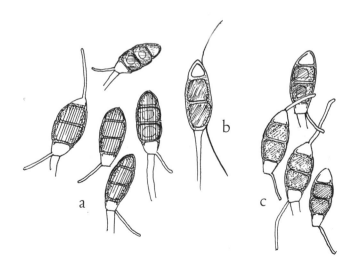

FIG. 98 [298].   (*a*) *Cryptostictis hysterioides* Fckl.   (*b*) *Cryptostictis hysterioides* Fckl.,
Symb. Myc. tab. IV, fig. 24, 1869.   (*c*) *Cryptostictis cynosbati* (Fckl.) Sacc.

(Fckl.) Hoehn. The fungus causes a canker and die-back of rose and is also found on leaves and fruits of rose and on other hosts such as *Rubus, Crataegus* and *Prunus* in Europe. It has been the subject of study by Brooks and Alaily (Ann. Appl. Biol. 26:213–226,1939) and Jenkins (Mycologia 29:725–731, 1937). Grove (Jour. Bot. 599, 1932, fig. 3, and British Stem and Leaf Fungi II, 327–331, 1937) created the genus *Coryneopsis* for these forms of *Coryneum*, naming this one *Coryneopsis microsticta* (Berk. & Br.) Grove. The fungus has also appeared as *Hendersonia rosicola* Sacc., *H. rubi* West., *H. canina* Brun., *H. rosae* Kickx, *H. henriquesiana* Sacc. & Roum., *Sporocadus rosicola* Rabh., and *Coryneum ruborum* Oud. Hoehnel (Mitt. Bot. Inst. Techn. Hochsch. Wien. 7:29–32,1930) found conidia with setulae at both extremities as in *Amphichaeta* and similar conidia without setulae as *Coryneum microstictum* in the type specimens of *Pestalotia compta* Sacc. on rose leaves. He named the non-setulate form *Stilbospora microsticta* (Berk. & Br.) Hoehn., a conclusion which is unacceptable. He named the appendaged form *Amphichaeta compta* (Sacc.) Hoehn.

Servazzi (Boll. Lab. Sper. R. Osserv. Fitopat. Torino 18:21–24,1939) listed six synonyms for *Monochaetia compta* (Sacc.) Allescher and reported an admixture of conidia. He regarded the form without setulae as *Hendersonia rosae* Kickx. Grove's view that the conidia are trimorphic, which is correct, would exclude the possibility of two distinct species.

Cryptostictis cynosbati was illustrated by Diedicke (Krypt. Flora Mark Brandenb 9:870,879, fig. 8, 1915) with 4-celled conidia, 2 intermediate colored cells, one setula at apex but none at the base. The fungus was named *Hyaloceras comptum* (Sacc.) Died. var. *ramicola* Berl. & Bres. This name was derived from *Pestalotia compta* Sacc. var. *ramicola* Berl. & Bres. (Ann. Soc. Alpinisti Tridentini 14:81,1889, pl. 6, fig. 9). Here the type description reports 4-celled conidia, one apical appendage, but pl. 6, fig. 9 shows 6-celled conidia like *Seiridium marginatum* Nees, which Saccardo (Syll. Fung. 10: 493,1892) has referred to as *Pestalotia seiridioides* Sacc., and which is more properly *Monochaetia seiridioides* (Sacc.) Allescher, a species common to *Rosa canina* L. It appears that Berlese and Bresadola were concerned with two distinct species on the same host.

Pestalotia compta Sacc. on leaves of *Rosa muscosa* Mill. [= R. centifolia L.], Selva, Italy, Sept. 1876. Hoehnel confused this species by asserting that *Monochaetia* Sacc. [= *Hyaloceras* Dur. & Mont.] (Frag. z. Myk. 11:561,1910), then later retracted his assertion (Falck, Myk. Unters. u. Ber. 1:301–369 and Frag. z. Myk. 18:963,1916).

Specimens examined: On canes of *Rosa* in herb. Curtis No. 3197 (herb. Farlow), Society Hill, S. C., 1851, also herb. Curtis No. 40, sub *Pestalotia* sp. [Fig. 98c]; Kansas Fungi No. 2059, Rooks County, Kan., Mar. 20, 1896 (Bartholomew), sub *P. monochaetoidea* Sacc. & Ellis; N. Am. Fungi No. 48, Port Byron, Ill., June 13, 1900 (Harper), sub *P. monochaetoidea* Sacc. & Ell.

On leaves of *Rosa*, herb. Berlin Bot. Mus. sub *Amphichaeta compta* (Sacc.) Hoehn.

Pestalotia monochaeta Desm. var. *rosae* Roum., Fungi Galliae Exs. No. 6162. On fruiting twigs of cultivated rose, France, May 1892, Fautrey.

Pestalotia intermedia Sacc., Bommer & Rousseau was described on canes of *Rosa pomifera* Herrm., Yvoir, Belgium. The type specimen (herb. P. A. Saccardo) bears in Saccardo's handwriting "*P. monochaetoidea* et *P. compta*" after the name "*Pestalotia intermedia* B.R.S." Diedicke and Servazzi assigned the fungus to *Hyaloceras comptum* (Sacc,) Died. and *Monochaetia compta* (Sacc.) Allescher, both of which are *Cryptostictis cynosbati* (Fckl.) Sacc.

Pestalotia discosioides Ell. & Ev. according to the type in Ellis & Everhart N. Am. Fungi, 2nd Ser., No. 2180, on rose leaves, Faulkland, Del., Aug. 1887 (Commons), is *Crytostictis cynosbati* (Fckl.) Sacc. Further examples of this fungus on leaves of *Rosa* are: herb. Dept. Plant Path., Cornell University, Aug. 18, 1918 (Burnham); herb. Canad. Dept. Agr., Ottawa, Canada, No. 1558. Bear Island, Lake Timagami, Ontario, Aug. 10, 1930 (Connors); culture No. 200A, L. M. Massey, Cornell University, Aug. 1935. On canes of *Rosa* in herb. Montagne, Mus. d'Hist. Nat. Paris, Bristol, England (M. Broome) sub *Coryneum marginatum* Nees. *Pestalotia discosioides* (wrong name) is the subject of a paper by Gomaz-Menor (Rev. Agr. Com. Santo Domingo 27:2304–2305,1936). He illustrated 5-celled fusiform conidia crowned with 3 setulae, agreeing with the genus *Pestalotia*. No measurements were given and correct identification is not possible.

Seiridina rubi Hoehn. was described on canes of *Rubus*, Vienna, 1906 (Hoehnel). The author considered the fungus like *Seiridium* except that the 4-celled conidia have one setula at each extremity. His herbarium has a specimen of the same fungus on the same host collected in Dalmatia and incorrectly named *Pestalotia funerea* Desm.

Pestalotia monochaetoidea Sacc. & Ell. var. *rubi* Ell. & Ev. nom. nud. On dead canes of *Rubus strigosus* Michx. Newfield, N. J., May 1879. On cultivated *Rubus* canes, Nat. Fungus Coll., U.S.D.A., Blacksburg, Va., Apr. 14, 1890, W. B. Alwood, sub *Discosia* sp., sub *Pestalotia calvescens* (herb. name).

Pestalotia monochaeta Desm. var. *rubi* Sacc. & Roum., Forêt de Fontaine-bleau (Seine et Marne), Dec. 1883. The type specimen has conidia without setulae like *Coryneum microstictum*. A similar fungus without setulate conidia appears in herb. Hoehnel, Melanconiales No. 4135 (herb. Farlow), on canes of *Rubus*, Dalmatia (Hoehnel), sub *P. funerea* Desm. On stems of *Sedum reflexum* L. Mendon-Fleury, April 1910, M. F. Ludwig, sub *P. monochaeta* Desm. Conidia 4-celled, elliptic, $11–15 \times 5–6 \mu$, 2 or 3 yellow-brown-colored cells, basal cell hyaline, apical cell often hyaline, an oblique setula projecting from base of lowest cell, 6μ long; pedicel thick, $15–20 \mu$ long; apical setulae absent.

299. **Pestalotia congesta** Berk. & Br., Jour. Linn. Soc. Bot. 14:89,1875; Syll. Fung. 3:786,1884.

Acervuli hypophyllous, subepidermal, then erumpent, congested, spreading, confluent forming black sooty masses, 200–500 μ in diam. Conidia 2-celled, elliptic, umber or dark, strongly constricted at septa, 23–29 × 8–11 μ; setulae 3–5, hyaline, 10–33 μ long, joined to or borne along axis of the short hyaline stalk projecting from the apices of the conidia; pedicels coarse, broad, deciduous, 8–12 × 2 μ.

On leaves of *Syzygium jambolanum* DC. [= *S. cumina* (L.) Skeels] Peradeniya, Ceylon, Feb. 1868 in herb. Berk. & Broome, Fungi of Ceylon, No. 805 in herb. Kew [Fig. 99]. The conidia have no hyaline exterior cells. The appendages are joined to a stalk at the apex. This fungus belongs to the genus *Neobarclaya* and is more properly *N. congesta* (Berk. & Br.) Petch (Ann. Roy. Bot. Gard. Peradeniya 9:165,1924). The conidia are variable from narrow clavate to broad ovate and show a total variation of 18–30 × 7–12 μ. The synonymy of the species is as follows:

Pestalotia congesta Berk. & Br. (see above).
Neobarclaya natalensis Syd., Hedwigia 38:134,1899.
Pestalotia evansii P. Henn. Engler, Bot. Jabrb. 41:273,1908.

A compilation of the species and collections of the fungus on *Syzygium cordatum* Hochst. [= *Eugenia cordata* Laws.] in South Africa were reported by Laughton (Bothalia 4:830–831,1948). The fungus *N. natalensis* Syd. was the subject of study and emended description by Ciccarone (Nuov. Gior. Bot. Ital. (n.s.) 54: no. 1–2, 1947, reprint, pp. 1–15). See *Pestalotia evansii* P. Henn.

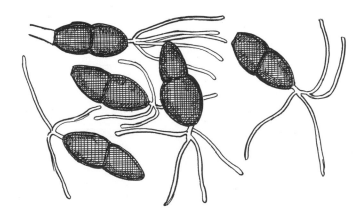

FIG. 99 [299]. *Pestalotia congesta* Berk. & Br. [= *Neobarclaya congesta* (Berk. & Br.) Petch].

300. **Pestalotia consocia** Peck, N. Y. State Mus. Rep. 39:48,1886, pl. 1, figs. 8, 9; Syll. Fung. 10:494,1892.

In spots on leaves of *Hamamelis virginiana* L. caused by the fungus *Phyllosticta hamamelidis* Cooke.

The fungus was renamed *Monochaetia consocia* (Peck) Sacc. (Syll. Fung. 18:485,1906). Conidia 6-celled, long elliptic to oblong fusiform, 4 brown intermediate cells, exterior hyaline cells; apical hyaline cell obtuse, crowned with one curved setula, one oblique or lateral setula projecting from base of lowest hyaline cell adjoining the attachment of the pedicel; pedicels coarse, erect, when detached showing the truncate base of the conidium. The fungus is renamed *Cryptostictis consocia* (Peck) Guba, comb. nov.

Specimens examined: On leaves of *Hamamelis virginiana* L. herb. N. Y. State Mus., Sandlake, N. Y., Sept. 1886, C. H. Peck [Fig. 100]; Catskill Mts. N. Y., August, C. H. Peck; Sydow, Fungi exot. Exs. No. 288, London, Ontario, Canada, Aug. 23, 1913, J. Dearness, all sub *Pestalotia consocia* Peck; herb. E. F. Guba, Ithaca, N. Y. Sept. 13, 1924, Guba.

301. **Pestalotia depazeoides** Welw. & Curr., Trans. Linnean Soc. (London) 24: pt. I, 284,1868, pl. 26, tab. 17, fig. 14; Syll. Fung. 3:408,1884; 15:242,1901.

On leaves of *Ficus andongensis* Gagnep., Pungo-Andongo, Africa. Dec. 18, 1856.

The type description states that the conidia are borne in small black pycnidia. Conidia pale brown, 1 or 2-celled, crowned with 3 setulae, 12–15 μ long. Figure 14 (see Welwitsch and Currey, above) shows 1- and 2-celled conidia bearing 3 simple setulae about the apex. In addition the elliptic

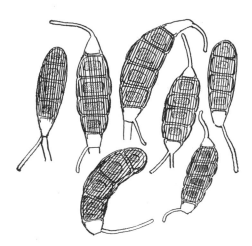

FIG. 100 [300]. *Pestalotia consocia* Peck [= *Cryptostictis consocia* (Peck) Guba].

conidia are illustrated with a septum across the apex separating a small additional cell bearing 3 setulae.

Type specimen Welwitsch and Currey, Fungi Angolenses No. 78 in herb. P. A. Saccardo [Fig. 101] shows elliptic-oblong, 1-celled hyaline conidia crowned with 1 (dichotomous) branched or 2 or more simple or much branched flexuous setulae: pedicel basal, coarse, deciduous. Septate and pale fuscous conidia were not found. Thus the type description of fungus *Pestalotia depazeoides* and the fungus studied by the writer are distinct.

Saccardo (Syll. Fung. 3:408,1884) designated the fungus *Robillarda depazeoides* (Welw. & Curr.) Sacc., which is not to be confused with *Pestalotia depazeoides* Otth (Mitt. Naturf. Ges. Bern 1868, pp. 58–59; Syll. Fung. 11: 579,1895) on leaves of *Rosa* sp. Steffisburg, Switzerland, which is *Cryptostictis cynosbati* (Fckl.) Sacc.

Pestalotia sessilis Sacc. [= *Robillarda sessilis* (Sacc.) Sacc.] is the type of the genus *Robillarda*. *R. depazeoides* (Welw. & Curr.) Sacc. is the second species.

302. **Pestalotia effusa** Vest.   Oefv. K. Vet. Acad. Förh. 10, 1:45,1897; Syll. Fung. 14:1027,1899; Allescher in Rabh. Krypt. Flora 1. Abt. 7:694, 1902.

On the periderm of living twigs of *Lonicera caerulea* L. Bot. Gard., Uppsala, Sweden, April 16, 1899.   T. Vestergren, Micr. rar. sel. No. 137 [Fig. 102].

The fungus does not belong to the genus *Pestalotia*. The acervuli are

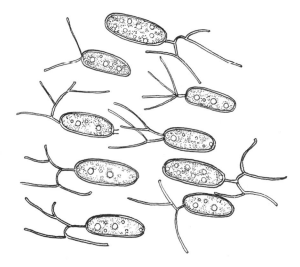

Fig. 101 [301].   *Pestalotia depazaeoides* Welw. & Curr. [= *Robillarda depazeoides* (Welw & Curr.) Sacc.].

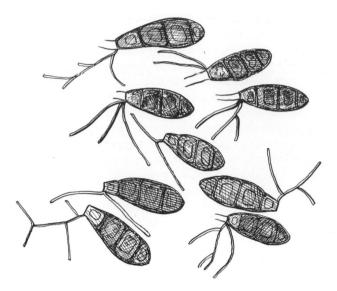

FIG. 102 [302].   *Pestalotia effusa* Vest. [= *Cryptostictis effusa* (Vest.) Guba].

elliptic to linear, immersed, then erumpent. The conidia are 4-celled, elliptic-fusoid, rounded at the apex, attenuated toward the base, the lowest cell conic-truncate, the walls thin, shrinking and collapsing; 3 upper cells honey colored, lowest cell yellowish or pale, sometimes all cells pale brown, concolorous; pedicels basal, short, coarse, usually detached; setulae 2 or 3, simple or usually branched, sometimes 1 and branched, eccentric and obliquely projecting from the base of the lowest cell and adjoining the point of attachment of the pedicel.

The type description places the setulae at the apex of the conidium, which is incorrect. The fungus is *Cryptostictis effusa* (Vest.) Guba comb. nov.

The genus *Cryptostictis* is characterized by polymorphic conidia. The setulae project from either or both extremities. They are simple or branched or both. In *Cryptostictis anomala* (Harkn.) Guba the apical setulae are sometimes branched. In *C. effusa* the setulae appear only at the base of the conidia and they are both simple and branched.

303. **Pestalotia evansii** P. Henn., Engler, Bot. Jarhb. 41:273,1908; Syll. Fung. 22:1222,1913; Centralb. Bakt. II. 24:270,1909.

Spots amphigenous, gregarious, round-angulate, dark-violet-colored. Acervuli carbonaceous, subglobose, erumpent, surrounded by torn shreds of epidermis, exposing black contents which issue in coils. Conidia 2-celled, elliptic, dark or black-violet, hardly constricted at septa, 15–26 × 9–12 μ, resting on a broad, hyaline attenuated, deciduous stalk; setulae filiform, flexuous, 2–4, usually 4, joined to a short, hyaline stalk or axis projecting from the apex, up to 30 μ long or a crest of 4 branches.

In spots on leaves of *Eugenia cordata* Laws., Barberton, Transvaal, Aug. 1906. I. B. Pole Evans, No. 234 [Fig. 103].

The author described 3-septate conidia with a superior hyaline papillae-form cell which, however, is more properly a short stalk. The fungus is the same as *Pestalotia congesta* Berk. & Br. Fungus is identical with *Neobarclaya natalensis* Syd. described on *Syzygium cordatum* Hochst. [= *Eugenia cordata* Laws.]. The correct name is *Neobarclaya congesta* (Berk. & Br.) Petch, Ann. Roy. Bot. Gard. Peradeniya 9:165,1924. Ciccarone (Nuov. Gior. Bot. Ital. (n.s.) 54:1–2,1947; reprint, pp. 1–15) published an emended description of *N. natalensis* Syd. based on the fungus on leaves of *Eugenia cordata* Laws., Natal, Durban, J. M. Hood, 1897, and *Syzigium guineensis* DC. [= *Calyptranthes guineensis* G. Willd.], Angareb River (Amhara), A. Ciccarone, 1939.

304. **Pestalotia exilis** Tassi, Boll. Lab. Ort. Bot. R. Univ. Siena 3:101,1900; Syll. Fung. 16:1015,1902.

The fungus, according to description, is characterized by small acervuli bearing narrow fusoid, 4-celled hyaline, almost filiform conidia crowned with 2 slender setulae. The fungus appears to be more properly *Hyalotia exilis* (Tassi) Guba, comb. nov. See No. 314, *Pestalotia laurina* Mont., for a formal description of the new genus *Hyalotia*.

On dead bark of *Eucalyptus eximia* Schau., New South Wales, Australia.

305. **Pestalotia flagellifera** Ell. & Ev., Jour. Mycol. 5:156,1889.

On branches of *Comptonia asplenifolia* Ait. [= *C. peregrina* (L.) Coult.] killed by fire. Newfield, N. J., June 10, 1889. J. B. Ellis.

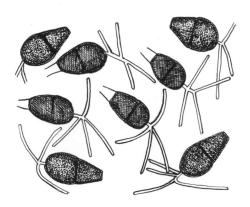

Fig. 103 [303]. *Pestalotia evansii* P. Henn. [= *Neobarclaya congesta* (Berk. & Br.) Petch].

Conidia elliptic-oblong, slightly curved, 1-celled, bi-guttulate, at length 2-celled, pale yellow or subhyaline; apex crowned with a long filamentous setula; pedicels stout, supporting conidia at base or slightly to one side, often deciduous.

The fungus was renamed *Barclayella flagellifera* (Ell. & Ev.) Sacc. (Syll. Fung. 10:476,1892; 15:242,1901), then changed to *Neobarclaya flagellifera* (Ell. & Ev.) Kuntze, Rev. Gen. Pl. III; 1,177,1893, not *Neobarclaya flagellifera* (Ell. & Ev.) Sacc. (Syll. Fung. 11:725,1895; 12,49,1897). The new designation was necessary to avoid confusion with *Barclayella* Diet. (Hedwigia 29: 266,1890; Syll. Fung. 9:316,1891) a genus of rust fungi. The fungus, although characterized by both 1- and 2-celled subhyaline conidia, is like the genus *Mastigonetron* Kleb., which has 1-celled, dark-brown conidia, 1 long setula at apex and pedicel at base.

Fungus is identical with *Harknessia hyalina* Ell. & Ev., which has pale-yellow conidia and a long apical setula which Hoehnel renamed *Mastigosporella hyalina* (Ell. & Ev.) Hoehn., the type of his new genus *Mastigosporella* Hoehn. (Sitzb. K. Akad. Nat. Wiss., Math.-Nat. Kl. Wien 123:135,1914). More recently it was named *Uniseta flagellifera* (Ell. & Ev.) Cicc. (Nuov. Gior. Bot. Ital. (n.s.) 54:711,1947). According to Wehmeyer (Genus Diaporthe, Michigan Acad. Sci. 8:218–219,1927; University of Michigan Studies in Science, Ser. 9:203,1933) the perfect form of the fungus is *Cryptodiaporthe aubertii* (West.) Wehm. var. *comptoniae* (Schw.) Wehm.

Specimens examined: Ellis & Everhart, N. Am. Fungi, Ser. 2, No. 2388, on branches of *Comptonia asplenifolia* Ait. [Fig. 204].

306. **Pestalotia funerea** Desm. var. **heterospora** Desm., Ann. Sci. Nat. Bot. II. 19:336,1843, and Mem. Soc. Roy. Sci. Agr. Arts, Lille, 1842:110, 1843.

The fungus was originally reported on *Cupressus* sp. It was distributed in Roumeguère Fungi Galliae Ex. No. 432 "ad folia emortua Cupressarum

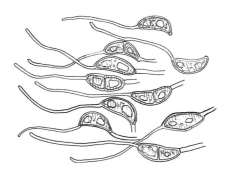

F ɪ ɢ. 104 [305]. *Pestalotia flagellifera* Ellis & Ev. [= *Mastigosporella hyalina* (Ellis & Ev.) Hoehn.].

Juniperi communis Thuyarumque in hortis." Klebahn (Myc. Centralbl. 4: 18,1914) studied type material and reported finding only colored 4-celled conidia without hyaline exterior cells, appendages or pedicels. He placed the fungus with the genus *Hendersonia*. He reported a colorless membranous mass at the extremities of the conidia. Two other collections by Cesati in Berlin Bot. Mus. on *Thuja* and *Cupressus* from Vercelli and Brixiae, Italy, respectively were examined by Klebahn but yielded neither *Pestalotia* nor *Hendersonia*.

The original description by Desmazières mentions an acervuloid fungus and two conidial types, one 5-septate and long-pedicellate without apical setulae; the other 4-septate, short-pedicellate, crowned with setulae, otherwise similar to the other [Fig. 105a]. Desmazières had before him two distinct species, *Coryneum juniperinum* Ellis and *Pestalotia funerea* Desm. The former came to my attention in Desmazières, Plantes Crypt. Fr., Fasc. 27: No. 1326. It has oblong-fusiform, 5-septate conidia, 4 intermediate brown or umber-colored cells, exterior hyaline cells collapsed more or less, basal hyaline cell obtuse, pedicels stout, long, easily detached or deciduous [Fig. 105b]. The same fungus appears in Klotzsch (Rabenhorst) Herb. Myc. Fung. II. 63:1855; see also Bot. Z. 12:151,1854 and 13:596,1855. *P. funerea* Desm. appears among the same specimens (Plantes Crypt. Fr., Fasc. 27: No. 1326) in distinct acervuli, hence the name *heterospora*.

Pestalotia heterospora Desm. var. *cupressi* Ces., Thuem. Fungi Austriaci No. 1062 (nom. nud.), on dry leaves of *Cupressus lawsoniana* A. Murr. [= *Chamaecyparis lawsoniana* (Murr.) Parl.], Tetschen, Bohemia, 1873. No fungus is present in the collection. The name suggests that the fungus was intended to belong to *P. funerea* Desm. var. *heterospora* Desm.

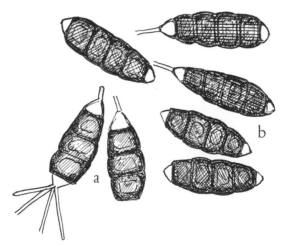

FIG. 105 [306]. *Pestalotia funerea* Desm. var. *heterospora* Desm. (a) *Pestalotia funerea* Desm. (b) *Coryneum juniperinum* Ellis.

307. **Pestalotia hendersonioides** Fautrey, Rev. Mycol. Fr. 15:116,1893; Syll. Fung. 11:579,1895.

On stems of *Ribes alpinum* L., Côte d'Or, France, Feb. 1893 in Roumeguère, Fungi Galliae Exs. No. 6370, 1893.

The species was given the new combination *Monochaetia hendersonioides* (Fautrey) Allescher (Rabh. Krypt. Flora, 1: Abt. 7:672,1902).

Apical appendages are deciduous early and in this state the conidia resemble *Hendersonia*. *Hendersonia ribis-alpini* Fautrey. (Rev. Mycol. Fr. 14:171,1892) in Roumeguère, Fungi Galliae Exs. No. 6129, 1892, on stems of *Ribes alpinum* L., Noidan, France, 1892 (Fautrey) is the same fungus. The conidia are essentially without setulae. It is renamed *Cryptostictis ribis-alpini* (Fautrey) Guba comb. nov.

308. **Pestalotia heteromorpha** Thuem., Inst. Rev. Sci. Litt. Coimbra, Ser. 3: 28: no. 575, 1880, 1881; Syll. Fung 3:794,1884.

On leaves of *Polygonum platycladum* F. Muell., Bot. Gard., Univ. Coimbra, Coimbra, Portugal, Aug. 1879. A. Moller No. 637 [Fig. 106].

The fungus is characterized by an acervulus and 4-celled fusiform, hyaline, conidia, 3 divergent setulae at apices, and short pedicels at base. The conidia are attenuated at both ends and constricted at the septa like *Pestalotia*. According to the original description, the apical conical cells are hyaline, the remaining three cells dilute gray with contents. This is a hyaline spored *Pestalotia* similar to *Pestalozzina fautreyi* Karst. & Roum. and both suggest the genus *Bartalinia*.

309. **Pestalotia hypericina** Ces., in Klotzsch, Rabh. Herb. Myc. II, No. 64, 1855; Bot. Z. 13:599,1855; Syll. Fung. 3:795,1884.

On dead bark of *Hypericum perforatum* L., Vercellis, Italy, Cesati [Fig. 107].

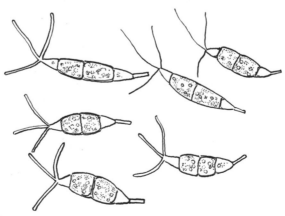

FIG. 106 [308]. *Pestalotia heteromorpha* Thuem. [=*Bartalinia*].

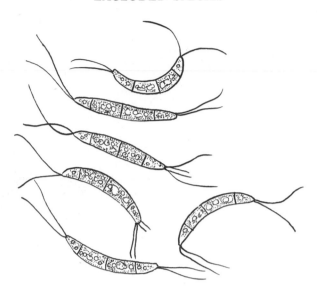

FIG. 107 [309]. *Pestalotia hypericina* Ces. [= *Diploceras hypericinum* (Ces.) Died.].

The conidia are 4-celled, narrow-cylindric, fusiform, curved, pointed at the extremities; two flexuous, simple, thread-like appendages at the apex, 2 similar appendages affixed to one side of the base; pedicels hyaline, filiform, deciduous; 2 central cells subhyaline or faintly olive or yellow, exterior cells hyaline.

Saccardo (Syll. Fung. 10:485,1892; 15:242,1901) changed the name to *Hyaloceras hypericinum* (Ces.) Sacc. and placed it in the subgenus *Diploceras* Sacc. Allescher (Ber. Bot. Ver., Landshut (Bavaria) 12:82–83,1892 and Bot. Centralbl. 42:106,1890) reported the same fungus on *Hypericum humifusum* L. from Munich, Germany (Sept. 1874), under the specific name *Pestalotia hypericina* Ces. var. *hyperici-humifusi* Allescher.

The fungus appeared as *Diploceras hypericinum* (Ces.) Diedicke (Krypt. Flora Mark Brandenb. 9:870,887 1915, fig. 17), a name accepted by Grove (Jour. Bot. 6, 1932, pl. 599, fig. 5, and British Stem and Leaf Fungi II, 353, 1937, fig. 130). The same fungus appears in Roumeguère Fungi Galliae Exs. No. 6864 as *Pestalotia truncata* Lév. Hoehnel (Fragm. z. Myk. 979, 92–94; Sitz. K. Akad. Wiss. Wien, Math-Nat. Kl. 1:125,1916) considered it a species of the genus *Diploceras*, closely related to *Pestalotia anomala* Harkn. [= *Cryptostictis anomala* (Harkn.) Guba]. Cl. & M. Moreau (Bull. Soc. Mycol. Fr. 64:187–192,1948) represented the conidia with only one basal appendage. Actually there are two.

Hyaloceras dilophosporum Cooke (Grevillea 19:5,1890) was referred by Saccardo (Syll. Fung. 10:484,1892) to the subgenus *Diploceras* Sacc. and designated *D. dilophosporum* (Cooke) Sacc. as the type of the genus *Diplo-*

ceras. It is characterized by hyaline or subhyaline, narrow-subfusoid, 4-celled conidia with 2 divergent setulae at both extremities; pedicels detached at the base of the conidia. This fungus was found on dead leaves of *Leptospermum scoparium* Forst., Australia (C. French).

310. **Pestalotia insidens** Zabr., Jour. N. Y. Microscop. Soc. 7: No. 3, 101–102, 1891.

On bark of *Ulmus americana* L., New Baltimore, N. Y., April 1872, Zabriskie [Fig. 108]; similar material collected by C. H. Peck in Catskill Mts., N. Y., in herb. N. Y. State Mus. Acervuli on a stromatic cushion, on maturity exposing the 6-celled conidia; 4 intermediate colored cells, olivaceous, the exterior cells hyaline, apex with one appendage, another projecting from base of the basal conic-truncate cell adjoining the pedicel. Other specimens examined: C. E. Fairman, Fungi of Orleans County, N. Y., No. 1068, Lyndonville, N. Y., May 1889; herb. Burt in herb. Farlow, Ames, Iowa, Aug. 18, 1894, F. C. Stewart. The fungus was reported by Bisby *et al.* in Fungi of Manitoba and Saskatchewan, 1938, p. 131. The species has been designated *Monochaetia insidens* (Zabr.) Sacc., Syll. Fung. 18:459,1906) but it is more properly a 6-celled conidial form of *Cryptostictis,* that is, *Cryptostictis insidens* (Zabr.) Guba, comb. nov.

311. **Pestalotia juniperi** Allescher, Ber. Bot. Ver. Landshut (Bavaria), 1890–1891, pp. 84–85 (publ. 1892); Syll. Fung. 11:580,1895.

On deformed branches of *Juniperus communis* L. killed by *Gymnosporangium clavariaeforme* (Jacq.) DC., Munich Forest, Grosshesselohe, Bavaria, May 1882.

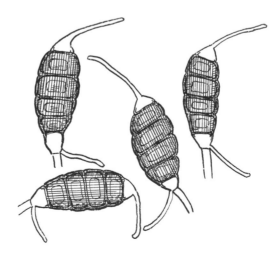

FIG. 108 [310]. *Pestalotia insidens* Zabr. [= *Cryptostictis insidens* (Zabr.) Guba].

The fungus is characterized by fusiform 6-celled conidia with long pedicels, 4 intermediate dark-brown cells, small hyaline, conical exterior cells, 25–30 × 6–9 μ; apical appendages lacking. Eventually the pedicels fall off, the exterior cells collapse or fall away and the conidia appear 4-celled and truncate at both ends. Allescher asserts that the conidia are borne in acervuli.

The fungus is like the 6-celled spored *Coryneum juniperinum* Ell. (Torrey Bot. Club 1882, p. 134, and Syll. Fung. 3:781,1884). It does not belong to *Monochaetia* or *Pestalotia* but is the same as one of the biotypes of *Pestalotia funerea* Desm. var. *heterospora* Desm., which is *Coryneum juniperinum* Ell.

312. **Pestalotia kriegeriana** Bres., Hedwigia 33:209,1894; Syll. Fung. 11:579, 1895.

The fungus was described on leaves of *Epilobium angustifolium* L. Koenigstein, Saxony. The type specimens appear in Krieger F. Sax. No. 999 and No. 999b [Fig. 109].

Conidia cylindric, subfusiform, 4-celled, yellowish or hyaline, provided with one setula at apex and one setula laterally disposed at base and adjoining the point of attachment of the pedicel; base of conidia truncate when pedicel is detached.

The fungus has been designated *Monochaetia kriegeriana* (Bres.) Allescher (Rabh. Krypt. Flora 1: Abt. 7:669,1902) and *Hyaloceras kriegerianum* (Bres.) Died. (Krypt. Flora Mark Brandenb. 7:877–878,1915). These erroneous allocations resulted from mistaking the laterally affixed basal setula for the

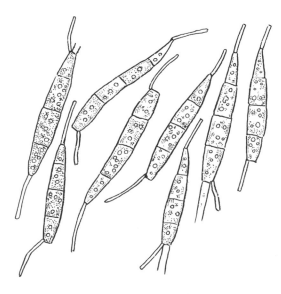

Fig. 109 [312]. *Pestalotia kriegeriana* Bres. [= *Monoceras kriegerianum* (Bres.) Guba].

pedicel. The pedicels are perpendicular with the conidia but usually deciduous and detached, leaving the truncate base. The fungus is neither a *Pestalotia* nor *Monochaetia*, nor any other genus of the Melanconiales. Being distinct, *Pestalotia kriegeriana* Bres. is represented as the type of a new genus of the *Melanconiaceae*, *Phaeophragmiae* as follows:

Monoceras gen. nov.

Acervuli simplices, lenticulares vel depresso-globosi, atri; conidia multiseptata, plerumque 4-cellulata, anguste fusiformia usque oblanceolata, infra incrassata, ad apices attenuata; cellulae apicales acutae, basales cylindricae, truncatae; cellulae omnes impletae, primo subhyalinae dein pallide flavidulae; setula una filiformia recta ad apicem, a cellula apicali distincta; setula una filiformis obliqua persistens ad basim affixa; pedicelli crassi, decidui.

Acervuli simple, lenticular or globose-depressed, black. Conidia multiseptate, usually 4-celled, narrow-fusiform to ob-lanceolate, broadened below, tapering toward the apices; apical cells acute, basal cells cylindric, truncate, all cells with contents, at first subhyaline then pale yellow throughout; 1 filiform erect setula affixed at apices, distinct from acute apical cells, 1 filiform oblique persisting setula affixed at bases; pedicels thick, deciduous.

Type, **Monoceras kriegerianum** (Bres.) Guba comb. nov., on *Epilobium angustifolium* L., Krieger, Fung. Sax., Nos. 999 and 999b. Koenigstein, Saxony, Germany. Similar to genus *Diploceras* except that the extremities of the conidia are 1-setulate. Differs from *Cryptostictis* (*Amphichaeta*) and *Pseudodiscosia*. See *Cryptostictis cynosbati* (Fckl.) Sacc. and *Pseudodiscosia dianthi* Hoesterman & Laub.

Specimens examined: On leaves of *Epilobium angnstifolium* L., Luck, Wisconsin, J. J. Davis, Aug. 25, 1916, sub *Hyaloceras kriegerianum* (Bres.) Died.; Ontario, Aug. 7, 1930, H. S. Jackson, Crypt. herb. No. 2098, University of Toronto, in herb. Farlow; Smarods, Fungi Latvici Exs., Zemgale, Kr. Jelgava, Ozolnieki, Aug. 15, 1932, J. Smarods; Parma, Italy, in herb. P. A. Saccardo. The fungus is listed by Davis (Trans. Wisconsin Acad. Sci. 19:691,1919) and Bisby *et al.* (Fungi Manitoba and Saskatchewan, 1938, p. 131). A similar fungus appears on leaves of *Rosa* in herb. P. A. Saccardo, Padua, sub *Pestalotia funerea* Desm.

313. **Pestalotia lateripes** Ell. & Ev., Jour. Mycol. 7:133,1892; Syll. Fung. 11: 578,1895.

The fungus was described on dead legumes of *Cassia chamaecrista* Walt. Newfield, N. J., Sept. and Oct. 1891, and was issued in Ell. & Ev. N. Am. Fungi No. 2786 [Fig. 110].

Acervuli pustulose or subhysteriform, with large irregular or linear openings. Conidia cylindric, clavate, yellow-brown, at length 4-celled with contents, apical cell subconic, narrow, curved, crested with 3 divergent setulae; basal cell narrow with an eccentric pedicel.

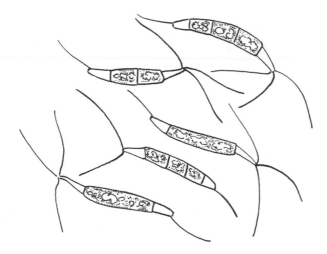

FIG. 110 [313].   *Pestalotia lateripes* Ellis & Ev. [= *Hyalotia lateripes* (Ellis & Ev.) Guba].

According to my studies the fruiting pustule is a globose pycnidium with ostiole. The conidia are cylindric-fusiform, usually 4-celled, hyaline or greenish, surmounted by a clear elongated oblique beak crested with 3 filiform setulae, base of conidia truncate with an oblique eccentric appendage adjoining the truncate base; pedicels detached or deciduous (not observed). This fungus is given the new name *Hyalotia lateripes* (Ell. & Ev.) Guba comb. nov. A related species *Pestalozzina laurina* (Mont.) Sacc. is established as the type of the new genus *Hyalotia* gen. nov. See No. 314, *Pestalotia laurina* Mont., for a formal description of the genus *Hyalotia*.

314. **Pestalotia laurina** Mont., Ann. Sci. Nat. Bot. III 12:312,1849; Syll. Fung. 3:800,1884.

On leaves of *Laurus nobilis* L. collected at Montaud lez-Miramas, France, Castagne.

Pustules gregarious, globose-depressed or hemispherical, innate-erumpent, hypophyllous. Conidia cylindric-fusiform, slightly curved, hyaline, usually 1-celled, the apical conical beak or cell empty, surmounted in an oblique manner and cut off from the rest of the spore by a septa, sometimes 2- or 3-septate, at length usually 4-septate (sometimes 5-septate according to Montagne); all cells with contents except conical apical cell, crested with 3 filiform divergent setulae, basal extremity conic truncate with an oblique or lateral filiform setula, the truncate base suggesting the point of attachment of the deciduous pedicel (not observed). This study is based on the type specimen in herb. Castagne No. 826 in Mus. d'Hist. Nat., Paris, France, associated with *Phoma lauri* Cast. [Fig. 111a].

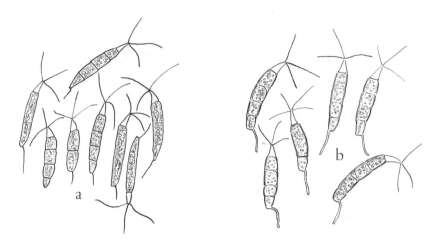

FIG. 111 [314]. *Pestalotia laurina* Mont. [=*Hyalotia laurina* (Mont.) Guba].

Saccardo (see above) placed the species in the subgenus *Pestalozzina* and later (Syll. Fung. 11:580,1895) it became *Pestalozzina laurina* (Mont.) Sacc. as the second species of the genus. *Pestalozzina unicolor* (Berk. & Curt.) Sacc., the first species, has colored conidia and is the type. The third species *P. callunae* (Ces.) Sacc. is according to Hoehnel (Fragm. z. Myk. 948,18,1916; Bot. Lab. Techn. Hochsch. Wien 2:26–29,1925) *Sphaerocista schizothecioides* Preuss. Thus, *Pestalozzina laurina* (Mont.) Sacc., being distinct, is the type of the new genus *Hyalotia*.

Hyalotia gen. nov. Melanconiaceae, Hyalophragmiae.

Acervuli simplices, hemisphaericales, depresso-globosi, uniloculati, atri vel obscures, innato-erumpentes, interiorem detegentes; conidia anguste fusiformia, primum continua, deinde plerumque 4-, rare 5-septata; cellulae omnes hyalinae, impletae, apicibus acutis setulis duis vel pluribus plerumque tribus, cristatis; cellulae basales ad bases truncatae, ad pedicellos obliquos filiformos hyalinos affixae.

Acervuli simple, hemispherical, globose-depressed, monoloculate, black or dark colored, innate-erumpent, exposing the contents. Conidia narrow-fusiform, at first continuous, then usually 4-septate, rarely 5-septate, all cells hyaline with contents, pointed apices crested with 2 or more, usually 3 setulae; basal cells truncate at base, resting obliquely on hyaline, short, liliform pedicels.

Type **Hyalotia laurina** (Mont.) Guba comb. nov. On leaves of *Laurus nobilis* L.

The genus *Pestalozzina* is emended and assigned to the *Melanconiaceae*, Section *Phaeophragmiae* with *Pestalotia unicolor* Berk. & Curt. as the type species.

The fungus was collected on *Parthenocissus tricuspidata* (Sieb. & Zucc.) Planch. in Bologna, Italy, by Goidanich [Fig. 111b].

A related species, *Hyalotia viridis* (Torrend) Guba, appeared in a culture from spots in leaves of *Casuarina equisetifolia* L. São Paulo, Brazil, April 1960, Luiza C. May.

˜315. **Pestalotia lupini** Sor. Z. Pflanzenkr. 8:266–271,1898, tab. V; Syll. Fung. 16:1014,1902.

The fungus was originally described on cotyledons and leaves of *Lupinus mutabilis* Lindl. collected at Nuremburg, Bavaria, Germany.

Sorauer reported that the fungus causes rusty-colored spots up to 2 mm in diam. surrounded by pale greenish zones and may form larger spots by coalescence.   The conidia are cylindric, 5- sometimes 6-celled, smoky gray or dark-olive-colored, 54–60 × 16 μ with granular contents, exterior cells lighter colored, apical cell bearing 3 to 4, rarely more or less, spine-like appendages up to 80 μ long, one or sometimes two of which are terminal and pointed outward, the lateral appendages oblique and projecting horizontally from the base of the terminal segment.

The same fungus occurs on *Cytisus laburnum* L. [=*Laburnum anagyroides* Medic.] in Miguia, Krypt. Germ. Austr. Helv., fasc. 6: no. 26, 1903, as "*Ceratophorum weissianum* Allescher in litt." but without description.

Cavara (Riv. Patol. Veg. 14:1–2,13–16,1924; Rev. Appl. Mycol. 3:10, 582,1924) designated the fungus *Mastigosporium lupini* (Sor.) Cav. and stated that it was considerably different from *Mastigosporium album* Riess (Fres., Beitr. Myk. 56, 1852, tab. VI, figs. 37–40; Syll. Fung. 4:220,1886) reported on leaves of *Alopecurus pratense* L.   The latter species has many-celled, hyaline, fusoid conidia with 3 setulae at and below the apex, thus belonging to the *Moniliaceae*.   A second record of *M. album* Riess for North America was reported by Johnson from Nova Scotia (U.S.D.A. Plant Dis. Rep. 41: 949,1957).

Doyer (Med. Phytopath. Lab. "Will. Comm. Scholt." 9:35–40,64–66, 1925) asserted that *Pestalotia lupini* Sor. is more properly *Ceratophorum setosum* Kirch. (Z. Pflanzenkr. 2:234,1892), a fungus originally reported on *Cytisus laburnum* L. [=*Laburnum anagyroides* Medic.] and *C. capitatus* Scop. [= *C. supinus* L.].   She found both identical in culture and also by cross infections of *Cytisus* and *Lupinus*.   Cavara saw only young hyaline conidia to influence him to name the fungus *Mastigosporium lupini* (Sor.) Cav.   Doyer collected the fungus on *Lupinus polyphyllus* Lindl. Pulselli (Boll. R. Staz. Patol. Veg. Rome 8:50–84, figs. 20,1928) found the same fungus on *Lupinus albus* L. and with it successfully infected *Cytisus adami* Poit. [=*Laburnocytisus adami* (Poit.) Schneid.].   Pulselli followed Kirchner in placing *C. setosum* in the subgenus *Pleiochaeta* (apex of conidia with more than one appendage). The fungus, being dark-spored, would belong with the *Dematiaceae*.

Saccardo (Syll. Fung. 11,622,1895) made *Ceratophorum setosum* Kirch. the type species of the subgenus *Pleiochaeta* Sacc. Hughes (Commwlth. Mycol. Inst. (London) Mycol. Papers No. 36, 1951) showed that *Ceratophorum setosum* is different from *C. helicosporum* Sacc., the type of the genus *Ceratophorum* subgenus *Monochaeta* (one appendage at apex of spore), and therefore *C. setosum* does not belong in the genus *Ceratophorum*. Other more significant differences are shown. Hughes raised the subgenus *Pleiochaeta* to generic rank with *Ceratophorum setosum* as the type, naming it *Pleiochaeta setosa* (Kirch.) Hughes. The conidia are elliptic to fusoid, 3–8-septate, hyaline or brown, with simple or branched apical appendages, without a basal appendage [Fig. 112a–d].

Gadd (Bull. Tea Research Inst. Ceylon 17:23–30,1937) collected the fungus on *Crotalaria anagyroides* H.B.K. and it also infected *Lupinus polyphyllus* Lindl. and *Crotalaria usaramoensis* Baker. Germar (Z. Pflanzenkr. 49:482–509,1939) offered an excellent biological treatment of the disease caused by this fungus and a fine bibliography. See also, Duplessis and Truter, "Brown spot disease of lupines caused by *Pleiochaeta setosa* (Kirch.) Hughes," Dept. Agr. Sci. Bull., Union South Africa, 347, 1953 and Hackbarth, "Infection of *Lupinus albus* and *L. luteus* by *C. setosum* Kirch" (Z. Pflanzenkr. 65:143–149,1958).

Clasterosporium uncinatum G. W. Clint. & Peck (N. Y. State Mus. Rep. 29:50,1878, tab. 1, figs. 9–10) was renamed *Ceratophorum uncinatum* (G. W. Clint. & Peck) Sacc. (Syll. Fung. 4:396,1886). The salient characters of the type are: mycelium effuse, dark brown; conidia rather large, subfusoid to cylindric, erect, 5–7-septate, 6–8-guttulate, chocolate-brown; septa obscure, basal end beaked into a long hook-like appendage. On leaves of *Quercus* sp., Buffalo, N. Y. The fungus in Seymour & Earle, Economic Fungi No. 160 in herb. Farlow [Fig. 112e] on leaves of *Carya amara* Nutt. [= *C. cordiformis* (Wangenh.) K. Koch.], Manhattan, Kan., Oct. 5, 1889, May Varney, is *Ceratophorum epiphyllum* (Schw.) Sacc., not *C. uncinatum*. This species also occurs on leaves of *Hicoria*.

The specimen on *Carya* has the following characteristics: The apex of the conidium is muticate, not rostellate or cuspidate, and the base is attenuated into a long hyaline, non-septate, hooked beak. The conidia are fusiform, cylindric, more or less opaque, obscurely many-septate. The long hooked beak at the base of the conidium appears as a late development as the conidium approaches detachment from its hypha. The position of the fungus in the genus *Ceratophorum* was clarified by Hughes (see above).

Pulselli (Boll. R. Staz. Patol. Veg. Rome 8:50–84,1928) placed *C. uncinatum* with seven other species in the subgenus *Monochaeta* of the genus *Ceratophorum* of which the type is *C. helicosporum* Sacc. The hyaline hook-like beak crowning the conidia is hardly comparable to the setulae crowning the conidia of *C. setosum* Kirch. [= *Pleiochaetia setosa* (Kirch.) Hughes].

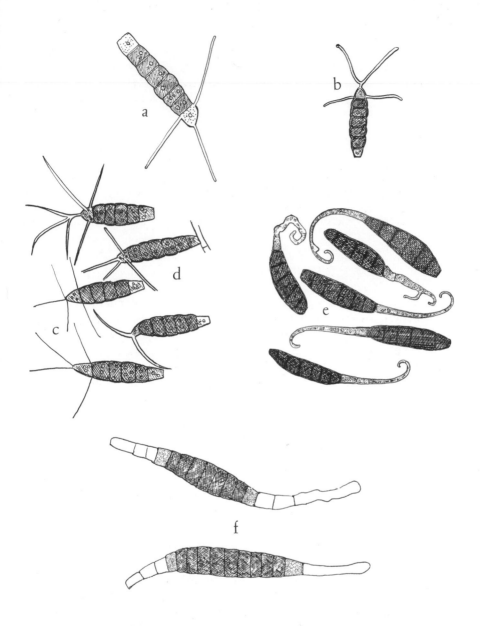

Fig. 112 [315]. *Pestalotia lupini* Sor. [= *Pleiochaeta setosa* (Kirch.) Hughes]. (*a*) Doyer, Med. Phyt. Lab. "Will. Comm. Scholt." 9 : 36,1925, fig. 20. (*b*) Ericksson, Pilzkrank-heiten II, 1928, fig. 228b. (*c*) Rostrup, Bot. Tidsskr. 26 : 312–14,1905, figs. 3–5. (*d*) Pulselli, Boll. Staz. Patol. Veg. Roma 8 : 50–84,1928, figs. 10, 16. (*e*) *Clasterosporium uncinatum* G. W. Clint. & Peck [= *Ceratophorum uncinatum* (G. W. Clint. & Peck) Sacc.]. (*f*) *Ceratophorum ulmicola* Ellis and Kell. [= *Dictyodesmium ulmicola* (Ellis & Kell.) Hughes].

Ceratophorum ulmicola Ell. & Kell. on *Ulmus fulva* Mich., based on specimen collected in Rooks Co., Kansas, Aug. 12, 1896, E. Bartholomew, herb. Farlow [Fig. 112f], is not typical of the genus *Ceratophorum*, and was named *Dictyodesmium ulmicola* (Ellis & Kell.) Hughes [Commwlth. Mycol. Inst. (London) Mycol. Papers *36*, 1951].

316. Pestalotia mariae G. W. Clint. in Peck, N. Y. State Mus. Rep. 27:102 1875, pl. 2, fig. 1–2; D. F. Day, Catalog of Native and Natural Plants of Buffalo and Vicinity, 1883, p. 139.

The fungus was found in spots on leaves of *Rhododendron maximum* L. at Buffalo, Aug. 22, 1873, by G. W. Clinton and designated *P. mariae-wilsoni* G. W. Clint. (herbarium name). Other collections are from Buffalo and Forestburgh by Clinton in Sept. 1873. The fungus has also been named as *Dochmolopha clintonii* Cooke (Nuov. Gior. Bot. Ital. 10:25,1878) and, more correctly, as *Cryptostictis mariae* (G. W. Clint.) Sacc. (Syll. Fung. 3:444,1884; 15:242,1901).

The fungus has 5-septate, fusiform conidia, with 4 intermediate pale-brown-colored cells and hyaline conic exterior cells, 1 apical appendage, 1 oblique appendage from base of inferior hyaline cell adjoining the pedicel. The conidia measure $16-25 \times 6-6.5 \mu$, the colored cells $15-17 \mu$ long, the setulae $6-16 \mu$ long. The pedicel is long and stout.

Cryptostictis mariae (G. W. Clint.) Sacc. was reported by Zeller (Mycologia 26:302,1934) on *Rhododendron californicum* Hook. [= *R. macrophyllum* G. Don] in the Pacific Northwest. *Coryneum rhododendri* Cooke reported as the cause of a leaf spot of *Rhododendron* (Schmitz, Phytopathology 10: 277–278,1920; Zeller, Mycologia 21:109,1929) is considered by Zeller to be the same fungus.

Specimens examined: on leaves of *Rhododendron maximum* L. (type), Buffalo, N. Y., Aug. 22, 1873 (Clinton), sub *Pestalotia mariae-wilsoni* G. W. Clint.; Mineola, Long Island, N. Y., June 1, 1923, Guba.

317. Pestalotia microsora Sacc., Michelia 2:284(1880),1881; Syll. Fung. 3: 800,1884.

The fungus has also been named *Monochaetia microsora* (Sacc.) Allescher (Rabh. Krypt. Flora 1, Abt. 7:669,1902). It was originally reported on stems of *Euphorbia spinosa* L., S. Giuliano, Toscana, Italy (Groves) [Fig. 113]. The conidia are 5-celled, $13-16 \times 6 \mu$, the 3 intermediate colored cells olivaceous, concolorous, $11-13 \mu$ long, exterior cells hyaline, apical cell obtuse conic crowned with a single filiform setula, 10μ long; basal cell conic truncate provided with an oblique appendage adjoining the base of the cell, the spore surmounted on a coarse, stout pedicel.

The fungus is more properly *Cryptostictis microsora* (Sacc.) Guba comb.

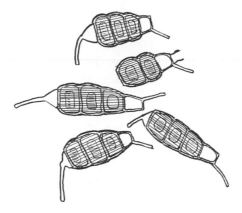

Fig. 113 [317]. *Pestalotia microsora* Sacc. [= *Cryptostictis microsora* (Sacc.) Guba].

nov. Sometimes the conidia are 4-celled with 2 intermediate colored cells, an exterior hyaline cell and a setula at both extremities.

318. **Pestalotia monochaeta** Desm. var. **libertiana** Roum. & Sacc., Rev. Mycol. Fr. 3 (no. 11):54, July 1881; Michelia 2:634(1880), Dec. 1882; Syll. Fung. 3:797,1884.

On stems of *Sambucus* sp., Malmedy, Prov. Rhenani, Belgium (Libert.). Voglino (Atti Soc. Ven.-Trent. Sci. Nat. Padova 9: fasc. 2:1885, reprint, p. 27) designated the fungus *P. saccardiana* Vogl. var. *libertiana* Sacc. It has also appeared as *P. libertiana* Sacc. (Syll. Fung. 15:242,1901) and as *Monochaetia monochaeta* (Desm.) Allescher var. *libertiana* Sacc. in Rabh. Krypt. Flora. 1: Abt. 7,667,1902. The fungus is renamed *Cryptostictis libertiana* (Roum. & Sacc.) Guba comb. nov.

319. **Pestalotia monochaetoidea** Sacc. & Ell., Michelia 2:375,1882; Syll. Fung. 3:798,1884; Saccardo, Fungi Ital., tab. 1117, 1881.

This fungus is more properly *Cryptostictis lonicerae* (Thuem.) Sacc. (Syll. Fung. 3:444,1884). Other synonyms are as follows:

Hendersonia lonicerae Thuem., Myc. Univ. 578:1876, non de Notaris.
Cryptostictis physocarpi Vest., Bot. Notis. 1899:166,1899.
Monochaetia monochaetoidea (Sacc. & Ell.) Allescher in Rabh. Krypt. Flora 1: Abt. 7:674–675,1902.
Monochaetia ellisiana Sacc., Syll. Fung. 18:485,1906.
Hyaloceras spiraeicola (P. Henn.) Died., Krypt. Flora Mark Brandenb. 9:880–881,1915, fig. 10, p. 870.
Monochaetia spiraeicola P. Henn., Sched. in herb. Mus. Bot. Berlin, Germany.
Amphichaeta physocarpi (Vest.) Hoehn., Fragm. z. Myk. XVI,871,1914.

Conidia ellipsoid, 4-celled, pale brown throughout or 2 intermediate cells colored; exterior cells hyaline; each extremity with 1 setula; pedicel thick, deciduous, basal cell truncate.

On stems of *Spiraea*, Newfield, N. J. (Ellis), May 1880, in Ellis, N. Am. Fungi No. 528 as *P. monochaetoidea* Sacc. & Ellis. Other specimens examined; on twigs of *Spiraea opulifolia* L. [=*Physocarpus opulifolius* (L.) Maxim.], Tamsel, Germany, May 1905 (Vogel), Sched. in herb. Mus. Bot. Berlin, sub *Monochaetia spiraeicola* P. Henn. On dry stems of *Philadelphus* and *Symphoricarpus*, Kassel, Germany, leg. Riess, 1852 and 1853, in Klotzsch, Rabenhorst, Herb. Myc. No. 1852, 1854; on stems of *Opulaster opulifolius* (L.) Kuntze [=*Physocarpus opulifolius* (L.) Maxim.], Albany, N. Y., Feb. 28, 1915, H. D. House sub *P. monochaetoidea* and May 28, 1918, S. H. Burnham sub *Monochaetia* sp.

Diedicke (see above) indicated that the fungus belongs in the genus *Cryptostictis*. Hoehnel (Fragm. z. Myk., XVI,871,1914) asserted that *Cryptostictis lonicerae* (Thuem.) Sacc. (Syll. Fung. 3:444,1884), belongs to the genus *Amphichaeta* McAlp. (Syll. Fung. 18:486). In Hoehnel's interpretation of *Cryptostictis*, the conidium has an oblique basal appendage and is without an apical appendage, which is incorrect. Actually, the two genera are identical. Saccardo, Fungi Ital. No. 1117, illustrated the conidia without the oblique basal setula.

Vestergren (Bot. Notis., 1899, p. 166) reported that the host plant of *Hendersonia lonicerae* Thuem. in Thuemen, Myc. Univ. No. 578 is probably *Physocarpus opulifolius* (L.) Maxim., not *Lonicera tatarica* L. At Uppsala, Sweden, the fungus occurs also on *Physocarpus amurensis* (Maxim.) Maxim. *Hendersonia lonicerae* Fries (Syll. Fung. 3:423,1884), according to Vestergren's study of the type, belongs to *Diplodia*.

320. **Pestalotia monochaetoidea** Sacc. & Ell. var. **affinis** Sacc. & Briard, Rev. Mycol. Fr. 8:25,1886, tab. 47, figs. 13; Syll. Fung. 10:493,1892.

This fungus is more correctly *Cryptostictis hysterioides* Fckl. (Fungi Rhenani No. 1838, fasc. IV, 1866, nom. nud.; Symb. Mycol. 392,1869, tab. IV, fig. 24; Syll. Fung. 3:343,1884; 15:164,1901). It has the following synonymy:

Hendersonia hysterioides Fckl., Symb. Mycol. 392, 1869, tab. IV, fig. 24; Syll. Fung. 3:443,1884; 15:164,1901.
Pestalotia sarmenti Pass., Atti R. Accad. Lincei, Sci. fisiche mat. nat., Ser 4:6,469,1889 (publ. 1890); Syll. Fung. 10:494,1892.
Monochaetia sarmenti (Pass.) Allescher, Rabh. Krypt. Flora 1: Abt. 7, 676,1902.
Pestalotia viticola Cav., Ist. Bot. R. Univ. Pavia, 1888, p. 28, pl. 3, figs. 15–16; Syll. Fung. 10:493,1892.

Monochaetia viticola (Cav.) Allescher, Rabh. Krypt. Flora 1: Abt. 7,676, 1902.

Hyaloceras viticola (Cav.) Died., Krypt. Flora Mark Brandenb. 9:881, 1915.

Amphichaeta europaea Grove, Jour. Bot. 55:134,1917; British Stem and Leaf Fungi II, 353–354,1937.

Pestalotia briardii Lendn., Bull. Soc. Bot. Geneva, Ser. II, 8:181–184,1916, fig. 1.

Monochaetia monochaetoidea (Sacc. & Ell.), Allescher var. *affinis* Sacc. & Briard, in Rabh. Krypt. Flora 1: Abt. 7:675,1902.

Monochaetia ellisiana Sacc. (Syll. Fung. 18:485,1906) var. *affinis* Sacc. & Briard (Syll. Fung. 25:610,1931) was introduced to replace *M. monochaetoidea* (Sacc. & Ell.) var. *affinis* Sacc. & Briard.

Pestalotia europaea Grove, Syll. Fung. 25:608,1931.

Cryptostictis hysterioides Fckl. on canes of *Vitis vinifera* L. is the type of the genus [Fig. 98a,b]. It was named at first without description. Fuckel (Symb. Myc. 1869, p. 392) described the fungus in detail as *Hendersonia hysterioides* Fckl. A similar fungus on fruits of rose was named *Hendersonia cynosbati* Fckl. but Saccardo (Syll. Fung. 3:443,1884 and 15:164,1901) returned both species to the genus *Cryptostictis*. Fuckel's illustration of the fungus leaves no doubt of its identity.

The conidia are 3-septate, 12–16 × 5–7 μ; 2 intermediate colored cells yellowish or pale brown; apical cell blunt, hyaline or usually colored, sometimes crowned with a single filiform setula, 10–20 μ long; basal cell dilute yellow or usually hyaline, provided laterally with an oblique filiform setula adjoining the thick deciduous pedicel, 10–20 μ long. Hoehnel (Fragm. z. Myk. XVI,871,1914) was in error when he asserted that the apex of the conidium never has an appendage.

Specimens examined: ex. herb. Castagne (Mus. d'Hist. Nat. Paris) Montond-les-Miramas, France, (Roussel), sub *P. pezizoides* de N.; Sükord, Hungary, May 1921 (Moesz), sub *Hyaloceras affinis* (Sacc. & Briard) Moesz; ex herb. P. A. Saccardo, Troyes, France (Briard), sub *Pestalotia monochaetoidea* Sacc. & Ell. var. *affinis* Sacc. & Briard, on canes of *Vitis*.

Pestalotia viticola Cav. was described on fruits of *Vitis vinifera* L., Stradella, Italy; *Pestalotia sarmenti* Pass. on canes of *Vitis vinifera* L., Vigheffio near Parma, Italy; *Pestalotia monochaetoidea* Sacc. & Ell. var. *affinis* Sacc. & Briard, on canes of *Vitis vinifera* L., Troyes, France. *Pestalotia briardii* Lendn. was reported on swellings on canes of *Vitis* from Switzerland; *Amphichaeta europaea* Grove, on canes of *Vitis vinifera* L., Kings Cliffe, England, March 1851 (Berkeley).

Grove reported that *Pestalotia monochaetoidea* Sacc. & Ell. var. *affinis* Sacc. & Briard and *Pestalotia briardii* Lendn. should be *Amphichaeta europaea*

Grove, a species with trimorphic muticate conidia borne in a simple acervulus. The genus was described by McAlpine (Proc. Linnean Soc., New South Wales, 1904:118,1904) and characterized by 4-celled elliptic-fusoid conidia, supported by a thick pedicel; subhyaline exterior cells or only the basal cell hyaline, translucent brown-colored intermediate cells, one setula at each extremity, the basal one projecting obliquely from base of lowest cell. Saccardo, aware of the genus *Amphichaete* Kleb. (Myc. Centralbl. 4:17,1914) but apparently unfamiliar with McAlpine's genus, substituted the name *Pestalotia europaea* Grove (Syll. Fung. 25:608,1931). *Amphichaeta* Kleb. is a genus in the Moniliales (Tuberculariaceae) characterized by 1-celled hyaline ovoid conidia (not 2-celled as stated by Saccardo), spinulose wall and 3 setulae at each extremity. *Amphichaete* Kleb. was changed to *Amphichaetella* Hoehn. (Sitz. K. Akad. Wiss., Math. Nat. Kl. Wien. I:125, 92,1916).

321. **Pestalotia monochaetoidea** Sacc. & Ell. var. **parasitica** Dearn. & House,
    N. Y. State Bot. Rep., 1921; Bull. N. Y. State Mus. 243–244:76,1923.

On living leaves of *Opulaster opulifolius* (L.) Kuntze [=*Physocarpus opulifolius* (L.) Maxim.], H. D. House, Aug. 27, 1919 [Fig. 114]. This fungus has 6-celled, long fusiform conidia. All 6 conidial cells are colored brown and with contents. The exterior cells are hyaline or subhyaline, the basal cell often empty and clear, the apex surmounted by a short appendage and another appendage projects obliquely from the basal cell at the junction with the pedicel. The fungus is more properly *Cryptostictis parasitica* (Dearn. & House) Guba. comb. nov.

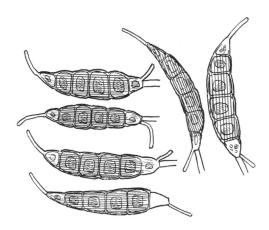

Fig. 114 [321].   *Pestalotia monochaetoidea* Sacc. & Ellis var. *parasitica* Dearn & House [=*Cryptostictis parasitica* (Dearn. & House), Guba].

322. **Pestalotia mycophaga** Vuill., Bull. Soc. Mycol. Fr. 12:35–37,1896; Syll. Fung. 14:1029,1899.

The species was renamed *Monochaetia mycophaga* (Vuill.) Allescher in Rabh. Krypt. Flora 1, Abt. 7:666,1902; Syll. Fung. 18:485,1906.

Pustules scattered, hypophyllous, black, at first covered by epidermis, finally pushing it away, 200–300 μ in diam. Conidia 5-celled, 27–32 × 7.3 μ; intermediate cells dark, opaque; exterior cells hardly colored, the apical cells conoid, short, bearing a slender, hyaline, curved or angular beak, 15–18 × 0.6–0.75 μ, basal cell attenuated; pedicels 100 × 1.3 μ.

On brown persisting leaves of *Abies pectinata* DC. [= *A. alba* Mill.], Gérardmer Vosges, France, cl. Mer.

The fungus appears to be like *Monochaetia pinicola* Dearn. but its proper disposition cannot be certain without a critical study of the type specimen. The description also suggests *Coryneum* with an apical hyaline attenuated beak of which there are several species according to Servazzi (Boll. Lab. Sper. R. Osserv. Fitopat. 12: no. 4, 1934).

323. **Pestalotia oenotherae** Ell. & Barthol., Erythea 26, 1896; Syll. Fung. 14: 1024,1899.

The fungus has been designated as *Monochaetia oenotherae* (Ell. & Barthol.) Sacc. (Syll. Fung. 18:485,1906), but it is more properly *Cryptostictis oenotherae* (Ell. & Barthol.) Guba, comb. nov.

Specimens examined: On dead stems of *Oenothera biennis* L., Marvin, Phillips Co., Kan., Mar. 7, 1895, E. Bartholomew. On stems of *Gaura parviflora* Dougl., Rooks County, Kan., Jan. 24, 1899, E. Bartholomew. Both specimens show the customary admixture of spore forms characteristic of species of *Cryptostictis* with 4-celled conidia. The 4-celled ellipsoid conidia have 2 intermediate brown cells, exterior hyaline cells, and a filiform setula at both extremities. Other conidia with 3 colored cells and hyaline basal cells lack the apical setulae.

324. **Pestalotia phacidioides** Ces., Klotzsch, Rabenhorst Herb. Myc II, 65,1855; Syll. Fung. 3:801,1884.

On stems of *Linaria bipartita* Willd. near Vercelli, Italy in Klotzsch Rabenhorst, Herb. Myc I, No. 724 [Fig. 115]; on stems of *Antirrhinum linaria* L. [= *Linaria vulgaris* Hill], Klotzsch, Rabh. Herb. Myc I:724, Bererloo, Belgium (M. Tosquinet), sub *Peziza linariae* Rabh.

The fungus is *Heteropatella lacera* Fckl. Grove (British Stem and Leaf Fungi II:157,1937) gives a fine description and historical review of the fungus. The filiform prolongation at the base of the spore, without contents, is the pedicel on which the conidium is mounted. The conidia are 1-celled, rarely or occasionally obscurely septate, narrow fusoid and tapering above into a

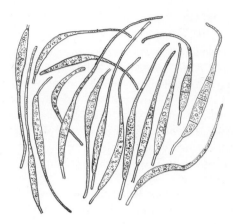

FIG. 115 [324]. *Pestalotia phacidioides* Ces. [= *Heteropatella lacera* Fckl.].

long, filiform, curved beak or prolongation, the contents throughout are hyaline and microguttulate. Clements and Shear (Genera of Fungi, 1931, p. 193) state that the base of the conidium is short ciliate, but this filiform persisting appendage is actually the sporophore.

Heteropatella is like the genus *Amphorula* Grove (Jour. Bot. 60; 82,1922; British Stem and Leaf Fungi I:362,1938) but Clements and Shear consider *Amphorula* a synonym of *Kellermania* Ell. & Ev. (Jour. Mycol. 1:153,1885).

325. Pestalotia primaria Ell. & Ev., Jour. Mycol. 2:103,1886.   Langlois, Cat. Prov. Plantes de la Basse-Louisiane, 1887, p. 32.

On stems of *Scirpus fluviatilis* (Torr.) Gray.

This fungus has elliptic-fusiform, 1-, at length 2-celled yellow brown colored conidia, rounded at the apex and slightly attenuated toward the base. The apices are crested with 3 short, hyaline filamentous setulae almost as long as the conidia.   The conidium is surmounted on a filiform pedicel.

The fungus was made the type of the genus *Barklayella* Sacc. (Syll. Fung. 10:475–476,1892; 15:242,1901) and designated *B. primaria* (Ell. & Ev.) Sacc. The generic name was changed to *Neobarclaya* Kuntze and the species to *N. primaria* (Ell. & Ev.) Kuntze, Rev. Gen. Pl. III:1,177,1893 not *Neobarclaya* Sacc. (Syll. Fung. 11:725,1895 and 14:46,1899).   In Syll. Fung. 12:49,1897, the fungus appears as *Neobarclaya primaria* (Ell. & Ev.) Sacc., the change being made to avoid confusion with one of the genera of rusts, *Barclayella* Diet. (Hedwigia 29:266,1890; and Syll. Fung. 9:316,1891).   The name appears as *Neobarclaya prunaria* (Ell. & Ev.) Lindau in Engler & Prantl, Die Natürlichen Pflanzenfamilien I:1,407,1900.

Saccardo described the genus *Barklayella* (Syll. Fung. 10:475–476,1892) to include another fungus, *Barklayella flagellifera* (Ell. & Ev.) Sacc., originally described as *Pestalotia flagellifera* Ell. & Ev. (1899), but the conidia of this species have only 1 long setula at the apex. With the change to *Neobarclaya* the fungus was designated *N. flagellifera* (Ell. & Ev.) Kuntze, Rev. Gen. Pl. III:1,177,1893, not (Ell. & Ev.) Sacc. (Syll. Fung. 12:49,1897). The genus, according to Saccardo, is characterized by colored conidia crowned with 1–3 setulae, but the conidia and the setulae in the two species are quite distinct. The two species represent distinct generic types in the *Melanconiaceae*. *Neobarclaya flagellifera* (Ell. & Ev.) Kuntze [= *Mastigosporella hyalina* (Ell. & Ev.) Hoehn.].

Saccardo asserted that the genus *Barklayella* is like *Robillarda* but with acervuli rather than pycnidia. Actually, the hyaline conidia of *Robillarda sessilis* Sacc. (Michelia 2:8,1880), formerly *Pestalotia sessilis* Sacc. (Michelia 1:261,1878), are totally different.

Specimens examined: On stems of *Scirpus fluviatilis* (Torr.) Gray, A. B. Langlois, Lousiana, May 1886, No. 443 [Fig. 116a]; March 12, 1887, sub *Pestalotia primaria* Ell. & Ev. in herb. Farlow, sub *Pestalotia versicolor* Speg., var. *americana* Speg. [Fig. 116], Nat. Fungus Coll., U.S.D.A. The conidia are, in these specimens, 1- and 2-celled, colored, elliptic, usually with 3 setulae about the upper half and sometimes arising laterally from the middle portion of conidia, occasionally or rarely branched; pedicels hyaline.

Saccardo (Syll. Fung. 15:241,1901) listed *Pestalotia americana* Speg. as a synonym of *P. versicolor* Speg. var. *americana* Speg. (Syll. Fung. 3:791, 1884), a species reported on *Scirpus palustris* L. [= *Eleocharis palustris* (L.) R. & S.] in Argentina. This fungus should not be confused with *Pestalotia americana* Montagne in Gay, Historia de Chile (Bot.) 7:481,1850, reported on fallen leaves in Chile and which is *Mastigonetron fuscum* Kleb.

Pestalotia versicolor Speg. var. *americana* Speg. (Anal. Soc. Ci. Argent. 13:21,1882 and Syll. Fung. 3:791,1884) was reported to be the same as *P.*

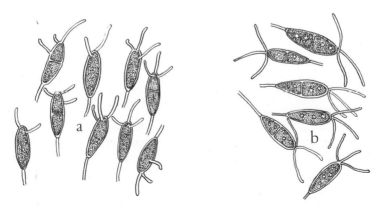

FIG. 116 [325]. *Pestalotia primaria* Ellis & Ev. [= *Neobarclaya primaria* (Ellis & Ev.) Kuntze].

scirpina Ell. & G. Martin (Am. Naturalist 19:76,1886) by Guba (Phytopathology 19:208,1929 and Mycologia 24:385–386,1932). Spegazzini's fungus from Argentina on *Scirpus* is a typical *Pestalotia* and totally different from Langlois's specimens from Louisiana.

The genus *Barklayella* Sacc. (Syll. Fung. 10:475,1892) was described to combine the characters of *Pestalotia primaria* Ell. & Ev., the type, and *P. flagellifera* Ell. & Ev., the second species as follows: "Acervuli subcutaneous-erumpent, black. Conidia oblong, 1-septate, colored, apex crowned with 1–3 setulae. Like *Robillarda* but without pycnidia." In contrast, *P. primaria* Ell. & Ev. (Jour. Mycol. 2:103,1886) was described as follows: "Acervuli hysteriform, black, erumpent, superficial, about 0.5 mm long. Conidia oblong-cylindrical, yellow brown, continuous, at length 1-septate, with a crest of 3 short, hyaline bristles, 6–9 μ long and slightly thickened at the tips; pedicels filiform, 10–12 μ long." Therefore the genus *Neobarclaya* Kuntze must conform to the type species *N. primaria* (Ell. & Ev.) Kuntze. Ciccarone (Nuovo Gior. Bot. Ital. (n.s.) 54: no. 1–2, 1947, reprint, pp. 1–15) has preferred to credit Saccardo for the new combination.

326. **Pestalotia salicis** Hollós, Ann. Mus. Nat. Hungary 4:369,1906, tab. IX, fig. 26; Syll. Fung. 22:1225,1913.

Acervuli covered by the epidermis, gregarious, globose, perithecioid, 250–280 μ diam. Conidia cylindric, elongate-fusiform, erect, or rarely curved, greenish-hyaline, with 4 cells all alike, constricted at septa, 24–32 × 4–6 μ, apex crowned with 3–5 hyaline setulae, 20 μ long; pedicels deciduous.

On fallen twigs of *Salix babylonica* L., Kecskemet, Hungary. All of the cells of the conidia are hyaline and the setulae arise at the summit. This would suggest the genera Bartalinia or Hyalotia.

327. **Pestalotia sessilis** Sacc., Michelia 1:261,1878; Mycotheca Veneta, No. 975, Padua, 1876.

The name was changed to *Robillarda sessilis* (Sacc.) Sacc. (Michelia 2:8, 1882; Syll. Fung. 3:408,1884:15:242,1901). It is the type of the genus *Robillarda*.

Pycnidia epiphyllous, covered by the epidermis, erumpent and protruding in a circular manner, lenticular. Conidia oblong, sessile, 9–11 × 3.5 μ, 1-septate, slightly constricted at septa, dilute olivaceous; setulae 3, crowning the apex, 14 μ long; pedicel none or obsolete.

On languishing leaves of *Rubus caesius* L., Colfosco, Treviso, Italy, Sept. 1876. The fungus appears in small, angulate white spots with reddish margins.

Grove (British Stem and Leaf Fungi II:189–190,1937) asserts that the fungus is identical with *Discosia artocreas* Tode ex Fries (Summa Veg. Scand. 423, 1846 and Syll. Fung. 3:653,1884). According to my study, this fungus is present in the type specimen and it does not agree with the conidial characters given in the original description of *Pestalotia sessilis* Sacc.

Another *Pestalotia sessilis* Sacc. (Ann. Mycol. 8:339,1910 and Syll. Fung. 22:1224,1913), described on leaves of *Diospyros mespiliformis* Hochst., Eritrea, Africa, is not valid since this name was used earlier (1878) for another fungus which is now *Robillarda sessilis* (Sacc.) Sacc. The new name *Pestalotia saccardensis* Guba nom. nov. is proposed for the species on *Diospyros*.

Pestalozziella subsessilis Sacc. & Ell. (Michelia 2:575,1882 and Syll. Fung. 3:737,1884) should not be confused with *Pestalotia sessilis* Sacc. The former fungus was found on leaves of *Geranium carolinianum* L., Newfield, N. J. (Ellis, N. Am. Fungi No. 1223 and Fung. Col. No. 444) [Fig. 117]. It is the type of the genus *Pestalozziella*.

Voglino (Atti Soc. Ven.-Trent. Sci. Nat. Padova 9: fasc. 2, 1885, reprint, p. 8) asserted that *Pestalotia sessilis* Sacc. and *Pestalozziella subsessilis* Sacc. & Ell. are the same, which is incorrect. The latter has an acervuloid fruiting structure and belongs with the *Melanconiaceae*. Conidia are elliptic oblong, 1-celled, hyaline or subhyaline, crowned with a short, coarse stalk from which arise 3–5 simple or branched frail appendages, the base of the conidium resting on a coarse pedicel. The short stem or stalk above the spore was overlooked by Clements and Shear (Genera of Fungi, pl. 51, fig. 16) and by the authors of the species.

Pestalozziella geranii-pusilli C. Mass. (Gior. Bot. Ital. 21:167,1889; Accad. Agr. Art. Comm., Ser. III, 65, 1889, extract, p. 103, tab. III, fig. 22; Syll. Fung. 10:470,1892) is the same fungus. It was reported on leaves of *Geranium pusillum* Burm., Tregnago, Italy, Oct. 1889. Massalongo illustrated 1-celled yellowish or faintly colored conidia.

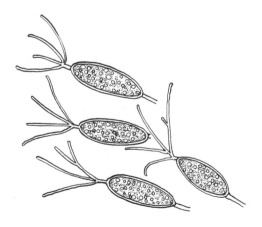

Fig. 117 [327]. *Pestalozziella subsessilis* Sacc.

328. **Pestalotia thuemenii** Speg., Thuemen, Die Pilze des Weinstockes, Vienna, 1878, pp. 14–15, pl. 2, fig. 21; Spegazzini, Riv. di Viticoltura Enologia Ital. 2:341–342,1878, pl. 6, figs. a–e; Voglino, Atti. Soc. Ven.-Trent. Sci. Nat. Padova 9:209–243,1885, pl. 8, fig. 8; Syll. Fung. 3:789,1884.
Pestalotia monochroa Tassi, Boll. Lab. Ort. Bot. R. Univ. Siena 2:160, 1899, tab. XV, fig. 7; Syll. Fung. 16:1016,1902.

P. perseae—drymifoliae Calvino, La Costa Azzurra Agricola-Floreale San Remo 18:3–4,57,1938, fig. 3.

Acervuli oblong-depressed, at first raising the epidermis, then rupturing it lengthwise, 300–350 × 60–90 μ. Conidia cuneiform, club-shaped, 5-celled, arising from sooty colored, septate, creeping hyphae; 3 intermediate colored cells, dilute olivaceous or yellow brown, 35 × 6 μ, exterior cells slightly paler, all more or less guttulate with oil drops; pedicels of different forms and lengths, 5–10 × 2–2.5 μ, the apical cells inequilateral, cymbiform, bearing 2 hyaline setulae 7–15 μ long, one arising from the apex of the cell, the other from the side.

On ripe berries of *Vitis vinifera* L., Conegliano, Venetia, Italy, Sept. 1877, Spegazzini [Fig. 118a]. On dead stems of *Casuarina equisetifolia* L., botanic garden, Siena, Italy, Oct. 1899 (Tassi), sub *Pestalotia monochroa* Fl. Tassi [Fig. 118b,c].

Pestalotia perseae-drymifoliae Calvino on withering twigs of *Persea drymifolia* Cham. & Schlecht, [=*P. Americana* Mill. var. *drymifolia* (Schlecht & Cham.) Blake], San Remo, Italy, April, 1937, is the same fungus [Fig. 118d]. Calvino asserted that the conidia are yellowish or pale brown, crowned with 2 or rarely 3 setulae. The color is greenish or yellowish and luminescent.

In Spegazzini (Riv. Viticoltura Enologia Ital.) the fungus carries the name *P. thuemeniana* Speg. with the description, but *P. thuemenii* Speg. on the plate drawings. The latter name, being the first published in Thuemen (see above), is accepted. According to Thuemen, the spots on the grapes are blackish, of irregular form up to 1 cm in diam, and bear densely grouped compressed-oblong pustules which on protruding, split the epidermis lengthwise. Reported on the Dall'Ochio grape, a variety of *Vitis vinifera* L.

The acervuli of *P. monochroa* Fl. Tassi, according to the original description, are oblong to hysteriform, and the setulae are 2, one at apex, 12 μ long, the other lateral and oblique, arising below the apex, 7–10 μ long, the pedicels often oblique, and arising from the side of the base off the axis of the conidia.

The fungus is assigned to the genus *Pestalozzina*, based on the type fungus *Pestalozzina unicolor* (Berk. & Curt.) Sacc. It is named *Pestalozzina thuemenii* (Speg.) Guba comb. nov.

Pestalozzina Sacc. emend. Guba *Melanconiales, Melanconiaceae, Phaeophragmiae.*

Acervuli simple without stroma, dark-colored or black, oblong or

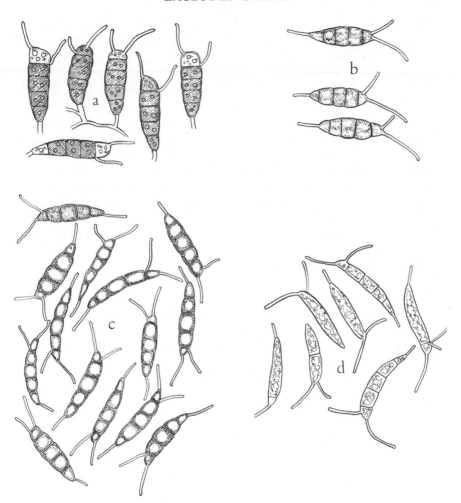

Fig. 118 [328]. *Pestalotia thuemenii* Speg. [=*Pestalozzina thuemenii* (Speg.) Guba]. (a) Riv. Viticoltura Italiana 2 : 1878, pl. 6, fig. d. (b) *Pestalotia monochroa* Tassi [=*Pestalozzina thuemenii* (Speg.) Guba], Boll. Lab. Ort. Bot. R. Univ. Siena 2, 1899, tab. XV, fig. 7. (c) *Pestalotia monochroa* Tassi [=*Pestalozzina thuemenii* (Speg.) Guba]. (d) *Pestalotia perseae-drymifoliae* Calvino [=*Pestalozzina thuemenii* (Speg.) Guba].

globose-lenticular, depressed, at maturity breaking and freeing the contents. Conidia 5-celled, cuneiform, clavate or somewhat fusiform, somewhat unequilateral, yellow or pale yellow brown, concolorous, color diminishing toward the extremities, all cells with contents; slightly constricted at septa, in form comparable to slugs or horned insect larvae; apical cells hemispherical; setulae flexuous, acropleurogenous (projecting from the side, base and apex of the apical cells); basal cells conoid, rounded at base, resting on a short pedicel.

Type *Pestalozzina unicolor* (Berk. & Curt.) Sacc. (Syll. Fung. 3:800,1884; 11:580,1895). On decorticated wood of *Juniperus*, Rhode Island. See description No. 330, *Pestalotia unicolor*.

329. **Pestalotia thujae** Hollós, Beiblatt Novenytani Kozlemenyek 6: pt. 2,67, 1907; Syll. Fung. 22:1226,1913.

Acervuli covered by epidermis, scattered, dark, punctiform. Conidia cylindrical, erect or somewhat curved, 4-celled, not constricted at septa, greenish-hyaline, 24–30 × 5–5.5 μ; setulae 3–5, up to 20 μ long.

On dry fallen twigs of *Thuja occidentalis*, L., Kecskemet, Hungary.

Pestalotia thujae Roum. nom. nud. (not P. tuyoe) in Roumeguère, Fungi Galliae Exs. No. 1876 (1882), was collected on dried fruits of *Thuja gigantea* Carr., St. Paul Garrai, Sept. 1881, by Angèle Roumeguère. It is reported to be close to *P. conigena* Lév., but my examination of numerous exsiccati specimens failed to reveal the fungus. Hollós's fungus appears to be more properly *Hyalotia thujae* (Hollós) Guba comb. nov.

330. **Pestalotia unicolor** Berk. & Curt., Grevillea 2:155,1873–1874; Syll. Fung. 3:800,1884; Frost, Boston Soc. Nat. Hist. 12:79,1869, nom. nud.; Bennett, Catalog of Plants of Rhode Island, 1888, p. 87.
   Pestalotia decolorata Speg., Anal. Soc. Ci. Argent. 9:158–192,1880; Syll. Fung. 3:784,1884.
   P. myrticola Bubak, Ann. Mycol. 14:154,1916; Syll. Fung. 25:604–605, 1931.

Pustules solitary or densely gregarious, punctiform, carbonaceous, globose-lenticular to hysteriform, erumpent, tearing the grayish wood fibers in a linear manner, frequently confluent and arranged without order, minute, 75–150 × 50–75 μ, or raised and prominently exposed, 215–500 × 115–215 μ, in gray fibers of woody matrix. Conidia 16–23 μ long, narrow, cylindric, club-shaped, fusiform or cuneiform, erect, equilateral, sometimes curved, slightly attenuated toward the base, 5-celled, only slightly constricted at septa, all 5 cells with contents, yellow or pale olivaceous, almost decolorous, the walls slightly darker, 11–15 × 4.5–6.5 μ, guttulate; the apical cells hemispherical or subglobose with 2 to 4, usually 3 divergent setulae arising at different levels, acropleurogenous, 8–20 μ long, the basal cell rather long-conic, sometimes short, pedicels 8–12 μ, deciduous.

On decorticated wood of *Juniperus*, Rhode Island, Bennett, No. 60, M. A. Curtis No. 6324, in herb. N. Y. State Mus., in herb. Farlow and herb. Berkeley, Kew, England [Fig. 119a]. The fungus was listed by Frost in 1869, on *Juniperus* in New England. On living leaves of *Myrtaceae*, Richuela, Argentina, Feb. 20, 1880, Spegazzini. This is the type of *P. decolorata* Speg. The specimen designated *P. decolorata* Speg. in Roumeguère Fungi Galliae Exs. No. 3984, on wilting leaves of *Myrtus communis* L., Bone,

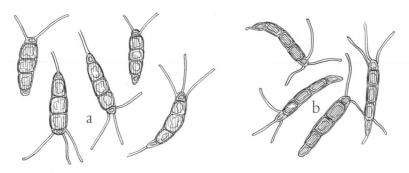

FIG. 119 [330]. (*a*) *Pestalotia unicolor* Berk. & Curt. [=*Pestalozzina unicolor* (Berk. & Curt) Sacc.]. (*b*) *Pestalotia decolorata* Speg. [=*Pestalozzina unicolor* (Berk. & Curt.) Sacc.].

Algeria, May 1886 (Major Duroux), is sterile. The same fungus was described as *P. myrticola* Bubak on *Myrtus communis* L. Tirol, Austria, Jan. 1, 1916. On living leaves of *Polygonum virginianum* L., Stanton, Del., Aug. 1894, A. Commons, No. 2560, in association with *Pestalotia polygoni* Ell. & Ev. On decaying scapes of *Synandrospadix vermitoxicus* Engler, Bot. Gard., La Plata, Argentina, Oct. 1910 [Fig. 119b], in association with the type specimen of *Pestalotia pallidicolor* Speg. [=*P. adusta* Ell. & Ev.]. On twigs of *Ulmus* sp. Arlington, Mass., E. A. Burt, May 21, 1894, in herb. Farlow, sub *Pestalotia insidens* Zabr. [=*Cryptostictis insidens* (Zabr.) Guba].

A leaf spot of *Myrtus communis* L. caused by *P. decolorata* Speg. was reported in Great Britain by Hewlett (Jour. Roy. Hort. Soc. 77:413,418, 1952). The disease was produced in wounded and unwounded leaves with a water suspension of conidia. The same fungus was isolated from galls on *Myrtus communis* in Cyprus by Nattrass (Ann. Rep. Dept. Agr. Cyprus 1933, 48–57,1934).

Pestalozzina Sacc. (Syll. Fung. 3:800,1884) was conceived as a subgenus of *Pestalotia*, differing in totally hyaline conidia. It embraced *P. unicolor* Berk. & Curt. the type, *P. laurina* Mont., *P. callunae* Ces. and *P. fautreyi* Karst. & Roum. (Syll. Fung. 10,496,1892). Saccardo (Syll. Fung. 11,580, 1895) made *Pestalozzina* a genus with *P. unicolor* as the type. Hoehnel (Mitt. Bot. Inst. Techn. Hochsch., Wien 2:26–29,1925) accepted this genus and included in its concept *P. laurina* Mont., *P. fautreyi* Karst. & Roum., *P. soraueriana* Sacc. and *P. rollandii* Fautr. *P. unicolor* possesses a unique conidial type. It is totally colored yellow brown and is therefore not within the original generic concept of *Pestalozzina* or *Pestalotia*. The character of the conidia and the disposition of the setulae set the species apart from Pestalotia. *Pestalotia unicolor* Berk. & Curt. is proposed as the type of the emended genus *Pestalozzina*, *Melanconiaceae*, Section *Phaeophragmiae* and is *Pestalozzina unicolor* (Berk. & Curt.) Sacc. (Syll. Fung. 3:800,1884; 11:580, 1895).

331. **Pestalotia viridis** Torrend, Broteria 11:180,1913, fig. 8; Syll. Fung. 25: 603,1931.

On leaves of *Acacia melanoxylon* R. Br., Madeira Islands, October, C. de Menezes.

Acervuli convex, globose-lenticular, 0.3–1 mm long. Conidia 4-septate, erect, cylindric to narrow-fusiform, hyaline and iridescent, $20-24 \times 3-4 \mu$ long, crowned with 2 to 3 filiform appendages, $18-22 \mu$ long. From fig. 8 (Broteria 11:1913) and the description, it appears that the fungus is more properly *Hyalotia viridis* (Torrend) Guba comb. nov.

Culture from *Casuarina equisetifolia* L., São Paulo, Brazil, April 1960, Luiza C. May; conidia 5-celled, $17-20 \times 3-3.5 \mu$; apical cells hyaline empty; 4 cells with contents, greenish; setulae 3, $15-20 \mu$; pedicels eccentric, $6-8 \mu$ long.

MISCELLANEA

Species Nos. 332–342

This section comprises a selected group of species whose conidial forms show analogies to some of the excluded species and which, in some instances, have been referred to the genera Monochaetia or Pestalotia. The descriptions follow the general pattern, including literature citations, critical treatment, and new combinations and names.

332. **Dinemasporium gramineum** Lév., Ann. Sci. Nat. Bot. III, 5:274,1846; Syll. Fung. 3:683,1884.

On *Andropogon scoparius* Michx. [Fig. 120].

Pycnidia subepidermal, erumpent, surrounded by torn epidermis, raised, cup-shaped or inverted boat-shaped, covered with black stiff hairs or setae. Conidia hyaline, 1-celled, narrow-fusiform, curved or falcate, with acute apex bearing 1 filiform appendage, the base blunt with 1 filiform appendage projecting somewhat off the base; pedicels indefinite and not seen.

Dinemasporiella hispidula Bubak & Kab., Hedwigia 52,358,1912; Miguła, Krypt. Flora Deut. 6:516,1910, pl. 67, figs. 10–13 (not *Dinemasporiella* Speg.), is the type of the genus *Dinemasporiella* Bubak & Kab., but this fungus is the same as *Dinemasporium hispidulum* (Schrad.) Sacc. (Michelia II,281,1881;

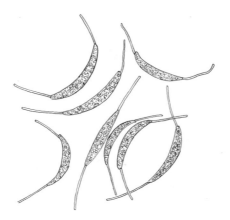

Fig. 120 [332]. *Dinemasporium gramineum* Lév.

Syll. Fung. 3:685,1884). *Dinemasporiopsis hispidula* Bubak & Kab. (apud Diedicke, Krypt. Flora Mark Brandenb. IX, 718, figs. 10 and 750), is described with 2-celled conidia. Clements and Shear (Genera of Fungi, 1931) considered both species synonyms of *Dinemasporium gramineum* Lév.

333. **Discosia artocreas** Tode ex Fries, Summa Veg. Scand. 423, 1846; Syll.
       Fung. 3:653,1884; Grove, British Stem and Leaf Fungi II:189–190,
       1937.

     The fungus is recognized by its unique appendaged, slightly allantoid spores. The conidia are oblong, rounded at the ends, bases occasionally somewhat truncate, usually 3-septate, hyaline or subhyaline, furnished at each end with one appendage affixed laterally or acrogenously or just beneath the extremity; with or without coarse deciduous pedicel at base. Wolf and Wolf (The Fungi I:399,1947, fig. 153–0) show allantoid, appendaged conidia (appendage at each extremity) and stout pedicel at base. The fungus has a wide synonymy (see Grove, above) and has been found by the writer with the following specimens: Ellis & Everhart, N. Am. Fungi No. 34 on leaves of *Ilex opaca* Ait. with fungus designated *Pestalotia stellata* Berk. & Curt.; herb. G. F. Atkinson, No. 2288, Cornell University, on leaves of *Quercus* with type specimen of *Pestalotia clavispora* Atk.; Saccardo, Mycotheca Veneta No. 975, on leaves of *Rubus caesius* L., Colfosco (Treviso), Italy, associated with *Pestalotia sessilis* Sacc. [Fig. 121]; herb. Farlow (Carver, No. 499), on leaves of *Rosa sp.* Tuskegee, Ala., associated with a 6-celled spored *Monochaetia* designated *Pestalotia seiridioides* Sacc. *Discosia artocreas* Tode is distinct from *Leptodiscus terrestris* Gerdemann (Mycologia 45:548–54,1953 and Phytopathology 44:451–55,1954) on roots of *Trifolium pratense* L. [Fig. 121b], although the conidia appear somewhat similar.

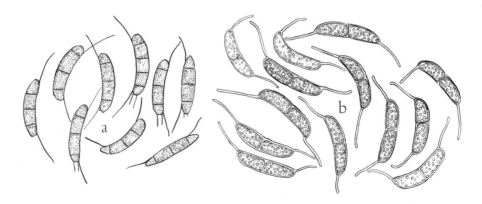

     Fɪɢ. 121 [333]. (*a*) *Dicosia artocreas* Tode ex Fries. (*b*) *Leptodiscus terrestris* Gerd.

334. **Heteropatella hendersonioides** Fautrey & Lambotte, Rev. Mycol. Fr. 18: 143,1896; Syll. Fung. 14:999–1000,1899.

The fungus was described on dry stems of *Bupleurum falcatum* L., Montague de Bard (Côte-d'Or), France, June 1896, F. Fautrey and issued in Roumeguère, Fungi Galliae Exs. No. 7227 [Fig. 122a].

There is no fungus corresponding to *Heteropatella* in the type specimens. The conidia are fusiform, hyaline, 1–3-celled, stuffed with protoplasm, apex with 2 to 3 appendages (rarely one), tapering to base, supported on a filiform flexuous pedicel. Fautrey and Lambotte described the conidia in reversed position placing the 3 appendages at the base rather than at the apex of the conidium.

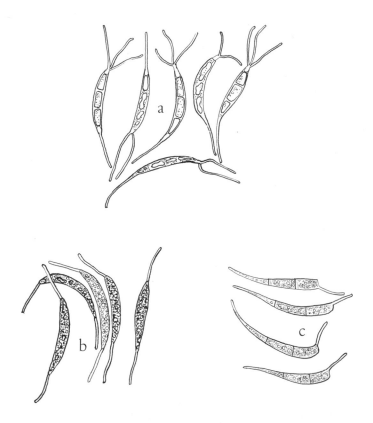

FIG. 122'[334]. *Heteropatella hendersonioides* Fautrey & Lambotte. (*a*) *Pestalozzina hendersonioides* (Fautr. & Lam.) Hoehnel. (*b*) Undetermined, not *Heteropatella lacera* Fckl. (Hoehnel, Mitt. Bot. Lab. Techn. Hochsch. Wien 2: 26–29,1915). (*c*) *Heteropatella hendersonioides* Fautrey & Lam. (Diedicke, Ann. Mycol. 2:182,1904, fig. 2); *Pestalozzina hendersonioides* (Fautr. & Lam.) Died. (Krypt. Flora Mark Brandenb. IX, 837, 1915, fig. 10, p. 823).

The type description of *Heteropatella hendersonioides* Fautrey & Lambotte embraces characters of two distinct fungi [Fig. 122a,b] and collectively it applies neither to *Heteropatella* or *Pestalozzina*. Both forms were described by Hoehnel (Mitt. Bot. Lab. Techn. Hochsch. Wien 2:26–29, 1915). The form with 3-celled hyaline fusiform conidia on a flexuous slender pedicel and 2 to 3 apical appendages was identified as *Pestalozzina hendersonioides* (Fautrey & Lambotte) Hoehnel. Diedicke (Ann. Mycol. 2:182, 1904, fig. 2) originally designated his fungus on *Bupleurum longifolium* L. as *Heteropatella hendersonioides* Fautrey & Lambotte. His figure 2 illustrates typical *Heteropatella* conidia with an oblique appendage-like pedicel and an attenuated apex [Fig. 122c]. The conidia are borne in an acervulus, thus placing the fungus in the *Melanconiaceae*, not the *Excipulaceae* in which the genus *Heteropatella* appears. Thereupon, Diedicke (Krypt. Flora Mark Brandenb. IX:837,1915, p. 823, fig. 10) transferred his fungus to *Pestalozzina hendersonioides* (Fautrey & Lambotte) Died., which was a mistake. Diedicke's fungus is a typical *Heteropatella*, that is, *H. lacera* Fckl.

Roumeguère's type specimen No. 7227 also bears a pycnidial fungus which Hoehnel designated *Heteropatella lacera* Fckl. The conidia are hyaline, 1–3- usually 1-celled, narrow fusiform and slightly curved, stuffed with protoplasm, one flexuous appendage at apex, flexuous pedicel at base [Fig. 122b]. The apex is not drawn out into a long beak characteristic of *Heteropatella*; therefore the fungus cannot be *H. lacera* Fckl.

Pestalozzina uniseptata Grove (British Stem and Leaf Fungi II:287–288, 1937, fig. 110) cannot belong to this genus. The conidia are hyaline, 2-celled, attenuated at each end into a hyaline beak which is not cut off from the conidium by a septum. Grove implies that his fungus and Diedicke's fungus *Heteropatella* on *Bupleurum longifolium* (fig. 2, 1904; 10, 1915) might belong to the genus *Pseudodiscosia*. The two genera are identical except for a variable fruiting structure. *Pseudodiscosia* is an acervuloid *Heteropatella* having the same spore form. Buddin and Wakefield (Trans. Brit. Mycol. Soc. 11:169–188,1926) showed that *Heteropatella antirrhini* Budd. & Wakef. has a hyphomycetous stage, *Cercosporella antirrhini* Wakef. Likewise *H. dianthi* Budd. & Wakef. (Trans. Brit. Mycol. Soc. 14:215–221,1929) is the pycnidial form of *Pseudodiscosia dianthi* Hösterman & Laub. The fruiting structures of the three orders of the Fungi Imperfecti overlap and are difficult to define in all cases. They cannot be the basis of three distinct genera especially when the conidium is identical throughout. Therefore, *Pestalozzina uniseptata* Grove is more properly *Heteropatella uniseptata* (Grove) Guba comb. nov.

Pestalotia hendersonioides Fautrey (Rev. Mycol. Fr. 15:116,1893) on stems of *Ribes alpinum* L. (Roumeguère, Fungi Galliae Exs. No. 6370, 1893), belongs to the genus *Cryptostictis* and is *C. ribis-alpini* (Fautrey) Guba.

335. **Pestalozzina camelliae** Pass., Rev. Mycol. Fr., 9:146,1887.

On twigs of *Camellia japonica* L. Bot. Gard., Parma, Italy.
The name appears as *Pestalotia camelliae* Pass. in Syll. Fung. 10:486,1892.
Fungus is characterized by simple acervuli and oblong-clavate, 4-celled,
hyaline conidia with muticate apical cells bearing 2 setulae. The name
Hyalotia camelliae (Pass.) Guba comb. nov. is proposed for this species.

336. **Pestalozzina cordylines** Speg., Ann. Mus. Nac. Buenos Aires 20:372,
    1910; Syll. Fung. 22:1217,1913.

Spots linear, determinate, dried out, dark gray, limited by purple band.
Pycnidia amphigenous, black, innate, sublenticular, 150–200 μ diam. with
rudimentary ostiole. Conidia fusoid or subclavate, 4-, rarely 3-septate,
hyaline, attenuated downwards, somewhat rotundate above, 20–24 × 6 μ;
exterior cells small, the superior cell abrupt, crowned with 3 filiform, horizontal setulae 10–15 μ long; pedicels short, filiform, 5–10 μ long.

On wilting leaves of *Cordyline dracaenoides* Kunth, Bot. Gard., La Plata,
Argentina.

According to Hoehnel (Mitt. Bot. Techn. Hochsch. Wien 2:26–29,1925),
the fungus belongs to the genus *Bartalinia* Fl. Tassi with the designation
B. cordylines (Speg.) Hoehn.

337. **Pestalozzina fautreyi** Karst. & Roum., Rev. Mycol. Fr. 12:127,1890.

The name appears as *Pestalotia fautreyi* Karst. & Roum. in Syll. Fung.
10:496,1892. On branches of *Lonicera caprifolium* L., Noidan, France, Dec.
1899, F. Fautrey.

Acervuli orbicular. Conidia elongate, cylindrical, 4-celled, hyaline, the
apex crowned with 4–6 setulae. Hoehnel (Mitt. Bot. Inst. Techn. Hochsch.
Wien 2:26–29,1925) believed that the fungus belongs to the genus *Bartalinia*
(Syll. Fung. 16:951,1902). The description suggests the new genus *Hyalotia*.
Bartalinia robillardoides Tassi (Boll. Lab. Ort. Bot. Siena 3:3,1900, tab. 1,
figs. 1–3) is a pycnidial fungus with hyaline, elliptic-fusiform, septate conidia
crowned with 3 setulae. The conidia set squarely on the pedicels. *Pestalozzina laurina* (Mont.) Sacc. [= *Hyalotia laurina* (Mont.) Guba], the type,
is an acervuloid fungus with narrow conidia and oblique filiform pedicels
projecting from the bases of the basal cells adjoining the point of attachment
of the pedicel. Thus the two genera are quite distinct. The type material
of *Pestalozzina fautreyi* Karst. & Roum. in Fungi Galliae Exs. No. 6161 in
herb. Farlow is empty.

338. **Pestalozzina rollandi** Fautrey, Rev. Mycol. Fr., 17:71,1895; pl. 153, fig.
    23; Syll. Fung. 11:580,1895; 14:1029,1899; Allescher, Rabh. Krypt.
    Flora 1: Abt. 7,630,1902.

On needles of *Pinus strobus* L., France, Dec. 1894, L. Rolland [Fig. 123].
Fautrey described conidia with one delicate setula at the apex inserted

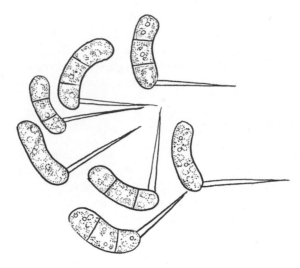

FIG. 123 [338].   *Pestalozzina rollandii* Fautrey [= *Cytotriplospora pini* Bayliss, Elliott, & Chance].

obliquely and longer than the conidium.   This was the error of the description.   Saccardo (Syll. Fung. 18:485,1906) made the combination *Monochaetia rollandii* (Fautrey) Sacc.   Bayliss, Elliott, and Chance (Trans. Brit. Mycol. Soc. 7:47–49,1920, fig. 6) erected the new genus *Cytotriplospora*, naming as the type *C. pini* Bayl., Elliott, & Chance, which is the same as *Pestalozzina rollandii*.

The fungus has 1–6-chambered pycnidia (acervuli according to Fautrey), hyaline allantoid conidia at first unicellular, then 2- or 3-celled, rounded at the ends, 15×4–7μ, pedicels acute, slender, erect, attached obliquely near the base of the conidia, resembling appendages.

According to Grove (British Leaf and Stem Fungi I:364,1935), the fungus reminds one of Berkeley's enigmatic *Sphaeropsis geniculata* Berk. & Br. (Ann. Nat. Hist. Mag. 5, Ser. II, 375,1950; Cooke, Handbook of British Fungi, No. 427) and *Phoma geniculata* Sacc. (Syll. Fung. 3:102,1884) and described at length by Grove (p. 76).   Grove asserted that Berkeley's fungus could be *Fusicoccum bacillare* Sacc. & Penz. var. *acuum* Fautrey (Rev. Mycol. Fr. 14:9,1892) described on *Picea excelsa* Link (not *Abies*).

However, Hoehnel (Mitt. Bot. Inst. Techn. Hochsch. Wien 2:26–29,1925) asserted that the fungus (Roumeguère Fungi Galliae Exs. No. 6761) was falsely described by Fautrey and is a typical *Strasseria* Bres. & Sacc. (Verh. zool.-bot. Ges. Wien 436, 1902) and that *Plagiorhabdus* Shear (Bull. Torrey Bot. Club 34:310,1907) is identical.   Hoehnel asserted that the fungus should be named *Strasseria geniculata* (Berk. & Br.) Hoehn.

Bayliss, Elliott, and Chance (Trans. Brit. Mycol. Soc. 7,47–49,1920, fig. b) described 1–3-celled conidia with a sporophore attached to one side of the base without a setula at the upper rounded end. *Strasseria* has allantoid, 1-celled conidia resting on conidiophores and the upper rounded ends are provided with one oblique stiff setula, thus differing from *Neottiospora* whose conidia are many setulate at apex and from *Cytotriplospora* which has no setulae.

Bayliss, Elliott, and Chance asserted that their fungus is like *Cytospora* (1-celled conidia) and *Cytodiplospora* (2-celled conidia). *Cytotriplospora* differs from the latter genus by having 3-celled conidia when mature; thus the new name *Cytotriplospora pini* Bayl., Elliott, & Chance.

339. **Pestalozzina soraueriana** Sacc., Syll. Fung. 11:580,1895; Sorauer, Z. Pflanzenkr. 4:213–215,1894, tab. 4, fig. 1–7.

According to Hoehnel (Mitt. Bot. Inst. Techn. Hochsch. Wien 2:25–29, 1925) the fungus is more properly *Mastigosporium album* Riess (Fresenius Beitr. Myk. 1852, p. 56, tab. VI, figs. 37–40; Syll. Fung. 4:220,1886). It has nothing in common with the genus *Pestalozzina*.

In 1894, Sorauer described the fungus as the cause of a new disease of meadow fox tail, *Alopecurus pratensis* L. in Germany and Austria.

The conidia are totally hyaline, fusiform, 3–5-septate, borne on short stout conidiophores, the apices bearing 1 or more filiform setulae, the setulae sometimes projecting from the first septum below the apex [Fig. 124a]. The fungus is a hyphomycete belonging to the family *Moniliaceae*.

The fungus occurs commonly on *Alopecurus pratensis* L. and *Deschampsia caespitosa* (L.) Beauv. in Europe. It was found for the first time in the United States in June 1954 near Ithaca, N. Y., by J. P. Ross (U.S.D.A. Plant Disease Rep. 38: no. 8, pp. 607–608, Aug. 15, 1954). Sprague (Jour. Agr.

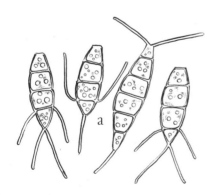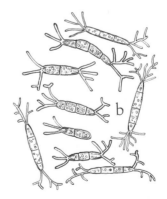

FIG. 124 [339]. (*a*) *Pestalozzina soraueriana* Sacc. [= *Mastigosporium album* Riess]. (*b*) *Dilophosphora alopecuri* (Fries) Fries.

Research 57:287–299,1938) emended the genus *Mastigosporium* to include both setulate and non-setulate forms.

Raino (Valtion Maatalouskoet, Julkaisu 87, 1936) asserted that *M. album* Riess and *Dilophospora alopecuri* (Fries) Fries are identical, but Sprague (Jour. Agr. Research 57:287–299,1938) regarded them as different. Sampson and Western (Trans. Brit. Mycol. Soc. 22:168–173,1938) showed that there was no connection between the two species. *Dilophospora alopecuri* is a pycnidial fungus and the conidia are cylindric-fusiform, hyaline, $12 \times 2.2 \, \mu$, 1–3-septate, with several branched appendages at each extremity [Fig. 124b].

340. **Pseudodiscosia dianthi** Hoesterman & Laub., Gartenwelt 25:65–66,1921; illus. also in Salmon & Ware, Gard. Chron. (Eng.) LXXXI, 196:216, 1927.

The fungus is the cause of a serious stem and foliage disease of carnations, *Dianthus caryophyllus* L., in Germany and elsewhere in Europe. It has also been the subject of studies by Buddin and Wakefield (Trans. Brit. Mycol. Soc. 14:215–221,1929). The fungus forms an acervulus under the epidermis. The conidia are hyaline, curved, 2–3-septate, $12–24 \times 3–7 \, \mu$, inverted club-shaped, upper end attenuated into thread-like tail, broadened below; pedicels filiform, attached to one side of the base and oblique.

The fungus is like *Heteropatella antirrhini* Budd. & Wakef. (Trans. Brit. Mycol. Soc. 21:169,1926) whose hyphomycetous stage is *Cercosporella antirrhini* Wakef. *Pseudodiscosia dianthi* is more properly *Heteropatella dianthi* Budd. & Wakef., the authors preferring to consider the pycnidial stage more advanced than the hyphomycetal stage. *Heteropatella* is a well-established genus and the pycnidial stage of *Heterosphaeria*. The imperfect structure is an excipulum which on modification becomes a perethecium. The fungus was originally named *Excipulina valtellinensis* Trav. (Ann. Mycol. 1:316,1903; Syll. Fung. 18:443). The correct name is *Heteropatella valtellinensis* Wollenw. (Z. Parasitenk, 3:499,1931) according to Grove (British Stem and Leaf Fungi II:156–157,1937), specimens of which on *Dianthus* collected in southern counties of England, are accompanied by *Pseudodiscosia dianthi* Hösterman & Laub. Carnation leaf rot caused by the fungus *H. valtellinensis* has been reported from New Zealand (N. Z. Gard. 9:9:607, 1953).

Heteropatella, Pseudodiscosia, Cercosporella and *Spermospora* represent variable fruiting structures embracing a common conidial type of spore. It would seem best to place these conidial forms with *Heteropatella* rather than to recognize several distinct genera and species among the three orders of the Fungi Imperfecti. The conidia are not ciliate or appendaged at each end and thus the characterization of the genus *Pseudodiscosia* by Clements and Shear (Genera of Fungi, 1931, p. 198) is incorrect.

341. **Spermospora avenae** (Sprague & A. G. Johnson) Sprague, Diseases of
     Cereals and Grasses in North America, 1950, pp. 430–431.
     Pseudodiscosia avenae Sprague & A. G. Johnson, Mycologia 28:183–184,
         1936.

In these two names we have both the melanconiaceous and moniliaceous
stages of the same fungus.   The fungus causes a leaf spot of winter oats,
Avena sativa L., in Washington and Oregon, and has also been collected there
on *A. byzantina* K. Koch and *Arrhenatherum elatius* (L.) Beauv.   Sprague
and Johnson assert that their fungus has less distinct acervuli and narrower
conidia (10–42 × 2–4 μ) [Fig. 125] than *Pseudodiscosia dianthi* (*Heteropatella
dianthi*), and that it is distinct from *Heteropatella graminis* Gizhitskaia (Nov.
pro Flora Myc. 8:102,1929) found on grass stems, Russia, in 1928.

The leaf spot of oats was reported originally by Sprague (Northwest
Science 9:15,1935).   It was reported on a wild grass, probably *Avena sterilis*
L., in western Anatolia, Turkey, by H. Bremer (Phytopathology 33:165–167,
1943).   Sprague (Diseases of Cereals and Grasses) removed the fungus from
its "dubious position in the *Melanconiales*" and placed it in the *Moniliales*,
in the new genus *Spermospora* as emended (Mycologia 41:495,1949).   The
fungus more properly appears to belong to the genus *Heteropatella* (see
Buddin and Wakefield, Trans. Brit. Mycol. Soc. 11:169,1926; 14:215–221,
1929).

342. **Spermospora subulata** (Sprague) Sprague, Mycologia 41:495,1949;
     Sprague, Diseases of Cereals and Grasses in North America, 1950 (lit.
     cit. pp. 430–433, fig. 80).
     Cercosporella subulata Sprague, Mycologia 29:202–203,1937.

The fungus was originally described on *Melica subulata* (Griseb.) Scribn.

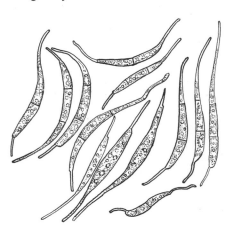

Fig. 125 [341].   *Spermospora avenae* Sprague [=*Pseudodiscosia avenae* Sprague & A. G.
Johnson]=*Heteropatella*.

and more recently (Mycologia 42:766,1950) reported on *Trisetum spicatum* (L.) Richt., *Bromus vulgaris* (Hook.) Shear and *Stipa lettermanii* Vasey in the northwestern states. More hosts reported by Sprague (Diseases Cereals and Grasses, p. 432) are *Agrostis alba* L., *Calamagrostis rubescens* Buckl., *C. scribneri* Beal, *Deschampsia caespitosa* (L.) Beauv., *Festuca rubra* L., and variety *commutata* Gand., *Melica bulbosa* Geyer, *M. smithii* (Porter) Vasey, and *M. spectabilis* Scribn.

The fungus was originally placed in the genus *Cercosporella*. The mycelium is aggregated into a thin stroma. The conidia are filiform, broadened toward the base and tapered above into a long whip-like distal extremity. The conidia are 1- or usually 2-septate, occasionally 3-septate, sometimes with an attached oblique basal appendaged pedicel. Because of the sperm-like character of spores and the subulate base, the fungus was transferred to the new genus *Spermospora* Sprague. Occasional specimens have conidia with an oblique short pedicel attached to the base. The genus was emended to include forms with an appendaged base (Mycologia 41:495,1949), such as *Spermospora subulata* var. *ciliata* Sprague on *Agrostis alba* L. and *Calamagrostis rubescens* Buckl. collected in Wyoming and Washington. The oblique appendage adhering to the base of the conidium is only occasional and appears to be the pedicel. In this respect the fungus appears to be like *Pseudodiscosia*, the acervuloid stage of *Heteropatella*.

This fungus is like *Heteropatella antirrhini* and *H. dianthi*, which also have fruiting stages conforming to the genus *Pseudodiscosia* and *Cercosporella* (see Buddin & Wakefield, Trans. Brit. Mycol. Soc. 11:169,1926; 14:215–221, 1929).

Specimens examined: on *Melica smithii* (Porter) Vasey, Priest Lake, Bonner County, Idaho, June 27, 1948, R. Sprague & C. G. Shaw (conidia usually 2-septate); on *Stipa lettermanii* Vasey, Waterton Lakes Natl. Park, Alberta, Aug. 7, 1949, G. W. Fischer (conidia 3-septate, an occasional one with oblique pedicel at base).

INDEX

INDEX